Ecton Copper Mines
Under the Dukes of Devonshire
1760-1790

Lindsey Porter

Foreword by His Grace the 11th Duke of Devonshire

During the late 18th century my predecessor, the 5th Duke, was lucky enough to be working the Ecton Copper Mine when a vast deposit of high-grade ore was located.

Much of the profit was used to finance the building of The Crescent and Stable Block (later the Devonshire Royal Hospital) in Buxton. The loss of this unexpected income, when the mine failed, created the incentive to invest elsewhere which, in turn, was to provide much of the income used by the 6th Duke to extend Chatsworth and furnish the house with its statuary and other treasures we see today.

For over thirty years this concern provided much employment at the mine, at its smelter and coal mines and amongst the many suppliers of materials the concern required. Its richness and huge depth for the period were well known at the time but have since been largely forgotten. I am delighted that the opportunity arose for the facts to be unearthed in the records held at Chatsworth.

Published by

Landmark Publishing Ltd
Ashbourne Hall, Cokayne Ave, Ashbourne, Derbyshire DE6 1EJ England
Tel: (01335) 347349 Fax: (01335) 347303
e-mail: landmark@clara.net
web site: www.landmarkpublishing.co.uk

ISBN 1 84306 125 2

© **C L M Porter 2004**

British Library Cataloguing in Publication Data: a catalogue
record for this book is available from the British Library.

Dedicated to Geoffrey Cox, Mineral Owner of Ecton Hill
1926-2003

Print: Cromwell Press Ltd
Design: Mark Titterton
Cover: James Allsopp
Editor: Kay Coulson

Cover painting: Ecton c. 1790 by James Allsopp

Title page: Silhouette of Cornelius Flint by White Watson

LANDMARK COLLECTOR'S LIBRARY

ECTON COPPER MINES
UNDER THE DUKES OF DEVONSHIRE
1760-1790

Lindsey Porter

Landmark Publishing

Ore and Metal output and Profit and Loss, 1761-1789

	Ore raised tons	Ore Sold tons	Cu Metal Sold tons	Cu metal made tons	Pb Metal Sold tons	Pb Metal Sales £	Total Expenses £	Revenue £	Profits £	
1761	576	574					4717	7592	2875	
1762	937	684					4631	9625	4994	
1763	1164	700					5450	9992	4542	
1764	1166	660					4054	8810	4756	
1765	927	704	9				5850	11588	5738	
1766	980	860	10				5028	14673	9645	
1767	788	922	5				4738	14229	9491	
1768	740	806	8				5032	11669	6637	
1769	397	510	3				4875	8694	3819	
Total	7675	6420	35	0	0		44375	96872	52497	
1770	795	400	15	?	4		6489	8210	1721	
1771	820	561	43	?			7886	12939	5053	
1772	716	410	88	?			7589	14900	7311	
1773	649	788	74	?			7276	12956	5680	
1774	709	416	83	?			6876	12851	5975	
1775	700		83	126			7000	6511	-489	
1776	750	20	41	182			7767	3258	-4509	
1777	785	21	222	172			8361	17150	8789	
1778	1042		152	164			7605	12164	4559	
1779	1200		279	80			11000	19705	8705	Col E Aug-Dec
Total	8166	2616	1080	724	4		77849	120644	42795	
1780	1530		342	533			15800	24878	9078	
1781	2200	20	527	600			17000	44577	27577	
1782	2060			450			17171	40500	23329	
1783	2250			380	500	5995	22270	35255	18980	
1784	2800			460	204	2822	20526	48242	20538	Col F ? more
1785	3100			470	258	3463	16426	39653	26690	
1786	3502			478	275	3749	20871	40555	23433	
1787	3208			468	302	4852	21046	40888	24694	
1788	2788			347	412	7458	20690	34177	20945	
1789	2600			261	?	?	20103	20097	-6	
Total	26038	20	869	4447	1951	28339	191903	358822	195258	
1790	2260			259						
1761-89	41879	9056	1984	5171	1955		314127	576338	290550	

Cu price 1782-89 assumed at £77 p. ton. Bold includes estimates

According to Mr Heaton (the Duke's auditor) the profit – including that from lead ores–amounted to £78, 2333. 19s. 9d from 1760-1775. The above figures are understated by £485 but exclude lead ore. Heaton also recorded the profit from 1760 to 1/1/1792 as being £293, 938. (Dev.Coll. L/60/20)

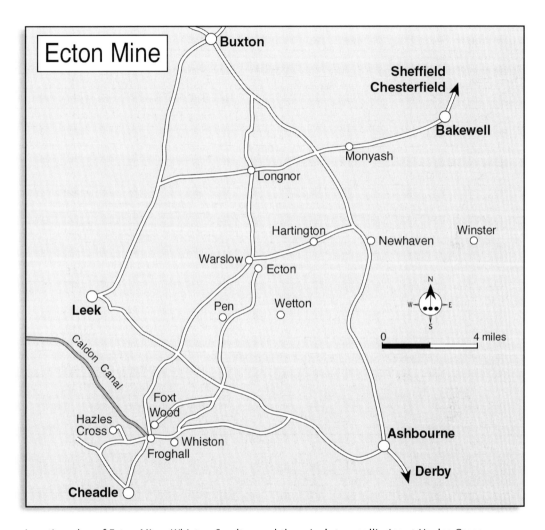

Location plan of Ecton Mine, Whiston Smelter, and the mine's two collieries at Hazles Cross, Kingsley and Foxt Wood

CONTENTS

CHRONOLOGY

1760	Duke commences operations at Michaelmas (September 21)
1762	Bote Level started
1763	Fourth Duke visits mine
1764	Calcining Furnace built
1766	Boat Level in use
1768	Smelter built (Clock House Smelter)
1770	Whiston Smelter constructed
1770	Certain roads to west and north of mine turnpiked
1770	Sale of Slime Ores cease
1773	Mine depth reaches 1,000 feet
1775	Deliveries of copper metal to London begin
1780	Apes Tor Adit level started
1780	Mine House built
1780	Kingsley Colliery (Hazles Cross) purchased. Large volume of coal deliveries from Hazles Cross Colliery start
1780	Whiston Smelter extended
1780	Sale of ore (copper) ceases
1780	Horses used underground for the first time. Coal deliveries from Foxt Wood Colliery begin
1780	Mine has a 4-wheeled vehicle (wagon)
1781	New building erected at Whiston
1782	New building erected at Ecton – lead smelter (with cupola) – and ? school
1782	First reference to coal from Goldsitch
1782	Reference to the Newhaven Sandhouse
1782	Brick production at Whiston started
1782/83	Saw pit constructed and ? thatched
1783	Capstan installed on Ecton Sough main shaft (Water Engine Shaft)
1783	Reservoir at Back of Ecton started (finished 1787)

1783	Fifth Duke visits mine
1783	First reference to Mine's Limekiln
1783	? 2nd cupola built at Ecton
1784	Whim erected on hill at top of Balance Shaft then being sunk
1784	Water Balance Engine set to work. Water Engine Shaft footway installed
1784	Slagmill Blast Furnace built (The New Smelt House)
1784	Mill for breaking down metal built at Whiston
1785	New road surveyed; Pen Farm – Butterton?
1785	Swainsley Mine started?
1785	Workshop built at Ecton; shade at the stone pit built; new furnace built; first reference to the Duke's Gravel Pit (R. December 1785)
1786	Brick Kiln built at Newhaven
1786	Second Water Balance Engine added at Ecton
1786	Limekiln built at Wetton Hill
1787	Brick Oven built at Hazles Cross Colliery
	Deliveries of coal from Goldsitch Colliery and Cheddleton canal wharf. One of Ecton's smelters replaced Brick making starts at Hazles Cross
1788	Production of copper ore and metal begins to fall
	Boulton & Watt rotative winding engine erected – winding shaft 1,212 feet deep, mine 1,278 feet deep
	Coke making starts at Hazles Cross
1790	Main ore deposit fails

ACKNOWLEDGEMENTS

My special thanks are to His Grace the 11th Duke of Devonshire and the Trustees of the Chatsworth Settlement who allowed access to the archive (The Devonshire Collection) over several years.

I have received significant assistance during the compilation of this work especially from the staff of the Devonshire Collection, Chatsworth: (Charles Noble, Keeper of Collection, Diane Naylor, Stuart Band, Andrew Peppitt and former Keeper Peter Day, now retired). Brian Rich, Dr J H (Jim) Rieuwerts and Wes Taylor offered help, practical assistance, answered many questions at unsociable hours and generally pushed me along. Wes also did some of the typing, if that is the right word these days. My neighbours, Ashbourne Library, sought books and papers; John Barnatt kindly saved many hours by making material available; John Cornwell, who allowed the use of the Bristol Coalfield photograph; Martin Critchley for the Ecton Deep Adit plan; Paul Deakin for his photographs of Ecton Deep Adit; Dr Trevor Ford, as always, was there when I needed him and cast an expert's eye over Chapter 2; Dr Lynn Willies allowed unrestricted use of his paper on Lead Mills in Chapter 9; A P (Tony) Woolrich found references I needed as did Roger Flindall whose work on newspapers is largely unrecognised and who unselfishly gave me everything he had on North Staffordshire; Rev Dr Richard Hills offered advice on machinery. His knowledge on machine tools and James Watt is unmatched; Len Kirkham, my soul mate on the mine and with whom much work has been done researching underground, both at Ecton and elsewhere. The late Edward Paget-Tomlinson who kindly offered to draw the likeness of the ship *The Ecton*; My youngest son, Phillip, who assisted me at Chatsworth; Penny Watts-Russell (researching Pascoe Grenfell, an ancestor) found the London metal prices I needed; Mick Cooper kindly made available his records of the 5th Duchess's Ecton mineral collection. Several other people are acknowledged alongside the reference/assistance provided where it appears in the text.

I am grateful to all of you and I hope I have not missed anybody!

A view of Ecton Hill from Warslow

Ecton in the 1980s. Most of the tips visible are of 19th century origin. The Dale Mine is on the left

Ecton Mine, near Warslow, North Staffordshire, is situated in the lovely Manifold Valley. It was worked principally for copper, with some lead ore (galena) also being extracted. Zinc blende was also extracted but dumped on to the waste heap until about 1796. The history of the mine has recently been republished as part of a larger study of non-ferrous metal mining around the Manifold Valley. (1) This 2nd edition followed the initial book on the subject (2) and incorporated additional material on the 16th and 19th century activities and other mines in the area.

Although the existence of detailed 18th century accounts have been known to exist for the period when the mine was worked by His Grace the 4th Duke of Devonshire, followed by the 5th Duke, no in-depth study has ever been made of them, probably because of the sheer volume of documents. For many years, most of the purchase invoices survive and the wage accounts survive for a longer period from 1760 to 1812.

As part of a PhD thesis, Mrs Pat Bromfield examined periodic batches of the records from a social history point of view and looked at these in the context of social history in the Staffordshire Moorlands. (3) No attempt was made to look at the records in their entirety, or in a mining/economic or general historic context. Indeed, she admitted in her thesis that she had no idea why a Revolution dinner was served at the mine in November 1788, one hundred years after the Glorious Revolution – an act partly orchestrated by three local noblemen: the Earl of Devonshire, the Earl of Danby and John D'Arcy. The Earl of Devonshire's involvement

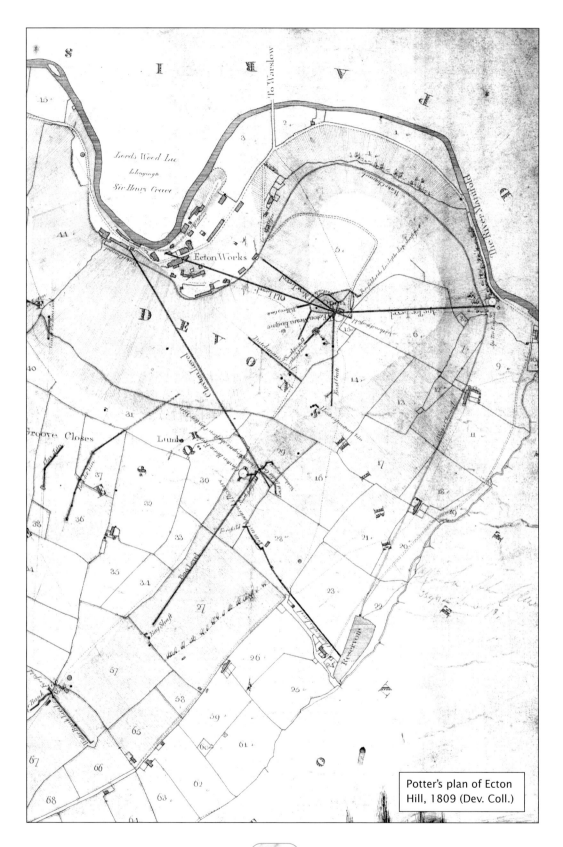

Potter's plan of Ecton Hill, 1809 (Dev. Coll.)

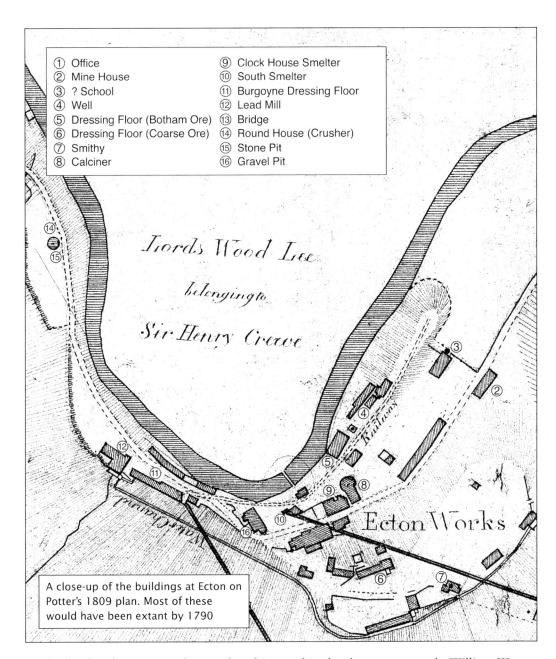

Key:
1. Office
2. Mine House
3. ? School
4. Well
5. Dressing Floor (Botham Ore)
6. Dressing Floor (Coarse Ore)
7. Smithy
8. Calciner
9. Clock House Smelter
10. South Smelter
11. Burgoyne Dressing Floor
12. Lead Mill
13. Bridge
14. Round House (Crusher)
15. Stone Pit
16. Gravel Pit

A close-up of the buildings at Ecton on Potter's 1809 plan. Most of these would have been extant by 1790

resulted in him being created 1st Duke of Devonshire by the new monarch, William III.

Consequently, the significance of the documents beyond their social interest was ignored. However, it is their mining and economic history interest which makes the records so important. For a few years in the latter half of the 18th century, the mine was perhaps the deepest mine in the country and one of the deepest anywhere. It was an early example of a vertically integrated industrial concern and at the time, one of the largest businesses to exist. In 1786 the annual costs of the mine, smelter and two collieries (which served both the mine and smelter) was £20,871, a figure which may be multiplied by 200 (at least) to equate to present day values.

However the records hold a further interest. They enable us to appreciate life in the area around the mine at that time. There are details of payments not only to miners and other mine

Top left: The site of the Water Balance Engine and the in-bye end of Apes Tor Adit Level. Above it can be seen the position of the penstock for the 1823 waterwheel

Above: The Water Engine Shaft and connecting passage to the Balance Shaft

Left: The pipe working at Ecton Sough level. This was probably known as Starr Shaft

workers, but also to wood cutters, brick makers, suppliers of ale, iron, ropes, candles, powder and much more. The movement of copper and coal created an industry in itself, revolving around the maintenance of packhorse teams, roads, payments to local tollhouses (perhaps the only daily records of these places to exist), etc. The tonnages of copper and coal combined were huge, extending to over 10,000 tons per annum abd reaching 11,150 tons in 1786. Some materials came from what were then long distances, such as timber from near Wincle in Cheshire and riddles or sieves from Hathersage, ropes brought by sea and up the Humber to the River Trent, ropes from Liverpool, gunpowder from Chesterfield and Manchester etc. Another value of this study has been to create a huge database of costings for labour and materials, from the price of candles and the carriage of coal, to the costs of building a boat and buying beef!

For local historians, this study will create a valuable source of primary records. For instance, the meagre record in the Staffordshire Moorlands VCH (4) relating to Pethills Forge can now be extended, not only in terms of ownership of the business, but also in terms of the type of products produced in iron, based on the extraction of local ironstone, outcropping in the area. In Ashbourne, Robert Longden, who lived in the building now occupied by the Derbyshire Building Society in the Market Place, supplied the mine and smelter with large quantities of iron-based materials, while in an adjacent street, Compton, J Ride & Son warehoused cakes of copper metal from Whiston before it was despatched to purchasers.

Detailed accounts also survive for the Duke's Whiston Smelter (situated near to Froghall in the Churnet Valley) and the Duke's two collieries near Kingsley and Foxt Wood, near Froghall. Although reference to these has been made (5), a detailed study of the Duke's records has never been attempted.

Finally, the accounts give details of ore extraction costs which have never been published in detail. The accounts do not present the complete picture, however, for annual copper metal sales figures do not survive for the 1780s and the true extent of the business cannot be fully judged. Although this is a disappointment, it is fortunate that such a lot does survive. One has to be thankful that the Devonshires never had a clear-out of domestic clutter, otherwise many items which today comprise the priceless records in the Devonshire Collection would not be available to us. (6)

In the text the individual reckonings are quoted thus: R.February 1786 i.e., the Reckoning Account and date. Occasionally, the actual number of the invoice in the account is indicated, especially where there are more than one from a particular supplier. Quotations are reproduced verbatim, indicating to the reader some of the difficulties of working out what was meant on occasions!

The research undertaken by myself for this book, examining the individual invoices and accounts from 1760 to 1790 has resulted in a fresh appraisal of the previous 18th century activity and in some cases, different conclusions. The latter is partly due to the amount of concentrated activity, giving perhaps a better overview, and partly by a different interpretation for which I am entirely responsible.

The many illustrations from the accounts and the two photographs of the 4th and 5th Dukes are reproduced curtosey of the Duke of Devonshire and the Trustees of the Chatsworth Settlement.

Ecton Hill today. The remaining tips are largely tree covered. The castle folly (left) dates from 1931

Ecton Sough with the mine water channel. The floor was formerly boarded

The walled-up in-bye end of the 1739 Ecton Sough

The second Smithy Shaft, now infilled after the death of a little girl who fell down it

The shaft side of the arch in the photograph (left). The stones have been worn by shaft ropes

The in-bye end of the walling of the 1774 Ecton Sough. The 1739 level is to the right of the photographer, Paul Deakin

The pipe working above river level descending to the Sough, now called Ecton Deep Adit Level. The top of this shaft may be seen on page 24

The pipe working at Sough Level. The working is thought to have been called Starr Shaft

The walls and pitching (stone floor) of the 1774 Ecton Sough. Pitching in Peak District ore mines is rare

References

1   Porter, L., & Robey, J., *Copper and Lead Mines around the Manifold Valley, Staffordshire*, 2000, Landmark Publishing

2   Robey J.A., & Porter, L., *The Copper & Lead Mines of Ecton Hill, Staffordshire*, 1972

3   Bromfield P., *Industrial workers in a Peasant Community: Manifold Valley parishes in the 18th century, with special reference to workers at Ecton Copper Mine c. 1760-1820* unpub. thesis, Keele University

4   Victoria County History, *Leek and the Moorlands*, Vol VII, 1996, p.214

5   Chester, H., *The History of the Cheadle Coalfield, Staffordshire*, 2002, Landmark Publishing

6   The surviving mine invoices in the Devonshire Collection (herein referred to as Dev. Coll.) are in the Ecton Voucher Boxes. These are 1760-74; 1775-1782; 1783-84; 1785; 1786-87; 1788-89; 1790-91; 1792-94; 1795-97; 1798-1804; 1805-07; 1808-1810; plus "Ecton - early 19th c unsorted". In the text of this book are many references to invoices in the reckoning of {date}. Payment was usually made a couple of months later

The Ecton and adjacent Clayton Mine mineral deposits were different from other ore deposits in the Peak in that the bulk of the ore was found in huge, vertical masses known as pipes. These differed from 'pipes' in Derbyshire, where they were more or less horizontal and also long and narrow. Many Derbyshire pipe veins were ancient caverns filled with ore and spar. They were not veins a few inches thick, which had to be separated from unwanted rock and spar. The descriptions of the Ecton deposits are few but those who recorded what they had observed seemed impressed by the beauty of some of the minerals.

Samples of the ore survive. There are samples in the Natural History Museum in South Kensington, London, and some attractive pieces collected by Georgiana, 5th Duchess of Devonshire which survive in a room in the former stable block at Chatsworth. A 19th century smelter's sample of ticketed ore (ore available for testing to ascertain its yield) may be seen at the Lead Mining Museum at Matlock Bath. It is addressed to Messrs Keys at Whiston and therefore dates from post-1846 when they purchased the smelter.

Perhaps the best description of the ore deposit was provided in 1802 by Mawe:

'The general produce of this mine is massive, rich, yellow copper ore, frequently in contact with galena and blende, but specimens occur of purple, steel-blue, brown or brass-yellow colours. The ore yields from 40 to 60% and is sometimes vitreous and black. Sometimes, though rarely, it is crystallised in the cube, and its modifications.

No specimens whatever can exceed the beauty of some from this mine, consisting of iridescent copper pyrites, on a white barytic gangart (gangue). The colours are beyond description; the topaz yellow and gold; the violet and azure, being blended in the brightest effulgence.

The calcareous spar of Ecton, is a singular modification of the rhomb, very transparent, sometimes of a rich topaz colour, and generally containing brilliant crystallised pyrites in the interior. Fluor, water coloured, or light blue, also appears, finely crystallised with galena. By the decompostition of the copper pyrites in the calcareous spar, arises a beautiful green efflorescence, clothing the spar and sometimes appearing to pass into pearl spar'. (1)

Another description helps our understanding further: (2)

'The top parts of the veins contains lead are poor in silver and Blende with copper ore, the latter predominating in the lower parts. The main ores are chalcopyrite and coloured copper ore with which occur also oxides and carbonates. The gangue is calcite, very transparent and sometimes of a beautiful yellow colour,

Fig 2.1 Section through Ecton Hill between Ecton and Clayton Mines (Dev. Coll, undated), from east (left) to west (right). No description acccompanies it

moreover colourless and bluish fluorspar, frequently with crystals of chalcopyrites in the interior, baryte, brown iron ore, iron pyrites and calamine.

The veins sometimes attain a considerable thickness, at one time there was an ore body which had the amazing thickness of 70 yards (65m).'

Mawe's reference to a yield of 40-60% is confusing. It is unlikely that any of the deposits contained ore which overall yielded 40-60% metal upon smelting. Yet if this is a reference to a yield of ore from host rock, spar etc, it is equally confusing for the main deposits were supposedly solid ore. The answer probably lies in the fact that he was writing after the exhaustion of the main deposits and the remaining deposits were raised with a higher percentage of unproductive material.

Dr Hatchet, writing following a visit in June 1796, described the ore as being yellow 'but part is also the pulverulent green ore and part the Hepatic Ore which they reckon the best. The Copper Ore is mixed with galena and Brown Blende – the latter did not appear to be known in the mine till pointed it out altho' in considerable quantities. The galena is in a great quantity'. (3) Brown Blende cannot be a reference to calamine or zinc carbonate. Nearby at Mill Dale on the River Dove a mill was built to smelt calamine and the earliest reference to it is in 1750. (4) It was combined with copper to make brass at Cheadle a major purchaser of Ecton copper. So this must be zinc sulphide, still known as zinc blende. However this had little commercial value as it was difficult to smelt.

Geisler, who visited Ecton during his tour of 1772-73 (5) wrote: 'they have found green thick copper ore with lime and quartz (presumably he means calcite or fluorspar)'. He described the pipe as an oblique cone, the base of which was oval (presumably he meant when viewed from above) and that it haded to the west. 'Sometimes it is easily loosened from the hill, sometimes it is more strongly held'.

At 80 fms below the adit (Ecton Sough) the ore was 'now dug out 15 fathoms in one diameter, east-west, and 10 in the other, always of uniform quality, only a little more or a little less of quartz and lime mixture'. He also stated that 'there must be 25% of ore', which is assumed to refer to the yield (i.e. the amount of metal recovered upon smelting).

The discovery recently of a scrapbook formerly belonging to White Watson gives some interesting details on the mines and its mineralogy. (6) This scrapbook records that somebody (the name is not clear, but it may well be Mr Flint) 'frequently told W.W. that in working they frequently left veins of ore to be worked when the principal vein then in work was faulty – which plainly shews the Cornish Miners were wrong'. White Watson was convinced that Captain Goldsworthy at the mine (a Cornishman) was wrong when he stated to him that the mine was worked out.

Flint informed Watson of a curious feature of the pipe vein in 1790. The deposit took a sweep of ten fathoms to the side before returning to the perpendicular in a D-shape. The left vertical element of the D was 'dead' i.e. unmetaliferous. Goldsworthy told him that the last mineral obtained at the mine was 'Sulpheret of Zinc termed Brown Hen', ie the ore 'found' by Dr Hatchet. This would seem to indicate that below the 110 fathoms level deposit, the copper ore started to be replaced by zinc ore. If the value of the latter was unrecognised as claimed by Dr Hatchet, this could account for the drop in ore value from the late 1780s (although copper ore was more valuable than either lead ore or zinc ore in this area). Perhaps the problems of smelting it were later overcome and its value was accordingly enhanced. It is a pity we do not know more about this. Goldsworthy had also shown Watson a drawing of the pipe, a copy of which he had promised to send on, but he failed to do so. He had described the ore as having 'lain in a belly form'. Watson drew the ore deposit from memory (see Fig 2.1).

The D-shape form of the pipe vein appears to have occurred at the 34 fathoms level: it is referred to on the pre-1759 section of the pipe working (Fig 3.1, see p27). The large opening at adit level containing the Water Engine shaft was not excavated for its ore – there was none. There was a widening of the deposit at the sough, or adit level, described by Harpur as being

30 yards wide, which is over stated. Harpur says the next deposit was about 80 yards (40 fathoms below) and we know it was actually at the 34 fathoms level. He says both of these excavated swellings (Harpur calls them vaults) were circular and that there were eight in all. The third was one of the largest and similar to the second in height (about 30 yards) and in cross-section. Some of the other excavations, i.e. the fourth to the seventh were oval and 'one or two' were triangular. The height seems to have varied between 15-30 yards high.

Watson and his Saddles

Only one attempt was made by a geologist to describe the mineralisation of the Ecton area and even in this case, the essential features of the pipes was largely ignored. The description was made by Dr Joseph Watson in 1860. (7) In parts, Watson's description is as ponderous as the title of his article, which explains why he ignored the features of the pipe deposits: he concentrated on the saddle deposits. He should not be confused with White Watson.

Watson conveniently mentioned the name given by the miners to different parts of an ore-bearing anticlinal / synclinal formation and these are perhaps best illustrated in diagrammatic form (see figs 2.2-3). An anticlinal formation was a 'huckle saddle' and the synclinal variation a 'trough saddle'. The breadth of the saddles from side to side ('wing' to 'wing') seemed to average forty feet. The axis of the fold was quite often associated with a fracture, known as a 'joint'. The general direction of the saddles, and therefore the joints, was NNW-SSE.

Watson distinguished the 'pipe veins' from 'rake veins' at Ecton. Neither should be confused with the pipe deposits which produced the great wealth from the mine. These appear to be a metaliferous replacement of disturbed or weak ground sometimes where east-west bearing saddles were cut by others at 90°. In other words, and probably in over-simplistic terms, they were formed on a vertical 'joint'. Watson would have been unable to view these in 1860, as the mine was allowed to fill up with water from 1856.

The 'pipe veins' were the most important of the two sorts of vein. They are described as being irregular cavities inclined at angles varying from 15°–30° to the horizontal, i.e. like Derbyshire pipe veins.

The Dale Mine lead deposit is a good example of such a feature. The 'rake veins' would appear to be subsidiary veins described as 'a series of vertical fissures falling in with the pipe veins, and occasionally passing through them'. They appear to have been generally vertical and only became productive close to the 'pipe veins'.

Further features were the 'Lums' or 'Cross courses' which were usually quite large and frequently intersected the saddle beds in the direction of their strike. 'Lums' had quite different characteristics, often being associated with clay, broken rock and differing mineral composition. Watson seems to suggest that a 'lum' was different from a 'cross-course' but the terms were used for the same feature at Mixon Mine, south west of Ecton.

Watson clearly shows that the 'saddles' occurred in distinct zones and a miner could expect a swelling of an ore deposit once a 'saddle-bed' (as he called it) was reached. The mineralisation of a pipe and a rake vein chiefly consisted of galena (lead ore) mixed with a small quantity of zinc blende 'which is deposited in the ordinary layer-like form on the walls of the fissure'. Clearly the nature of the zinc deposit changed below the 110 fathoms level, the gangue or vein stone being calcite or barytes. Sometimes the pipe veins enclosed large lumps of ore embedded in soft decomposed limestone, with no vein stone. This usually happened where the veins 'squat' [Watson's term] i.e. having moved from one set of beds to another set below, the deposit swells out in a direction parallel with the coursing in the beds above.

When the vein reached the saddle-beds, the volume of ore expanded, as the size of the vein 'expanded rapidly'. The vein assumed a more banded structure, the gangue alternating with ribs of ore and more water being present, hence the miners following water whenever possible. Another associated characteristic was the adjoining rock being thickly threaded with small ore-bearing features. At the junction of a pipe vein with a saddle 'large deposits are the rule... and

Strings of spar. These were usually metaliferous above a saddle bed. Those shown here are barren of ore

any very considerable returns are seldom expected until these points are reached, unless, as is rarely the case, the rake veins are found to be very rich at the intersections of the pipe veins above the saddles. The first appearance of the contortions is marked by a universal fissuring of the rock, most of the fissures bearing ore, and the ceasing of the pipe to retain any longer the distinctive character of a separate vein.'

It would be at such features that the volume of zinc blende would have expanded. Unfortunately, an economic method of smelting the blende was not developed until the 1830s and high quantities of it were thrown away. It was Melville Attwood who was to reclaim this ore and send it to Cheadle to be smelted. How this fits with the reports above of the mining of zinc blende is not clear. The construction of the lead smelter in 1782 must have coincided with the exploitation of a pipe vein, or indeed perhaps more than one, when it reached a saddle.

Watson's description indicates a couple of examples of when the ores were associated with host rock, 'stone' as the accounts refer to it, rather than being in solid masses of 'pure' ore. In the 1780s, much more stone seems to have been removed via Apes Tor Shaft compared to earlier years and there are many references to 'getting stone away' from the dressing floors. The latter had become a feature by 1783 and continued for some years. This would seem to indicate a change in the nature of the deposit.

Watson went on to describe and also illustrate the ore-bearing nature of a saddle (see fig. 2.2). A marks the huckle or crown of a saddle, which was usually unmetaliferous. C marks the wings of the saddle, where some of the principal ore deposits could be expected (a). B is the saddle joint, the distance between B & A being ore-bearing, the ore dying out below B. The troughs marked f and the parts richest in ore are shown a. Here, very large and solid deposits were often found. D-D is the trough joint which was usually more productive than a saddle-joint. Wxyz mark the fissures, usually mineralised, which ran up to the pipe vein. They often contained enough ore to be worth following and sometimes were also sufficiently numerous that the whole of the rock containing them was removed.

The ore-bearing parts of the saddles consisted of two parts 'the thick beds and the thin beds, the latter lying beneath the former. The thin bed deposit was usually exploited by driving a cross-cut from the troughs of the thick beds (see dotted line o-o). The ore was free of vein stone or gangue in the saddles, although calcite was often found plated with ore on the cheeks of the fissures and spar (presumably calcite) also existed beneath the ore on the 'wings'.'

In place of vein stone on top of the ore, the miners often found a soft decomposed limestone (e), which they took as an indicator of ore. Known as way-beds, or way-boards, one of these was found recently by Len Kirkham, Peter Thompson, Wes Taylor and the author in Royledge

Mine (now closed) about three miles west of Ecton. It consisted of a pure white substance with the texture of semi-soft butter. It was above a mineralised band of copper pyrites disseminated in a sandy matrix.

It has been indicated above that as the pipe vein approached a saddle bed, it increased in size and the volume of galena increased. However upon reaching the saddle, the galena was replaced by copper ore: 'some lead as usually found at first in the saddles, but as the beds near the limestone [Watson must mean the thick beds of limestone] the proportion of copper ore invariably increases, until the whole deposit consists of this mineral'.

If one imagines the inclined pipe vein cutting into the saddle beds, there would then be the large deposit of ore in the saddle formation and this extended out to a width of two or three saddles on either side of the main ore bearing beds. Watson states that the breadth of a saddle from 'wing' to 'wing' averaged 40 feet or so, therefore the deposit could be up to seven saddles or 280 feet in width i.e., 40ft x 7. An example of this is unusual in the accounts but one seems to support Watson at this point. In the December 1788 reckoning James Kirkham & Co was paid for 'driving across range of the vein, 5 fathoms 4 ft' (i.e. 34 feet). It will be realised that

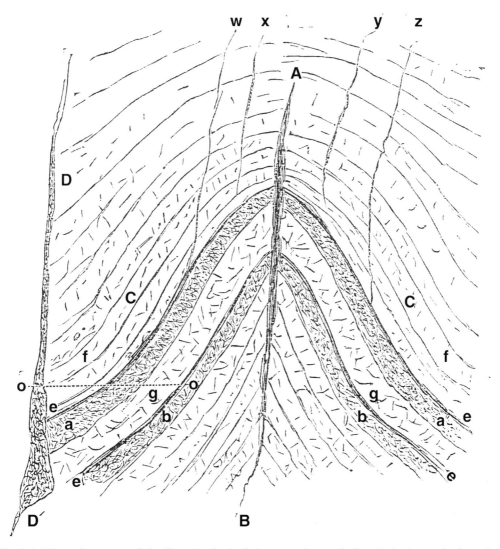

Fig 2.2: Vertical section of the "bearing beds," showing the mode in which the ore is deposited

a 'joint' was regarded as an indicator of ore and the miners followed them wherever possible. Early in 1788 Michael Twigg & Co were driving a trial 'gate' in a joint in a southerly direction and later in the year, George Beresford & Co were driving and sinking a trial in the NorthWest joint. Such references are common.

What is unclear is whether all eight large deposits of ore below adit level in Ecton Mine consisted of mineral replacement of a vertical fractured zone especially in the two areas of double saddles (where saddles crossed at 90°) or whether the latter (at the 34 and 110 fathoms level) were also in association with huge saddle formations as described above. It certainly seems to be the latter case. In other words, the vertical zone of mineral replacement was associated with six huge saddles (or up to six) and two 'double saddles' (or more than two). These eight areas of mineral extraction produced cavernous vaults, as Harpur described them. Partly this would be because of the extraction of the zone above a huckle saddle as Watson indicated. One is tempted to wonder if these vaults were created by the extraction of huge trough joints or an extensive mineralisation between the wings of a huckle saddle and its adjacent saddles. The complex nature of the double saddles really does defy speculation of its mineralised characteristics.

Another feature of the saddle was that the wings often flattened out. This seems to be the case in Royledge Mine where two mineralised zones have been worked out and are connected by worked out and back filled horizontal beds. This may also account for the early reference (see p 18 and Fig. 3.1) which described the workings at a depth of approximately 50 yards below adit level in Ecton mine as having become horizontal as the pipe vein was followed. Although as mentioned above, this seems to have been D-shaped.

In addition to the huge width alluded to above, Watson also states that ore penetration of the saddle joints could extend up to 80 fathoms away from the main deposit, hence a miner's expression that a saddle 'carried away the ore'.

Although we cannot prove it and indeed Watson was unable to describe it, it would appear that his article goes a long way towards helping our understanding of the way the main eight ore deposits at Ecton Mine were formed although the size of the joints (? trough joints) would seem to have been substantial features in their own right. To this end, Watson's account seems to have been under-valued in the past, especially his contention that the main ore deposits – whether in the main pipe or elsewhere, he did not enumerate – fell into distinct zones of saddles which he described as the 'saddle beds'.

Although Watson could not see the deposits in the Ecton Mine, it was possible for him to see such features in the Clayton Mine and also in the large openings in Good Hope Mine. There were also saddles in the neighbouring Dale Mine and that was working too. Unfortunately, Watson did not give the location of the saddles he saw and described.

Ecton Ore Samples at Chatsworth

White Watson amassed a significant geological collection for Georgiana, 5th Duchess of Devonshire and catalogued it in 1804. Mick Cooper has identified the items recorded in 1804 and a large number came from Ecton. (8)

References

1   Mawe J., *The Mineralogy of Derbyshire*, 1802, pp 109-112

2   The Ecton Copper Mines in England by B. Hooper Brough, *Berge-u-Huettenmaennische Zeitung*, 1883, No 52, p 613. Brough was assistant to the Professor of Geology at the Royal School of Mines, London.

3   Hatchet Dr., *A tour through the counties of England and Scotland in 1796 visiting mines and manufactories*, edited by A Raistrick, 1967, p 66

4 Porter, L., & Robey, J.A., *The Copper & Lead Mines around the Manifold Valley, Staffordshire*, 2000, p 245

5 Althin, T., 'Eric Geisler and his Tour Abroad 1772-73', *Med Hammare och Fackla*, Vol XXVI, 1971

6 White Watson's Scrapbook, pp 137-139, Derby Local Studies Library. I am grateful to Dr J. Rieuwerts and Roger Flindall for making this known to me. Re Watson's reference to Brown Hen: in Derbyshire, this isa term for very poor quality lead ore

7 Watson, J.J.W., *The Geologist*, Vol. 3, 1860. Notes on the Metaliferous Saddles, or ore-bearing beds in the contorted strata of the Lower Carboniferous Rocks of certain parts of Derbyshire & North Staffordshire, pp 357-369

8 The Ecton samples include the following list:
A466 'copper ore'
A467 copper ore (copper ore, galena)
A468/9 copper pyrites (sphalerite and chalcopyrite)
A470 copper pyrites (chalcopyrite on baryte)
A471/8 copper pyrites (chalcopyrite on calcite and baryte)
A479 copper pyrites (chalcopyrite, sphalerite and calcite)
A480/91 copper pyrites (chalcopyrite on baryte)
A492/3 copper pyrites (chalcopyrite on calcite)
A494 copper ore (chalcopyrite on calcite)
A495/8 copper pyrites (chalcopyrite on baryte)
A499 copper pyrites (chalcopyrite on calcite)
A500/2 copper pyrites (chalcopyrite on calcite and baryte)
A503 copper ore
A505 iron pyrites (pyrite)
A506 copper pyrites (chalcoprite)
A507 copper ore

Additionally in the garden at Chatsworth is The Grotto, lined with calcite and copper pyrites from the mine. It is, however, not opened to the public (and in need of a good spring clean to bring back the sparkle it must have enjoyed). Additional Ecton samples may be seen in the Natural History Museum, South Kensington, London, although when last seen, some of the samples were wrongly captioned. They were in the former Geological Museum Collection. Further samples are housed in Cambridge at the Sedgwick Collection. The Manchester Museum has a good 'nest' of green cave pearls from Waterbank Mine, presented by this author and the late David Sales of Leek in 1967.

See list below for details of some papers etc on the geology and mineralogy of Ecton Hill.
Ford, T.D., Geology of Ecton and Other North East Staffordshire Mines, *Mining History*, 2000, Vol 14, No. 4, pp 1-22
Ford, T.D., Sarjeant, W.A.S., Smith, M.E. 1993. Minerals of the Peak District, Bulletin of the Peak District Mines Historical Society, Vol 12, No 1, pp 16-55
Ford T.D., in Porter L., & Robey J.A., the Copper and Lead Mines in and around the Manifold Valley, N. Staffs, 2000, pp 16-26
Masheder, R. & Rankin, A.H. 1988. Fluid inclusion studies on the Ecton Hill copper deposits, North Staffordshire, Mineralogical Magazine, Vol 52, pp 473-482

The top of the pipe working. One Chatsworth plan marks it as "The Engine Shaft"

Contorted Strata off the Ecton Engine Chamber. These beds are situated in the same level as the photograph on page 20

THE DUKE'S TAKEOVER

The Pre-1760 Period

In 1723, a group of adventurers set about reworking an old abandoned mine at Ecton Poyser in the Manifold Valley. Some work had been done here in the previous century, but much of it had been a little higher up the hill where Deutchmen had reworked some ancient shafts for a partnership consisting of the Earl of Devonshire, Sir Richard Fleetwood of Wootton Hall and others. Mining had been pursued by a John Clayton at about the same time. The two mines concerned are now known as Dutchman & Clayton Mines.

Nightingale states that a Cornish miner found ore on the surface of the hill attached 'to some fine spar'. He goes on 'on viewing the situation and height of the hill, he concluded that it might contain vast quantities of copper ore... He, therefore, communicated his discovery and his sentiments to some adventurers at Ashbourne...' These were the 1723 lessees and it is known that they included Ashbourne people. Who the Cornishman was, is unknown however. (1)

The 1 November 1723 lessees were: Baptist Trott of Mapleton, near Ashbourne, Thomas Sleigh of Stanshope, John Sleigh of Ashbourne, William Chancy and Joseph Hayne of Derby, Hall Walton of Stanhope, Wm Wardle of Boosley (Bosley or Boosley Grange) and Samuel Longford of Leek. The 1723 adventurers worked a vertical vein slightly north of Dutchman Mine. It probably yielded ore as it progressed deeper but it also haded a little, so it was not truly vertical, making it more difficult to draw out ore, rock and water. These speculators also decided to drive a level into the vein at river level to 'prove' the vein at that depth and make it easy to remove the ore, rock and water. It was called Ecton Sough. However, the money ran out before the sough reached the vein. This, as it turned out, was a pity for the ore was more plentiful at that depth and would have contributed more to covering the expenses.

Two of the richer adventurers pressed on with a new 21 year lease from 1739 terminating at Michaelmas 1760 (29 September), joined by other investors. The 12 December 1739 lessees were John Gilbert Cooper of Locko, Derbys; Ann Chancy of Ashbourne; John Thompson of Ashbourne; Samuel Longford of Leek; and Alexander Taylor of Buxton Hall. The lessor was the Duke of Devonshire. For the last 150 feet (25 fathoms) above the sough, the ore had become wider and it remained like that for some depth (see below for more details on this).

Pre-1760 Ore Yields

The accounts of Andrew Barker, one of the 4th Duke's agents charged with estate rent collection, include detail of royalties received from Ecton Mine. The royalty was 1/9th and the accounts are fairly complete from 1743-1760 (1747-48, 1750-51 are missing). From 1752 until the end of the lease, tonnages raised were of the order of 500-600 tons p.a. With the end of the lease in sight, the tonnage rose in 1759 – to about 700 tons, but in 1760, 1,490 tons were raised. Clearly, the lessees were raising every last ton they could get their hands on – as Charles Roe and Co did at Parys Mountain in Anglesey in the 1780s.

The Duke was incensed by the large increase in ore extraction. The lessees had, by March 1760, increased the numbers of 'hands' by two to three fold deliberately to gain all they could before the lease ended. Such activity usually was at the expense of careful extraction working practice.

The lease was checked to see if the Duke had any remedy. He had none, but it was realised that whilst the royalty of 1/9th had been paid, there was another aspect of the lease which had been overlooked. It contained a clause requiring the payment of 4d per dish for cope. This was a payment which released the miners and gave them the choice of selling to whom they chose. It was usually 4d per load in the High Peak and 6d per load in the Low Peak. (2)

This duty had never been made and the Duke now sought to determine if it was enforceable. The case stated for Counsel's opinion (from two Members of the Bar) included the statement that shortly after entering onto the mine, the lessees started to get great quantities of copper ore and the mines had ever since continued to be very rich and prosperous. Some £7-8,000 p.a. had been produced. This is probably correct in the 1750s, if not in the 1740s. Cope was determined by measurement i.e., by the dish, rather than by weight. The Duke, or his agent, had not provided a dish or demanded payment. The difficulty was that copper ore could weigh differently according to the richness of the ore.

One opinion was that although the cope could be claimed for the remaining six months of the lease, as no dish had been provided, the lessees had been put in a position of being unable to fulfil the covenant, although if fraud could be proved, a Bill in Equity would succeed. The alternative view was more optimistic, stating that notwithstanding the non-provision of the dish, there was an obligation on the lessees to fulfil the covenant and pay the 4d a dish. The outcome of all of this is unknown. If one takes just the known tonnage (see below) and assumes the weight did not vary, it is possible to gain some idea of the sum of money involved. A dish held about 22lb of ore. A dish of Derbyshire ore by comparison weighed about 60-65 lbs. The known tonnage of 6,114 tons therefore equates to 622,516 dishes and at 4d a dish, this amounts to over £10,000. No wonder the Duke was annoyed.

	Copper raised (tons)	Value £
1743-45	225 (est)	1,802
1746	75	597
1747		
1748		
1749	120	716
1750		
1751		
1752	485	6,617
1753	518	6,283
1754	592	3,662
1755	205	2,131
1756	586	5,109
1757	564)	
1758	526)	16,208
1759	709)*	
1760	1,490	10,535
1761	19	127**
6,114		53,787

John Heaton, the Duke's auditor recorded the Duke's profit for these early years:

1729-1739 – £42.19.8.
1739-1760 – £8,238. 6. 8.

Thus at 1/9th royalty this shows sales for 1739-1760 of some £74,145 – more if the Duke's profit excludes carriage costs to Warrington etc. (Dev, Coll., L/60/20)

** Slimes due to old partnership. These figures are based upon the 1/9th royalty received by the Duke. It is considered that the total tonnage of slimes produced in 1761 was this amount, i.e., these figures should not be multiplied by 9. The Duke would not have sent any money to the previous partners having been denied his 4d a dish.   *Estimated

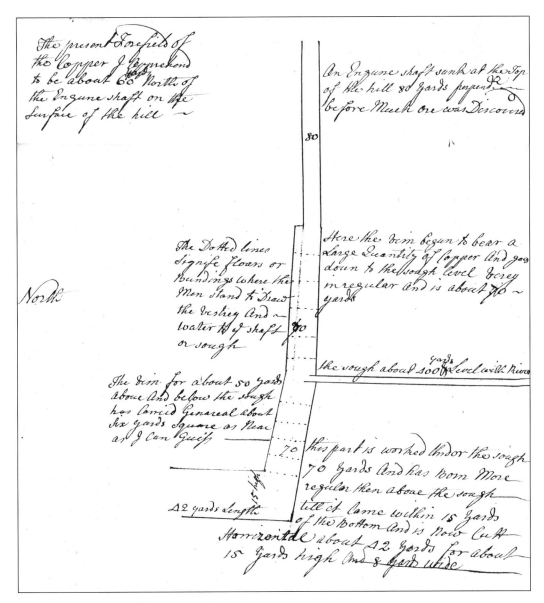

Fig 3.1 Pre-1759 plan of the pipe working

Suspicions of Fraud

The extraction of over 1,400 tons of ore in 1760, could reflect the discovery of a deeper large swelling of the ore-pipe but even if this was true, the sudden rise in price in 1761 under the Duke raises the prospect of whether the correct price was being accounted for to the Duke. It seems likely that the smelters, the purchasers of the ore, would have willingly accounted for their purchases to the Duke as they did in the 1770s.

This means, notwithstanding the non-payment of cope, that there was an increase in ore quality or in ore values in the market place. That it occurred just at the time the Duke took over control of the mine seems most fortuitous. Not only was the volume of ore increasing, the price rose helping to mitigate the effect of later reductions brought about by the monopolistic activities of Thomas Williams (see chapter 14).

The Duke's ore (which he had to have smelted himself) was sent usually to Patten & Co., at Warrington. By the end of the lease, it was being sent by packhorse (or mule) to Roe & Co., at Macclesfield.

Consistent volumes from 1752 would appear to suggest uniformity of the pipe working, but the price obtained was £6-£8 per ton. Once the Duke took over, prices rose in 1761 to a range of £9-£14.17s.0d. In 1762, the minimum price obtained was £12.12s.6d and it was 1774 before the price dropped below that. Even if values were rising, it seems likely that the quality was also rising. During this period (1743-1760), some 6,700 tons are known to have raised and with figures for four years missing, the true figure could be 7,500-8,000 tons. The known value of the ore raised was nearly £54,000 (see Table page 26), but allowing for the missing years, the value was £74,145. (3)

Little other detail of pre-1760 activity at the Ecton Mine is known, other than that given below. It is interesting to consider how long it took for the Duke's ore to reach Warrington and whether it went the whole way by pack horses. It is possible that the ore went to Patten & Co at Cheadle (or the Warrington company as it was sometimes called).

A year prior to the takeover by the Duke, an estimate of a monthly expense of working the mine was made by Jonathan Roose. It is dated 8 September 1759:

'44 Workmen at	1. 12. 0 p month	70. 8. 0
27 Pumpers at 1. 3. 4	Do	31.10. 0
22 Labourers at 1. 0. 0	Do	20.16. 0
12 Carters at 1. 0. 0	Do	12. 0. 0
3 Barrels of Powder	Do	17. 5. 0
32 Duz of Candles	Do	8.16. 0
Ropes	Do	1.10. 0
Timber	Do	5. 0. 0
Iron	Do	5. 0. 0
Cooper Work	Do	1.10. 0
Leather Nails & Spades	Do	1. 0. 0
Coles	Do	-.12. 0
Dressing 45 Tuns of copper soposed to be got out of the mine this last month at 15s pr Tun		33.15. 0
Carpenters Wages per month		4. 0. 0
Blacksmiths & overseers wages pr	Do	10. 0. 0
	Monthly charge	£223. 2. 0
Soposed to be Raised out of the Mine the Last Month	45 Tuns at £8	£360. 0. 0
Raised from ye Hillocks	32	
	77	
		£136.18. 0'

Roose worked at Cow Close Mine, near Youlgreave, from 1753-59 and was probably acting as an umpire. He later went to Penrhyn Ddu in North Wales and then found the Mona Mine deposit for Roe & Co. A note to this account states that 24 of the 44 workmen (i.e. miners) were employed at the bottom of the mine. The other 20 were working 12 fathoms above the sough level. The sough was 45 fathoms above the mine bottom. Roose hoped that the deposit being worked above the sough would continue down to where the other miners were working. If this was to happen, the mine might 'be very rich for a great many years'. The number of workers was therefore 105 plus the carpenter, blacksmith and overseer, making 108 in all.

If the output and expenses are projected onto an annual basis, the profit would be some £1,650 per annum. No wonder the Duke decided to work the mine on his own account. Even after the Duke had turned down the request for an extension of the 1739 lease, it was not clear that he intended working on his own. Henry Scott of Doveridge wrote on behalf of the daughters of the late Alexander Taylor of Buxton Hall, who held a 1/24th share of the mine, asking that they be included in any new arrangement. Additionally, A. Chauncy wrote from Bath to state that his/her grandfather and father 'were the first who worked the mine... and were at very Great Expense in so doing having for twenty years together the largest Shares in it; at a time when it got nothing, to the no small detriment of their family'. They sold the greatest part of their shares to cut their costs. Clearly, the revenue which better days had brought was insufficient to redeem the outlay. The grandchildren hoped to continue to redeem the difference; it was not to be. In the 1739 lease, one of the lessees was Ann Chaney, widow of Wm Chaney, a physician of Ashbourne, Derbyshire (which may mean he was one of the 1723 lessees). Although the names are slightly different, it seems that William was the grandfather referred to.

A simplified section of the mine survives which is undated (see Fig 3.1). From the 1759 Account given above, the mine bottom was 45 fathoms below the sough. On this section, it was 35 fathoms which, if correct, makes it pre-1759. The Engine Shaft had gone down perpendicular for 40 fathoms before much ore had been discovered. Here the vein became richer yielding 'a large quantity of copper'. This continued down to the sough level, a distance of 35 fathoms, in a irregular way. The vein, for about 25 fathoms above and below the sough was about six yards square. Below the sough, the vein continued down 35 fathoms, described as being more regular than above the sough. At that depth the vein would appear to have turned horizontal. The working was 21 fathoms in length and $7^1/_2$ fathoms high, presumably working copper. There were five bundings or platforms for working the ore in the 35 fathoms above the sough and another five below the sough. This sough is not the current sough (now known as Deep Ecton Adit level). The original sough was slightly to the north, but had to be replaced in 1774 because of unstable ground.

The 35 fathom level (actually 34) became one of the main horizons of the mine, the site of the boat level and the haulage whim for ore and water. This level was also the horizon for the geological feature known as the 'double saddle' (see p 22) and the change of the vein from vertical to horizontal must have been as a result of this unusual geological occurrence. (See Chapter 2). (4)

Work Begins 1760-69

To recap, the main period of development of the Ecton mine may be traced back to 1723 when a lease was granted to adventurers or speculators, to try their luck at Ecton Hill. They ran out of funds, although the date is unknown. The Company was successful in finding the topmost of eight large deposits of copper ore arranged vertically. They increased in size with depth. Described as being like a bell this description is misleading for it creates the impression of a mass of ore which was bell shaped and this is not the case. There were eight separate deposits which increased in size, so that the whole deposit – known as a pipe – including the intervening limestones took on the appearance of a bell. Regrettably the analogy was more apocryphal than the writer could have imagined for the deposit had a bottom which cut off at the 110 fms level with no large scale commercial deposits below it. No recent activity by borehole exploration has been undertaken to prove if further deposits at a greater depth exist – or indeed if they exist anywhere else nearby. The success of the 1739 lessees was sufficient for the 4th Duke of Devonshire to turn down a request for a further lease in 1760; he decided to exploit the deposit on his own account, a decision which the 5th Duke must have been grateful for, given the huge wealth the mine created.

For the first ten years or so, the mine appears to have carried on much the same as before,

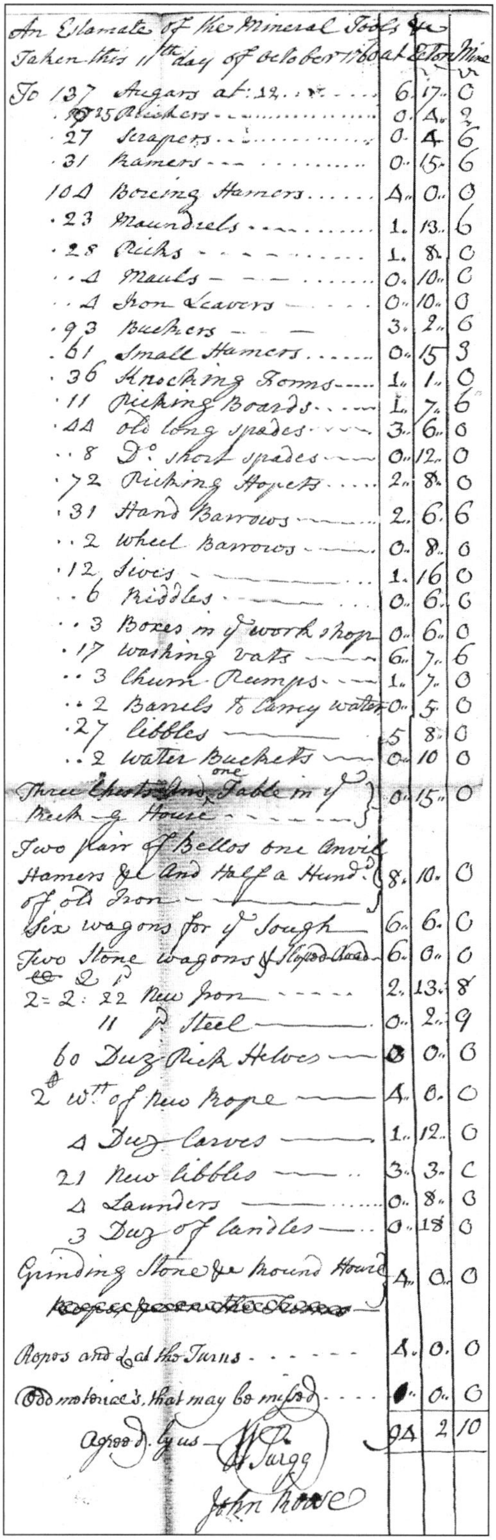

Fig 3.2: The 1760 inventory

selling the ore to the same suppliers, sinking ever deeper to prove the deposit at depth in the hope that the pattern of large swellings of ore would be repeated by yet another one somewhere below their feet. The mine was not advanced in the 1760s in a technical sense, the amount of water was not great and the concentration of ore near to the main shaft meant that extraction costs could be kept to a minimum. Production generally grew as the records of costs, general activity, the number of people employed and of course the volume of ore extracted indicate. By 1770, the mine was smelting a lot of the ore to coarse copper metal at the mine in order to reduce the volume to be carried away to the smelting houses over the hills. In this year, a smelter was opened at Whiston by the Duke. The closure of one of the customers, Cooper & Rotton of Derby, enabled the mine to purchase much of their fixtures and fittings for use at Whiston.

The payment books were made up to six or seven week periods so that there were always 8 reckonings per year. The first one was on 29 November 1760. Ninety one people were paid wages and all were male. It is not clear whether this was the final payroll under the lessees or whether more people were taken on to assist in the removal of the fixtures and fittings of the lessees. It would appear that the Duke did not purchase the fixture and fittings, for this first reckoning includes a payment for raising '1,486 waggon full of gear and other utensils of the old proprietors'.

Wages for five 'lads' began at 2s per week for the youngest, with one – Wm Marsden – receiving 4s per week. Thirteen labourers and 29 pumpers were paid 10d per day, for a six day week. There were eight shaft drawers who were marginally better paid at 1s per day. Three men, described as 'Counts and sets to the Shaft' received 7s per week, while 25 workmen (presumably miners) received 8s per week. Two of these worked the pumps on Sunday and received 7s 6d extra for the 7 week period. Also earning 8s per week were four 'Derbyshire workmen'. There were two smiths, earning 12s and 7s per week – clearly the smith and an assistant. Two carpenters were paid per their account, but there was one on the payroll at 8s per week. Finally there was one copper dresser, David Malampy, who was paid 10s per week.

The next reckoning (of 3 January 1761) indicates that ore raising and dressing had recommenced for there is the first reference to 'wimen' – two at 3s per week and one (Ann Parker) at 5s per week. The number of employees seems to have fallen to 78 people, with even fewer (43) by February 1761, although at this point the need for caution appears – the employment of a 'knocker' (to break up lumps of ore). The payment for 18 weeks could mean the payment for three people at 6 weeks each or simply a late payment since that person commenced work! It is likely to mean three people but problems like this prevent meaningful analysis at times.

By mid-1761, there were about 150 people drawing wages plus contractors, miners paid a rate for doing a particular job. However this figure dropped in September 1761 to 65 on wages and with slight variations either side, this general level is maintained to the end of 1762. Clearly a new system of paying the miners was introduced and the number of men underground is no longer apparent.

Ore production increased throughout 1761, with 575 tons of copper being raised. By March 1761 the dressers included Ann Parker's team (six in all), responsible for washing at 4s 6d per week, 16 knockers under Elizabeth Keeling earning 2s 6d per week and 21 'pickers' under Thomas Wint earning 1s 6d per week making 45 people in all, plus four 'coper dressers', earning much higher wages, 13 at 10s per week and one at 8s per week.

The number of hours per day in the lead mining area of Derbyshire was usually six rather than eight (5) to allow for the agricultural interests of the workers. There is a clear indication of the working day at Ecton for Efford (6) states that the shift was 6 hours in 1769. The loss of production 'during the hay' was generally common and Ecton may appear to be no different. Each September, the ore-raised figure for the previous reckoning shows a reduction in the period 1762-1767 (except 1763, when it occurs in August). The cause of this could have been the time off for the annual wakes or an indication that hay was cut and carried later than now. The former is more likely. It is possible that the ore dressers worked for ten hours per day (see under Ore Dressing, Chapter 5).

Clearly the major activity of the mine concerned the exploitation of the huge deposit of ore in the Ecton Mine. However exploration continued elsewhere. In September 1761 George Mitchell & Co are recorded as driving the Lead Sough at £4 per year – a reference to Chadwick Mine, and work here continued for some time. Although the sough is now flooded, access from the inner end reveals that is was originally constructed as a 'coffin level' (shaped like a coffin in cross-section), with the characteristic of sweeping pick marks away from the worker, from the roof of the level to about 3 feet off the floor, then a change in direction with the marks being towards the worker. Much of this pick work has been removed by subsequent enlargement which may be dated to the 1760s and later. It is the only known surviving example of a coffin level in the North Staffordshire orefield.

Further work was also being undertaken in September 1761 at 'Duchmans Engine' where men were driving. References to some areas, such as Owls Nest unfortunately remain a mystery. The 'Engine' would be a horse whim used for haulage up the shaft.

Ore Production

Copper ore production in the decade reached a peak in 1763 and 1764, producing around 1,165 tons in each year. (See page 4 for the complete figures). In 1762, 1765-66, production was between 900-1,000 tons per annum with a reduction thereafter each year to 1769 when only 400 tons was raised. However it is known that the mine had 2,800 tons of ore and metal on the bank in 1769 and the reduced production must have been because of this. Once the decision to smelt their own ore had been taken, ore was stockpiled until the decision was taken concerning where to build the smelter. The sight of 2,800 tons of yellow ore and metal glistening in the sun would have been quite impressive. The amount of ore dressed is substantially less throughout the period compared to the amount raised – a difference of several hundred tons in some years. Clearly the dressers could not keep up with the miners.

At an early date, it was realised that the waste being dumped on the waste tip (the hillock) contained retrievable ore and workers were paid by the ton extracted to retrieve this. They appear to have dressed it themselves as it was likely to contain much more waste material than the more concentrated ore being raised from the main areas of the deposits. The coarse ore was dressed on the hillside where the late 19th century dressing floor was situated. The dressers were paid by the volume of ore recovered. The ore was raised up the Smithy Shaft, whilst the good quality ore was trammed straight out of the level and treated separately by the river.

The need to carefully control the dressing process was highlighted by Efford in 1769 when he recorded that the recovery of fine slimes (or particles) of ore from water was managed by an old Cornishman (Philip Tangye). Even so, considerable ore must have been lost through dressing, for over 40 tons of fine copper slime (fine grains of ore) was raised from the river bed in 1836 (7), The adjacent Burgoyne Royalty dressing floor, used for mines not owned by the Duke, could have contributed to this, however.

Efford described the dressing as being done by women and girls sitting at benches, breaking up the ore with flat hammers. No attempt has yet been made to describe where this operation took place. Papers in the court proceedings *Roscoe v New Dale Mining Co and R. Niness* (8) include a plan indicating that the Duke's dressing floor was adjacent to the river. A surface plan of the mine in 1809 shows the mine buildings well. There are three long buildings marked adjacent to the river and it is suggested that these are the buildings which were used for dressing. A lot of mines dressed ore in the open, so the female workers were clearly better off. Although several buildings were built with a tiled roof (presumably the smelters and smithy), the purchase of thatch indicates that others were not tiled and it is likely that the knocking shed of Elizabeth Keeling and her workers would have been one of those which was thatched. It is also likely to have been open-sided to allow in more light and let out the dust. Thatch was purchased from Pikehall, east of Newhaven. Upon the death of the 4th Duke, the amount due to his executors by the mine was £11,402. 7s 4d. (9)

Lead Ore

The reckoning book records the payment for 165 loads 5 dishes between 1762-1769 with (curiously) 1 ton 17cwt in 1761. This makes a total tonnage (with 4 loads to the ton) of some 42 tons of lead ore from the mine in this period. It is likely that much of this came from Chadwick Mine.

Profitability of the Business

The mine was an economic success right from the start of the Duke's involvement – presumably reflecting the pattern of the previous few years. Annual costs for the first decade (the 1760s) averaged £4,666 p.a. The sale income details for 1768, 1769 are not available, although C Roe & Co bought ore worth £3,900 in 1768. However sales were being reigned back ahead of the decision to build the Whiston Smelter. On top of this, it is known that a substantial amount of ore remained at the mine. Robert Shore detailed the stock in 1770:

	Ton	£ Per Ton	£ Total
'Botham Ore' ready for use	177	16	2,832
ditto undressed	40	16	640
ditto carrd to Whiston	50	16.10s	825
Undressed Corse ore	2,000	4.0.0d	8,000
Ore from the catchpits	30	12.0.0d	360
Copper for refining	6	120.0.0d	600
			£13,257

Plus
Ore belonging the Executors (of the 4th Duke)

	Tons	£ per Ton	£ Total
At Whiston	100	£5.0.0d	£ 500
At Ecton dres'd	100	£4.10.0d	450
At do, undres'd	100	do.	450
At do. Undres'd	200	£3.0.0d	600
(very corse)			£2,000

NB All the corse ores undres'd are only computed the quantity when dress'd may be more.'

Thus some 2,797 tons of ore remained unsold at the end of 1770. Ore raised in 1770 amounted to 795 tons (dressed ore 533 tons) so a substantial amount of stock remained to be sold in 1769 worth in excess of £10,000. Ignoring the stock, the sales of £96,872 exceeded costs of £44,378, yielding a surplus of £52,494 for the period 1760-69, an average of £5,832 p.a. (10)

Ore Volumes and Receipts

The amount of ore raised was less than 1,000 tons p.a. except in 1763 & 1764. The total tonnage for 1760-69 was 7,675 tons of ore raised. However ore dressed in this period amounts to 5,759 tons. This figure includes ore recovered from the 'hillocks' and termed hillock ore – i.e. ore originally thrown away and not having been dressed because the ore was not concentrated enough. This difference in volumes raised and dressed may be explained in part by ore lying 'on the bank' awaiting treatment, but it cannot be the whole story. In 1763/64, 2,331 tons were raised and 1,245 tons were dressed.

The average ore sales figure for 1761-69 is £10,763 p.a. This compares with say Dolcoath at Camborne in Cornwall where the average sales figure from 1740-1777 was £12,162. (11) However, the profit at Ecton would have been higher per ton because of the low pumping costs. Because the Ecton ore deposit was a vertical one, rather than a horizontal one, the extent of the workings were small in width and the interference with the water table remained, for the most part, of no great consequence. Unfortunately, the profitability of the concern at Dolcoath during this period is not quoted by Harris. Another mine near to Dolcoath working during this period was South Crofty, where between 1747-56, Sir Francis Basset made £111,000 profit i.e. £11,000 average p.a. albeit from tin, not copper, but better than the average sales at Ecton. (12)

None-the-less, the profit on the first ten years of activity produced a substantial revenue for the Duke and the figures indicate that the mine was getting richer. The receipts in 1766 were £14,673 and in 1767 £14,229. (13) John Heaton's accounts (Dev.Coll., L/60/20) indicates that the profit from 1760-75 was £78,233.19.9d and from mid-1775-80 it was £31,224.12.3d. Profit levels were originally lower than South Crofty, but were to reach an average of £15,700 for 1780-91 (see chapter 12 Profit and Loss)

In the period 1761-69, the total cash (i.e. surplus) sent to the Duke amounted to £39,086. From a cash flow point of view, the mine gave 5% discount 'for ready money'. By contrast, in the mid 1770s the main purchasers were borrowing money from the Duke to fund their buying, at 5% interest.

A document has survived dated 15 September 1774 which is headed: 'Stock of Ores and Copper at Ecton and Whiston & Value'. It reads as follows:

	£	s	d
'Ore undres'd as it Rises out of the Mine at Ecton			
350 Ton at £11.17.0 pr Ton	4,147	10	0
Dres'd Ore 70 Ton at £12.12.0d	882	0	0
Coarse handaways undres'd 3,500 Ton			
At £1.10s pr Ton	5,250	0	0
Do. Belonging the younger sons of his Grace the			
Late Duke of Devonshire			
190 Ton at £1.10s per Ton	225	0	0
Whiston			
Botham Ore ready for smelting			
110 Ton £13.10.0 pr Ton	1,485	0	0
Wast Ores 70 Ton at £6 pr Ton	420	0	0
Slime ore 70 Ton at 7/10 pr Ton	525	0	0
Calcyin'd Regale 2 Ton at £60 pr Ton	120	0	0
Fine Copper 10$\frac{1}{2}$ Ton at £92	966	0	0
	£14,020	10	0'

This amounted to 4,110 tons of ore lying on the bank at the mine and a further 250 tons of ore waiting to be smelted at Whiston. A surprise is the amount of 'handaways', an expression not previously recorded in the Peak District ore field. It presumably relates to the ores held in host rock of gangue, such as calcite, which was awaiting separation. Another is the amount of ore awaiting dressing. This is alluded to in a letter dated 24 November 1774 written by Robert Shore from his Snitterton address:

'I have carefully examined the quantity and quality of all the waste ores at Ecton and Whiston. Belonging the Younger Sons of his Grace the late Duke of Devonshire; and Valued them as follows:

(Viz)300 Ton at £5.15.0d pr Ton	£1,725
60 Ton at £3.10.0d pr Ton	210
	£1,935

If his Grace will be pleased to allow for the above as Valued think it will be much the best on all sides. For by putting a small quantity of coarse ores into every Charge of Botham Ore; it makes ye s'd waste ores produce rather than smelting them by themselves; and they help the botham Ore by way of Flux'.

Clearly it made sense commercially to mix the poorer ores with the better (botham) ores whoever owned them – the 4th Duke's Trustees or the 5th Duke. Even ten years after the 4th Duke's death, stock of ores attributed to his estate were still valued at £1,935. The time to pay off the Trustees and run one business had arrived and this appears to have been done. Up until this date, all the smelting at Ecton appears to have been done to the 4th Duke's estate account only.

In 1780, the ore on the bank at the mine was said to be worth £20,000 (see p 209). In 1770, it had been valued at £15,257. Ore prices in the ten year period to 1780 had dropped marginally and ores was selling at £15 per ton. Much of the ore would no doubt be the poorer ores but we have no idea of actual tonnages. What we do know is that tonnages of ore on the bank were growing. The increased smelting capacity from 1780 once the fires at Whiston were relit presumably started to eat into this stock.

A Remarkable Survivor

The 1760 equipment inventory refers to a grinding wheel 'in Round House', valued at £4. This appears to have survived – or at least half of it has survived! On the west side of the Boulton & Watt winding engine house is an embanked drystone wall supporting the ground made up to house the counter-balancing drum. Exposed in that wall is about 50% of a 4ft 6in diameter massive limestone crushing wheel. It seems to have failed on a line of weakness across the wheel. It has a thickness of 15 inches and would appear to have been strengthened (perhaps after the weakness was observed) as slots across the face of the wheel exist for metal inserts. Having parted into two pieces, the surviving stone was reused as a base plate for a vertical timber. This was set into the stone with a little run off for rainwater. It would appear to have supported the pivotal post of something, perhaps the counter-balancing drum of 1788.

It would not have been the central post of the whim as this rotated. It would have had a spigot at the bottom and the edge runner would have had a hole cut into the recess to carry the rotating spigot. Moreover, the recess would been round, not square. If the central post of the counter-balancing drum rotated, it is unclear what function the stone performed.

The reference to the 'Round House' indicates that it was formerly in a building and was worked by a horse (ie it was not a hand operated grinding wheel – which would not have cost £4 in any event). This building is not marked on Potter's plan of 1809, if (as is likely) the wheel was used for reducing ore. Curiously, Potter marks a round building at the quarry midway between Ecton and Ecton Lee, indicating that a similar crusher for reducing limestone existed at this point. It is unlikely that the 1739-1760 adventurers were working a limestone quarry as their mine was producing stone which they could have used. This quarry was probably started by the Duke to provide building stone after 1760.

The replacement for the edge-crusher may be found in a reference of November 1782 – 'Going to Grin Moor for stone = 6s 0d.' Grin Moor, south of Buxton, is on limestone and owned by the Duke. Clearly Ecton had no need for a cart load of limestone.

This edge-crushing stone would appear to be the oldest recorded crushing stone in any Peak District mine to have been recorded, predating the previous earliest record by 57 years. (14) It is remarkable that half of it appears to have survive.

The grinding wheel surviving by the engine house

References

1   Nightingale, Rev., *Description of the County of Stafford*, c.1808, p 1011

2   Rieuwerts, J. H., *Glossary of Derbyshire Lead Mining Terms*, 1998, p 48

2a John Gilbert Cooper wrote in May 1760 to Godfrey Heathcote stating that the inclusion of the 'cope clause' was a draughtman's error. The 1723 lease included the clause as it was common to do so in lead mining leases from the Duke. In 1739 (Gilbert Cooper claimed) he had objected to the clause, saying 'how could copper ore and callamy [zinc ore] be subjected to a dish when it was sold by weight'. The clause could not be removed as the Duke had already signed the lease and as the cope had not been claimed under the 1723 lease, 'durst say....it would not be claimed under the new lease'. *Caveat Emptor*. The lease was signed in Ashbourne

3   Dev. Coll. A S Series: L/91/1/1-3; L/91/3/2; AS/ 1062-65

4   The documents referred to above, are from the Dev. Coll. Ecton Voucher Box series

5   Willies, L., 'John Taylor in Derbyshire, 1839-1851' *Bull. PDMHS*, vol 6, No. 5, p 228

6   Efford, W., Gentleman's Magazine, reprinted in *Bull. PDMHS*, 1961, vol 1, No.5, pp 37-40)

7   Porter, L., & Robey, J., *Copper and Lead Mines Around the Manifold Valley, Staffordshire*, p 226

8   op cit., pp 231-234

9   Dev. Coll., AS/1053, p 4

10 Figures taken from the audited accounts; Dev Coll. Voucher box 1760-74

11 Harris, TR., *Dolcoath: Queen of Cornish Mines*, 1974 p 22

12 Buckley, JA., *A History of South Crofty Mine*, u.d. p 31.

13 These figures are confirmed by Sir Joseph Banks' Journal

14 Rieuwerts, J. H., op. cit., p 54

Remains of a shoe found near Starr Shaft

4th Duke of Devonshire *(Devonshire Collection)*

5th Duke of Devonshire as a young man *(Dev. C.)*

When the Duke took over, the business of running the mine was on the cost book system. This meant that the shareholders of the mine (in this case, the Duke) were responsible for covering the costs. Consequently at certain times each year, the additional costs over sales were met by a 'call' on the shareholders. The opposite of this was the wonderful experience enjoyed by a minority of investors of seeing income exceeding expense, resulting in a dividend. At Ecton, the Duke was an 'arms length' owner/investor. Men of his rank (and there were few that equalled him financially or socially) were considered unworthy if they 'worked for a living'. Therefore all the work was done by people on his behalf. The level of profit certainly seems to have assisted many an interesting night at Brooke's Club according to Amanda Foreman (1), although the source of the 5th Duke's income is not discussed by her.

Only one visit by the mine owner to the source of such wealth is on record, a staggering display of indifference. The Fourth Duke visited the mine in 1763. His successor, who enjoyed the majority of the huge fortune which amounted from the mine, also only seems to have visited it once, in 1783.

The mine was initially managed on the Duke's behalf by Robert Shore of Snitterton, near Matlock, Derbyshire. He was paid £70 per annum with the first quarter's payment recorded in the Reckoning June 1761. His salary was increased to £100 from the reckoning of October 1763. He was responsible for employing miners and ancillary staff and prosecuting the development of the mine. He paid all wages and costs, the books of account being audited by Godfrey Heathcote, the Duke's attorney. As will be seen later, Shore's activities at the mine were to be eclipsed by the man's lack of honour. He was to be found guilty of fraud, both in c.1769 and in 1779. Luckily, he had an extraordinary employer. Not only did the 5th Duke content himself in only spending the profits of his most successful investment, he drew the line at committing Shore to trial and certain imprisonment. He could have easily achieved this under criminal law or under civil law for debt.

Fraud by the Manager

Following the death of the 4th Duke, (he died in September 1764), the November and December Reckoning costs amounted to £1,090.16s.9d. It is unclear whether there was an initial mistake on Shore's part, but he charged both the Executors of the 4th Duke and the Guardians of the 5th Duke with this cost and failed to account for the over-payment. The problem was noted at the time and is specifically mentioned in the audit by Godfrey Heathcote of both the Executors' and the Guardians' Movement of Funds, dated March 1766.

It is probable that the disbursements at the mine were made with cash belonging to the Guardians and that Shore then billed the Executors with the same amount, for a note in Heathcote's hand states that 'By the 3rd Article on the debtor side of the Account with the Extors he (Shore) charges himself with the said summe of £1,090.16s.9d' i.e. he pocketed this amount.

It was some years before the problem was realised and Shore took out a mortgage and bond dated 6 February 1770 (it was exactly 6 months later before Heathcote received it) to repay £1,000 plus interest at 3%. The rest he paid by cash and bills. A further document (a copy of a receipt given to Shore and dated 17 May 1779) refers to a payment of £139.18s.0d, being 3% interest on £1,090.16s.9d from 6 February 1776 to 6 February 1779. However the reverse side of the same document makes it clear that Shore had been paying interest plus a sum of £100 per annum to repay the principal outstanding (£1,000) on a yearly basis and that in 1777 (and probably in 1779), £600 remained due there being no payment in 1775 and 1776, so why the £139.18s.0d was paid is not clear.

Shore would appear to have been dismissed in 1779. Robey (2) states that some £5,000 was involved at this time, but it is not clear on what this is based. A document listing Shore's effects dated 13 May 1779 seems to indicate that part of the Reckoning of November 1778 plus most of the January and February 1779 reckoning remained unpaid – amounting to £2,869.13s.11d and there was another £905 for the March Reckoning due. It is endorsed with a later note referring to a comment by Cornelius Flint that the total unpaid at 27 March 1779 was £3,052.7s.0d.

The Reckoning for February to August 1779 is missing so some vital information for this period – such as the date of Flint's appointment, cannot be quoted. On the basis that lightning can strike twice, but usually in a separate spot, Heathcote sought confirmation from Messrs Cooper & Rotton, Patten and Roe, the three purchasers of ore and coarse metal, of details of their purchases and what they had paid for them.

Amongst those records are two telling sets of figures relating to payments by Roe & Co for ore to the Trustees of the 4th Duke's younger sons, formerly described as the Executors of the 4th Duke.

Shore's figures for 1765 - 67:   £4,349 (3)
Roe & Co's figures 1765 - 67:   £3,297 (4)

A difference of £1,052, but an over-payment compared with the actual cash received.

The matter does not rest here, however. Patten & Co supplied Godfrey Heathcote with details of ore purchase for the period of 1761 - 66 amounting to £16,374 (5). The equivalent figure from Shore's books is £20,430 (6), a difference of £4,056. This compares with Roe & Co where there was a shortfall paid to the Duke of £5,438 (7). The difference between the figures from Patten and Roe is £1,382 i.e. £5,438 - £4,056. (The account for Cooper and Rotton for 1761-67 shows a difference of £406, incidentally).

So, on the 4th Duke's Trustee's account, the books show Shore stating sales were £1,052 more than they really were. On the Guardians of the 5th Duke's account, Shore shows the Patten account as being £4,056 more than it is, while for Roe's he underpays £5,438, netting £1,382. If it was finishing here he nets £1,382 on the 5th Duke's account, but he overpays the figures on the 4th Duke's Trustees account to the tune of £1,052.

The irregularities mentioned here display good reasons for Heathcote to be concerned. It should be remembered that Shore was the most highly paid member of the Ecton workforce, earning £100 per annum. The figures involved here were therefore clearly significant. However, they show an accounting nightmare rather than fraud and regrettably one is unable to point directly at what Shore was up to from this alone.

Robert Shore appears to have got himself substantially in debt in the late 1770s. He was in partnership at a paper mill at Matlock with George White from April 1770. In January 1778, he agreed to continue the business on his own account. However, he was soon in debt to White. By 10 March 1779, he owed £400 rent (to Christmas 1778) plus other debts to the value of £650, all to White.

This detail is from a Chatsworth document (8) which also states that 'Shore was greatly behind in his payments to the work people at Ecton Copper Mine' With other complaints being made against him, the Duke's auditor (John Heaton) 'finding a great deficiency discharged Mr Shore'. The latter had not yet paid off the money still owing from the previous decade and the total due amounted to c. £5,000 (i.e. the old monies and the new debt). Shore had been misappropriating money owed to the creditors of the mine and smelter. (9)

Shore agreed in May 1779 to convey his estate to the Duke, but it was feared that it would not realise enough to cover the amount owed. He had previously surrendered his copyhold estates to the Duke in February 1771. (10) A meeting of his creditors was called to meet at the White House, Bakewell, on 1st December 1779. His mine shares were put up for sale in 1780. (11)

The list of assets of Robert Shore 'taken from his own mouth at Buxton Town Hall on 13 May 1779' was:

The rental on various properties £49

A freehold house used as a paper mill at Matlock which cost £1,400 and which could bring in a rent of £300 ($\frac{1}{2}$ share held by Shore)

Stock on the farm at Snitterton (where he lived) and household furniture

Freehold wasteland upon Morridge, about 60 acres near Leek and cost £540 about 2 years ago.

House thereon

Clock and bedding at Ecton

Bedding at Whiston

'Lease of Rowson's Farm and the crop thereon and on another farm' (? the one at Morridge) and 'stock of candles and gunpowder and stock in the shop and warehouse at Ecton Mine'.

This is the only reference to a mine shop at Ecton and presumably enabled miners to purchase materials at the mine.

Shore also had shares in various mines and these were: 1/6 and 1/24th of Orchard Mine, Winster; 1/96 and 1/192 of Drake and Limestone Mine, Winster; 3/22 of Over Pitts, Winster; 1/24 of Pitt Moss and Derbyshire Founder Mine at Grassington, Yorkshire and 5/24 of Mixon Copper Mine, south west of Ecton. However, the note of this is endorsed 'has got nothing'.

Misappropriation of funds must have been an ever-present temptation to the overseers of the income-generating side of the Duke's estates. In addition to the experience of Robert Shore's fraud in 1764 and 1778, another case occured in 1784. This was at Buxton and concerned the 'Agent of the Baths'. His account shows income of £485.2s.10d but only £240 was forwarded. It is endorsed 'The remainder was misapplied by him and will be lost'. (12)

A large number of records survive which take a close look at the sales of ore and coarse metal to Roe & Co, Cooper & Rotton and Patten & Co. The details of purchases by Pattens agree with Shore's account book, but between May 1767 and the end of the year there are several discrepancies in the other two accounts. Most of it (in value terms) concerned the Roe account. Some £602.9s.9d of sales had not been accounted for by Shore. The amount on the Cooper & Rotton account was £296; the total being £898.9s.9d. If the intention had been to take this sum too, then it was thwarted by Godfrey Heathcote, the sum when paid going to the Duke's account as a result of Heathcote's diligence. Additionally, two purchases by Patten & Co (for £64.10s.0d and £436.14s.3d) were allocated by Shore to both the Guardians and the executors' accounts.

Clearly Patten & Co would not have paid twice. It is not possible now to determine whether this was a symptom of an overworked and stressed employee or not. The mists of time have clouded the opportunity of making any assessment. However, Shore did defraud the mine of over £1,000 and one wonders whether these different irregularities were meant to draw a veil over this in the hope that they would help to mask what had really been perpetrated. What we do know is that the man did steal a second time and was dismissed for it.

The legacy of unpaid debtors from the Shore era lingered longer than might have been expected. Six bills were included in the Reckoning of March 1787 of Benjamin Wigley, who was probably deceased (the payment was made to his brother, William) The amount was significant too: £117.6s.9d. The bills are endorsed 'none of these 6 Bills has ever been ch[d] (charged) suppose Mr Shore were in partnership.'

Appointment of Cornelius Flint

The removal of Robert Shore brought Cornelius Flint to the position of 'Overseer' at the mine in 1779. He was from Great Longstone and had experience in mining. He had been the agent at the Hubberdale Lead Mine, not far from Flagg and may have had other responsibilities for the Duke in addition to the Ecton Mine. (13)

Cornelius Flint married Mary Lomas on 19 August 1781, when she was 30 years old. They were married at Earl Sterndale by Joshua Flint. She was described as 'an agreeable young lady with a handsome fortune'. (14) They had four children – Joshua (1782-1805); Mary (1785-1809); Dorothy (1787-1811) and Charles (1789-1861). The latter became the Medical Officer of Health in Leek and became an investor in local mines. He bought a share in the Botstone Lead Mine, Wetton Mill, from Richard Gaunt, also of Leek, for instance. (15) Cornelius Flint died in 1822 and is buried at Hartington.

It is traditionally held in the village that the Duke built what is today called 'The Old Vicarage' for Flint. It is situated on the bottom corner of Church Street with Dig Street. At the time of its completion, however, it is held locally that the vicarage burnt down and the Duke initially moved the vicar into the house, rather than Flint! The house has a well within the building, lined with limestone and looking just like a flooded mine shaft. No doubt the cost of construction of this former estate house and well lie buried in the mine accounts. However the date stone shows that it was built in the 1780s, so Flint lived elsewhere initially.

For many years after his death, the Hazles Cross Colliery was known as 'Flint's Pits' such was his reputation. Following his appointment at Ecton at £100 per annum, the majority of the individual invoices drawn against the mine have survived. They give us a far greater insight into what was being purchased and delivered to the mine or Whiston, or costs incurred at the two collieries, Hazles Cross and Foxt Wood.

An early exercise by the new manager was the reduction of costs. Across the board, Flint seems to have forced down expenses. There is a local tradition that is accorded to the Clayton deposit known as 'Smackers Open' but which may have its origins in this period. The story goes

Left: The grave of Cornelius Flint, Hartington Church

Below: The home of Cornelius Flint and his wife Mary, now called The Old Vicarage, Hartington

that during the excavation of the huge deposit, the miners worked high off the floor, standing in hammocks and were only allowed to work three days a week as 'they would earn too much money'. Did this actually allude to Flint's exercise in cost reduction? Perhaps at a time when ore output was greater than smelter production or the demand for the copper metal justified.

Examples of this are the reduction in carriage and candle costs:

Ecton–Whiston	9/1770: 8s 4d per ton	9/1780: 6s 8d per ton
Highmoor Pen–Whiston	9/1770: 5s 0d per ton	9/1780: 3s 4d per ton
Ecton–Highmoor Pen	9/1770: 4s 2d per ton	9/1780: 3s 4d per ton
Hazles Cross–Whiston	3/1780: 4s 0d per ton	9/1780: 3s 4d per ton
Candles	2/1782: 6s 6d per doz	8/1783: 6s 0d per doz

The invoices allow such an intense analysis of purchases that their importance cannot be over emphasised; whether it be of the tonnages being moved of all sorts of commodities; the nature of the goods being purchased – shovels, candles, invoices from long forgotten businesses: and so on. An invoice from the end of 1782 confirms that carts were being used to convey coal from Hazels Cross to Whiston, thereby ending a suspicion that this was so and the frustration of not being able to prove it. An invoice of 1779 shows that wagons (i.e. 4 wheeled two-axle vehicles) were in use where road conditions permitted. Bills from the Dale and Holme End (now Hulme End) toll bars indicate that there were times when the mine had to pay to bring items down the turnpike, probably owing to size – perhaps timber. For this legacy we have to be grateful, but the invoices for the years of Robert Shore would have been even more important with their references to purchases of 'cast mettle wheels' and other commodities early in the Industrial Revolution.

It was Cornelius Flint who was at the helm of the mine as it entered its period of maximum output and profitability, with responsibility for all aspects of this vertically integrated business. From January 1782 his salary rose to £148 per annum (£18.10s.0d per Reckoning).

Payment of Wages and Expenses

The majority of the money due to the mine from ore/metal sales was paid by Bills – the 18th century equivalent to a cheque. These were either banked or, in some cases, sent directly to the Duke when the income was far greater than the requirements of the mine. Cash was obtained in Chesterfield, but it is not known whether an Ecton Account was held there or whether it was from a Chatsworth General Fund. Other income from the sale of scrap iron, grass from land surrounding the mine or coal pits etc was usually small and often settled per contra account. In 1777, the mine went for most of the year with a cash float of about £1,000 held at the mine. It was used up at the December Reckoning but whether this was usual is not known. Some payments to the mine were made by cash. Patten & Co sent £210 by cash in December 1771 for instance. (16)

Cash was obtained by the mine from Messrs Wilkinson at Chesterfield. The agent (Robert Shore and then Cornelius Flint) fetched it from Chesterfield. Flint later described the procedure as being accompanied by 'two stalwart miners' and these were Ralph and Joseph Bonsall. All three went by horse-back and they also accompanied Flint to Whiston where payments were also made (and presumably also for the two collieries). There is no note indicating that they were ever robbed, nor any oral tradition of this. A statement of disbursements in 1777 indicates that there was no pattern to the days when money was collected; it appears to be purely at random. In January 1782 the mine purchased a 'pair of saddle pistols with bags and moulds' for £1.7s.0d. They were purchased off Hervis and Redfern of Birmingham and cost 1s.6d to transport by coach to Derby, where they would have been collected by the mine from the Duke's Town House. A check of the gun collection at

Chatsworth to see if these survive was unproductive. The trip to Chesterfield took two days and the Whiston trip one day.

All payments at the mine were receipted and paid two – three months in arrears. Quite often payment was collected on behalf of the debtor. For instance one bill for riddles, 'sives' (from James Hodgkinson of Hathersage) in 1779 indicates that they were left at the Red Lion in Tideswell for collection and the money was probably left at 'Thomas Armes at Tadenton (Taddington).' Debts were not paid by Bill of Exchange but by cash.

The Movement of Goods and Services

Clearly local businesses used publicans they could trust to look after money and commodities, presumably paying a fee for the service. Another example of this is an order to George Critchlow of Pethills Forge near Winkhill on the Leek-Ashbourne road. In November 1780 he provided 1cwt or so of steel and '1 doz Miners Spades made strong' (they cost 2s 0d each). These were left at 'Botham House', now Bottom House. Here was an inn where two turnpike roads crossed. One of these was the road from Froghall to Warslow used by carts and wagons en route to Ecton. No doubt one of the carriers picked up the items and carried them on to Ecton. The pub, The Green Man, is still there on the A523 at its junction with the B5053 (see also Chapter 10 on local routes for details of Critchlow's deliveries).

The acquisition of materials for the mine often meant arranging for them to be left at a certain point and then collected. Towards the end of 1780, 36cwt of chain was purchased from J Rowbottom of Foolow (for use to lower horses down into the mine). They were taken to 'Middleton' (Stony Middleton) by the maker and then collected. Also, a John Barton (address unknown) made 'six dozen spaids' at 2s.0d each. His instructions were to send them to Longnor 'to be left at Thos. Besicks at The Cock'. In order to get smitham riddles of the size required, it was necessary to send a man to the maker with a peg shaped to the right gauge (R. February 1780). Refreshments were provided on the mine's pay-days. In March 1781 Cornelius Flint claimed his expenses for providing 15 bottles of rum (they cost £2) for pay-days since the previous June. He also claimed for six pay-day expenses at £2.14s.0d, possibly for food etc.

By the 1780s the mine sat at the centre of a huge organisation from the point of view of the movement of materials. Ore and metal left the mine; the ore was bound for Whiston, although where the metal went (to Whiston or direct to purchasers) is not known. Coal was continually being brought to the mine for smelting copper and the smaller output of lead ore that was raised.

Additionally, from 1786, coal was required for the newly built brick kiln at Newhaven. Fireclay was needed for the Ecton Furnaces and was dug up at Newhaven. When the furnaces needed to be replaced, the stone was brought Revidge, northwest of Warslow. The furnaces also needed bricks – in fact the mine seems to have been a prodigious consumer of them.

Initially both burnt bricks and unburnt bricks, i.e. clay in the form of bricks to be burnt in the Ecton furnaces, were sent to the mine plus white bricks made from silica sand at Newhaven. From 1782, Whiston had its own brickworks. The furnaces also needed sand, lots of it, and stone at Revidge was reduced to sand to provide it. Lime ash was used during the reduction process (see p 129) and this was sent as required. To aid the smelting of the lead ore, pigs of lead were purchased from the Shacklow lead mill of Barker & Wilkinson. It was situated at the bottom of Taddington Dale on the A6 north west of Bakewell.

At Whiston, large quantities of coal were needed (at the rate of 3 tons or so, possibly more, to one ton of ore). It came from Ross & Shaw Pits initially and later from Ross Colliery, plus Hazles Cross and Foxt Wood Collieries which were owned by the Duke. Fireclay came from Cauldon Lowe and Milkhillgate Green, east of Cauldon Lowe village. The stone and sand came from Whiston Common. Wood Ash was purchased for the refineries while Lime Ash was used at Ecton as noted above.

The mine itself consumed lots of timber. Initially it came from the slopes of the Manifold Valley at Casterne, and Biggin Grange Wood south east of Hartington. Later, timber was brought from Barleyford in the Dane Valley, north of Rushton and from the woods around Whiston and on the Shaw Estate of Mr Beech, near Cheadle. Cut timber, deales or dales, were also purchased in Stoke on Trent and taken to Etruria to be shipped down the Caldon Canal to Froghall, bound for the mine, probably via the turnpike road to Warslow. The purchases each month of timber have to have been significant, if only because of the prodigous quantities of nails which were bought: from August 1779 to December 1780, for instance, 185,500 nails of different sorts were purchased. An additional 27,200 were also purchased, but these may have been bound for the new buildings at Whiston.

Regular shipments of iron were sent from various forges to both Ecton and Whiston. The Alderwasley Forge of Francis Hurt at Ambergate sent bar iron, brewers squares, ladles, ladle moulds, hoop iron (for strengthening barrels etc) to both works. The materials for Whiston were sent to Ashbourne where they were collected. Other works were the Ashbourne foundry of Robert Longden; the Bassett Foundry at Mayfield and George Critchlow's works at Pethills on the River Hamps, between Ford and Winkhill in North Staffordshire. Mr Bird (perhaps of Chesterfield) and the Chesterfield Foundry also sent supplies. Specialist castings were also ordered from other manufacturers, such as Smith & Knifton of Oakamoor and initially from Walker's foundry at Rotherham.

Gun powder chiefly came from Wilkinsons at Chesterfield in barrels and half barrels. The barrels were returnable too, with a deposit payable on each purchase. Candles were sold on to the miners at cost. Most came from Mr George Creswell, of Ashford, near Bakewell; others from Anthony Bradley of Ashbourne and Richard Roberts of Winster. In the seven week Reckoning of November 1780, 1,321 candles and 742lb of powder were delivered to the mine. More candles were used at Whiston. Deliveries to the mine were regularly of over 10,000 candles and $3^{1}/_{2}$ tons of gunpowder per annum.

Sieves (sometimes called riddles), barrels, spades, hammers etc were needed as replacements or for extended production. The sieves mainly came from Hathersage, although some 'sieve bottoms' came from Alderwasley Forge on occasions. Ropes were continually in demand – wear and tear clearly being a major factor, although the damp conditions must have taken a toll too. Fires were kept burning near the adit level capstan to try and keep the ropes in the main haulage shaft as dry as possible. They seem to have been purchased from several suppliers, but Caleb Willock of Winster regularly provided them. At one point he requested more time to make them in the winter (if possible) so that he could ensure the best quality by making them only when it was dry. Later wire ropes were to be used on the Balance Shaft, brought from long distances. Even hemp ropes came from as far away as Manchester and Liverpool.

Provisions for the mine horses – hay, oats and bran – had to be brought in too, although the carriers to and from Whiston paid for the feed for their own animals except when fodder rose drastically in price. The mine carriers must have been substantial purchasers of fodder.

On top of all this were the office materials – including paper which chiefly survives in the Chatsworth Muniment Room. It was used for most suppliers to create their invoices, some clearly being prepared for them, and for the accounts of labourers' and smelters' wages etc. Oil for machinery ('train oyle') was regularly bought together with soap. In the ten months from November 1779 to August 1780, the mine purchased 44lb of 'sope'. In the same ten month period, 42 quarts of oil, 2 pints of ink, a stone of 'tarr' and 5 stones of pitch were sent to the mine, plus many more items. Other 'domestic' items included pack thread for sewing the ore bags, materials for the mine house and even rum for hospitality as indicated above. Today it is, rightly, not appreciated just how much was being carried by pack horse, pack mule or by cart and the occasional wagon. Only through the actual invoices has the detail come to light.

Additional to the everyday activity described above were two other areas of activity. The lesser of the two were the exceptional purchases. The Christmas/New Year party of 1780 saw local ale-house brewers sending over 150 gallons of ale, over 100lbs of beef and cheese and over 250 bread cobs to keep everyone happy. One hundred clay pipes for the smokers (most of the men, one supposes) were provided to round off the event. In contrast, a 'scale beam' of over three tons in weight must have taken a huge effort to transport to the mine in 1780, but large, sometimes very large, consignments were not unusual.

Nearly two tons of chains were ordered to lower horses into the mine (see above). Most carts at this period would carry a ton, perhaps exceptionally up to one and a half tons. The construction of the Fishpond at Back of Ecton to feed water to the blast furnace waterwheel saw an order for about a mile of gritstone blocks with a channel cut through one side to convey the water when laid end to end. These came from a quarry at Sheen, possibly the one where Belle Engineering Ltd is situated. The largest item sent to the mine would have been the component parts of the steam engine provided by Boulton & Watt from their works in Birmingham and also from John Wilkinson of Bersham near Wrexham. It was a small affair compared to those of a century later, but for the time, they would have been an unusual and cumbersome item to have to transport.

The second area of daily activity around the mine would, of course, be the workers, wending their way to the mine, mostly on foot, (unless they were lucky) and in all weathers, from neighbouring villages. In some cases, such as Butterton, the more direct route would not have been available. The Butterton-Swainsley road was built in the 19th century and presumably workers went via Wetton Mill, the now removed Lees Bridge which existed between Wetton Mill and Swainsley or via Warslow, unless an unknown set of stepping stones created a shortcut. Alternatively, Wetton villagers had a direct route via Pepper Inn to help them on their way. In 1781, as output expanded, there were at least 250 people working at the mine – or at least that many attended the Christmas/New Year party and therefore must be fairly close to the number of employees. At Whiston, another 60–70 people were employed and yet more at the collieries. In 1780 the employees were stated as being as 300 at Ecton and 200 at the smelter/collieries.

The impact the mine had on the local community was clearly great, both from the management point of view and the movement of materials and employees. One readily thinks of men toiling in the mine, women breaking the ore down and 'washing' it to separate the ore from rock and spar. Clearly, there was a larger picture: men cutting timber many miles away and hauling it up valley sides; candle makers making over 10,000 a year to keep the mine going (no candles, no ore); carriers moving ore and coal in a continual stream by pack mule and cart with others producing hundreds of tons of fodder to sustain the animals; brick makers; providers of sand, stone, iron, implements, ropes, feed for the mine horses, clay, nail makers making huge quantities to satisfy the mine's requirements and keeping yet more carters in employment, some working full time fetching and carrying the needs of the mine. More men took away copper and lead metal.

From the management point of view, Cornelius Flint had to not only keep production on track, using his experience and that of his miners to exploit ore reserves to the full and in a safe and expedient manner; he also had to arrange for all the external activities to run smoothly. It was a time when deliveries could take weeks, cash had to be fetched on horseback from Chesterfield in large quantities with the ever-present risk of robbery – either between Chesterfield and Ecton or between Ecton and Whiston. Even ordering simple items often meant sending the shopping list by hand. On 12 December 1786, William Salt was sent to Ashbourne to pick up some 'lether' together with the post, which cost 2s 0d. During the construction of the steam engine, plans from Messrs Boulton & Watt were despatched to the Blackmoor's Head Inn in Ashbourne (now Wigley's Shoe Shop and adjacent shops in St John Street) for collection by the mine.

All this, in a business which was one of the largest in the country running one of the deepest pits in the world, with little technology, in a simplistic but clearly efficient manner. It was a great achievement, but one over which the passage of time has drawn a veil, until now. On top of this he had responsibility for the Whiston Smelter brickworks and the two coal mines. From 1786 he had to oversee the Newhaven Brickworks and shortly afterwards, a brick works and a coke works at Hazles Cross Colliery. He was clearly a busy and resourceful man.

References

1. Foreman, A., *Georgiana, Duchess of Devonshire*, 1998

2. Porter, L., & Robey, JA., *The Copper & Lead Mines Around the Manifold Valley, Staffordshire,* 2000, p 53

3. Dev Coll., 2/23. References 3 to 7 (below) relate to specific documents in the Voucher Box for 1779

4. Dev Coll., 2/7

5. Dev Coll., 2/15

6. Dev Coll., 2/23

7. Dev Coll., 2/11

8. Dev. Coll., AS/1251

9. Dev. Coll., AS/187

10. Dev.Coll., AS/187

11. Derby Mercury, 19/11/1779 and 19/5/1780

12. Dev. Coll., AS/1717

13. Porter & Robey, op. cit., p 54

14. Derby Mercury 16th August 1781

15. Draft conveyance in the possession of this author

16. Dev.Coll., AS/187

A small shaft at the in-bye end of Ecton Sough; it was possibly a climbing shaft

This shaft is just off the engine chamber but its function is not known

DRESSING AND SALE OF ORE

5

Work on the Dressing Floors

The report of Efford (1) gives us a good insight into the dressing techniques of the 1760s. There were two dressing floors, once the Clayton Adit level was used for drawing ore, but although the level was commenced in 1755, there is no note of when the Burgoyne royalty dressing floor was built.

The Devonshire dressing floor was situated close to the entrance of the Ecton Sough. It was clearly close to the river and a note on the 1753 calculations of the Duke's royalty (1775-1782 Voucher Box) was to remind the writer to check if there had been much copper ore 'taken away by the flood'. Certainly the ground-up waste in the 19th century was thrown in the river to await removal in the winter by flood waters and it is safe to assume that this was the practice in the 1760s.

Efford's account (see below) supports the view that the main dressing floor was by the river for he indicates that the ore was carried out by boys and thrown in a heap where it was reduced by men with hammers. Had the dressing floor been on the hillside this process would not have happened as the tubs were hauled up the Smithy Shaft. A hillside dressing floor existed to keep apart the coarse ores which needed a more protracted dressing to separate the ore from waste and then ensure all the small particles were recovered. The ores from the large deposits contained no waste and were treated separately.

Further evidence comes from a plan in the author's possession which was prepared for the case of *Roscoe v The New Dale Mine Ltd and Richard Niness, 1871*. (2) Many of the depositions made by miners for this case contain memories going back to the 1820s and this plan was prepared to show where the old Ecton and Clayton dressing floors used to be. The former is shown close to the calciner, by the side of the river.

The method of treatment of ores was primitive, although Efford states that the process was done in a building – which was unusual.

Efford states that:

'The ore is carried out by boys and thrown into a heap and two men with large hammers or sledges are employed to break it up into small pieces. Next, it is carried in small hand barrows by small boys to a place under a shed erected for the purpose, to be picked, sorted and laid in different parcels: Best, second and worst. This operation is performed by little girls from 8–12 years old.

Next the ore is carried to another large and convenient shed where about 50 women sit back to back on benches to buck or beat the ore with flat hammers still keeping each particular sort together. (The flat hammers were called 'buckers'). The ore is reduced to a fine sand: Sometimes when the ore was very rich it was only broken into pieces the bigness of a nutmeg; but poor ore was broken small with flat hammers until hand driven stamping mills were erected and a convenient supply of water was laid at hand.

The ore, now reduced to a small sand, it is again removed to the 'Buddles' for washing, where an old Cornishman has the sole suprintendency of it, as a great deal of the finest ore would be lost if this operation was not properly performed. Here, then, it is correctly washed and cleansed, and afterwards exposed for sale in the open air, in various heaps, 'ticketed' accordingly to the different qualities and quantities. 'Ticketing the ore' is taking a couple of handfuls off any heap of ore and putting them into a canvas bag, by way of

Name	Days	price	£	s	d	Signature
William Phillips	34½ at	12	1	14	0	Wm Thom Phillips
d° Getting Stone away				13		
Francis Beresford	35½	12	1	15	6	Francis Beresford
d° Getting Stone away				8	6	
Ann Kidd	35	9	1	6	3	Ann Kidd x
Mary Wall	36	d°	1	7		Mary Wall x
Hannah Beresford	35	d°	1	6	3	Hannah Beresford
Sarah Beresford	36	d°	1	7	—	Sarah Beresford x
Sarah Howarth	35	d°	1	6	3	Sarah Howarth x
John Barker	37	10	1	10	10	Jn° Barker x
William Stubs	37	d°	1	10	10	Wm Stubs x
Adam Beresford	35	d°	1	9	2	Adam Beresford x
Joseph Barker (B	31½	4		10	6	Joseph Barker x
Sarah Goodwin	34	3		8	6	Rachael Goodwin x
Benjamin Baker	30½	d°		7	7	Benj° Baker x
Ann Stavely	22½	3		5	7	Ann Staley x
Ann Beresford	35	4		11	8	Ann Beresford x
Joseph Barker (ts	27½	d°		9	2	Joseph Barker x
William Millard	23½	d°		7	10	Wm Millard
Ann Harrison	24½	3		6	1	Ann Harrison x
Thomas Wheeldon	35	4		11	8	Tho° Wheeldon x
William Bennett	28½	d°		9	6	Wm Bennett x
Thomas Beresford	23½	3		5	10	Tho° Beresford x
John Goodwin	36	8	1	4	—	Jn° Goodwin x
Joseph Twig	17½	5		7	3	Joseph Twig x
William Baker	30½	5		12	8	Wm Baker x
Sarah Whint	24	4		8	—	Sarah Whint x
Mary Lovatt	34	5		14	2	Mary Lovatt x
George Wheeldon	26	3		6	6	Geo° Wheeldon x
Elizabeth Heathcote	23½	d°		5	10	Eliz Heathcote x
Joseph Howarth	21½	d°		5	4	Sarah Howarth x
Rachael Goodwin	20½	6		10	3	Rachael Goodwin x
Rachael Halley	36	4		12		Rachael Halley x
Mary Sutton Son	15	6		7	6	Mary Sutton x
Wm Mellor	36	8	1	4		Wm Mellor x
Rob° Green	36	d°	1	4	—	Robert Green
Moses Smith	38	d°	1	5	4	Moses Smith
Iron Millard	34	d°	1	2	8	Iron Millard x
Samuel Wiltshaw	35	14	2	0	10	Wm Samuel Wiltshaw
George Wheeldon	35	13½	1	17	11	Geo Wheeldon x
d° Getting Stone away				10		Samuel Wiltshaw
Rowland Milington	36	10	1	10	—	
			36	17	3	

Name	days	price	£	s	d	(signature)
Brought forward			36	17	3	
Hannah Hall	36	9		1	7	Hannah Hall x
Ellen Twig	35	do		1	6 3	Ellen Twig
Martha Woolliscroft	35	do		1	6 3	moses Smith
Susannah Bold	34	do		1	5 6	Susannah Bold x
Hannah Holme	30½	do		1	2 10	Hannah Holme
Elizabeth Slack	33½	do		1	5 2	Eliz Slack x
Martha Bagnall	36	do		1	7	Martha Bagnall x
Sarah Bagnall	33½	do		1	5 2	Sarah Bagnall x
Wm Beresford	31	12		1	11	William Beresford x
do for taking care of Water					1 6	
Joseph Redfern	39	do		1	10	Joseph Redfern x
Ralph Belfoot	34½	do		1	14 6	
do for Getting Lead Ore out of Break House					4	Ralph Belfoot x
Richard Green	31	12		1	11	Richard Green
William Birch	32	do		1	12	Wm Birch x
do for making Fires this Reckoning					7	
Joseph Frost	33	12		1	13	
William Frost	32	do		1	12	Wm Frost
do for Getting Stone to the Road to repair it, from the children					3	
James Wheeldon	35	12		1	15	Robert Kyly
John Lomas	13	do			13	John Lomas
Thos Kidd	34	7		1	1	Tho Kidd x
Jacob Bowden	25	3			6 3	Jacob Bowden x
James Wheeldon Jns	32	6			16	David Wheeldon
Sarah Barker	3	9			2 3	Sarah Barker x
Peter Billinges Thisbrother	76	7		2	4 4	Peter Billinge x
Charles Barker	9	5			3 9	Charles Barker x
Wm Barker	9	do			3 9	Wm Barker x
John Salt	19	12			19	John Salt
Geo: Sutton	13	4			4 4	Geo Sutton x
Wm Salt Junr	9	12			9	William Salt
Samuel Belfoot Getting Lead Ore out of B. House					4	Saml Belfoot x
Knocking						
Sarah Easting	13	6			6 6	Sarah Easting x
Elizabeth Hope	27	do			13 6	Eliz Hope x
Dorothy Gold	2	do			1	Dorothy Gould x
Sarah Harrison	24	do			12	Sarah Harrison x
				70	5 1	

samples; then little labels are fixed to the bags, signifying the quantity of each parcel. When a load of ore was ready, notice was given to the smelting house whose proprietors or managers attend, and each bids what price he thinks proper (generally from £7 to £16 per ton) the highest bidder being the buyers; it is fetched away at the buyers expense.

The refuse part of the ore, which is not fit for sale, is beat down small and carried to the smelting house on the premises erected by his Grace, and there run into large pigs or bars, and is then sold for around £70 to £90 per ton. Upon the whole nothing is left. The great advantage to the country around arises from the number of hands employed, and the circulation of between £3,000 and £4,000 cash annually, in a poor place and thinly inhabited before this place was discovered, but now quite improved, and more than 300 men, women and children employed winter and summer, who have proper overseers for every department, and where everything goes on with the utmost harmony and cheerfulness. The miners, as before hinted work at 2d per hour, six hours at a time; women, by task, earn 4d to 8d per day, and are paid by measure according to the quantity of ore they can 'buck'; girls and boys from 2d to 4d a day, some more; thus there is constant employment for both sexes and all ages from 5 to 60 years of age.

The carpenter's shop, the smith's forge, the cooperage, with neat dwelling houses of the suprintendents, little kitchen gardens and out-houses annexed, are all singular in kind, and happily adapted to make life agreeable in that solitary place which lies between two monstrous hills, separated at least two miles from other inhabitants. This copper mine, in the state above described, clears annually between £8,000 and £40,000 profit, and if worked with the spirit which accompanies large returns, double the sum might be made of it; but his Grace, it seems is content that employs all the labouring poor who present themselves for work from the neighbouring parishes.

On the opposite side of Ecton Hill is a lead mine, [Clayton] which is likely to turn out to great advantage, the viens of lead approaching very near to the copper, and they are driving an 'adit' parallel to the other...'

Efford does not mention the round house and its edge-runner crusher a round stone on its edge which was used for crushing, being moved along a circular metal plate by horse power. It existed in 1760 (see Chapter 3: A Remarkable Survivor) and as has been mentioned, half of it probably exists to this day. This must have been used for breaking down lumps of ore. Efford states that ore was reduced to the size of nutmegs before being smelted, but it would appear that the manual reduction of ore by women must have been alongside the ore reduced by this crusher. This is hinted at by the reference in March 1787 to Sampson Hambleton & Co. being paid for weighing copper from the round House Pen to the new Smelt House Pen, which would relate to moving the dressed copper from the crusher direct to the smelter. (2)

Despite the use of the word 'washing' – both by Efford in the accounts – the expression was to indicate the need to clean or separate the ore from ground rock or spar. The ore was not dirty as such. As the ore was now in a ground up state, separation was achieved because of differing specific gravities, i.e., the ore settled to the bottom quicker because it was heavier. Agitation of the ground up ore and rock etc in water allowed the ore to accumulate at the bottom of the tub. This was recovered and dried whereupon it was known as 'slime ore' (or sometimes 'waste ore' see below).

Ore which was not so concentrated – perhaps from smaller veins etc was handled separately. Pickers were employed to recover the ore from this. This was more tedious work and the pickers washed and dressed their own ore, being paid more for it (by the ton) by the mine because of all the extra work involved. Once recovered, this ore was known as 'hillock' or 'waste ore'. The main ore recovered from the main part of the pipe working was known as 'bottom ore', except that it was often spelt 'botham' in those days.

In 1783, George Bettey and his son George were paid 15s 0d a week each in charge of the Slime and Belland dressing (R Nov. 1783) Slime and Belland are both tiny particles of ore.

Ecton Ticketts: 29 April 1768 bid from the Warrington Copper & Brass Co.

The Tickett from C. Roe & Copper Co. for the same parcel of ore

Robert Rotton's Tickett

Perhaps the two words describes its recovery in different dressing techniques. The word slime was perculiar to Ecton and does not appear in Derbyshire until the mid-1800s, when it was used to describe waste particles (e.g. slime pits) rather than ore particles. (4) To complicate matters, there is a reference to a slime pit being emptied in the Dressing Account for September 1785 and this was probably waste particles!

Sir Joseph Banks gives us a further insight into the method of selling the ores:

'The method of selling ore is worth observing. The ore is all beat down small before it is weighed which is done when certain people who are bidders are present – two hundred weight at a time is what their scales weigh – a man who stands by for the purpose takes from everyone of these a small quantity upon the point of a trowel which he puts into a tub for that purpose – a great deal of labour is bestowed upon this that it may be piesed (pieced) together as much as possible as many sorts of copper came from this mine and the values of all are to be judged of from an assay of these – the buyers take everyone a small quantity of this mixture and declare themselves bidders for the quantity of ore on a certain day then fixed about six weeks or thereabouts. This they call sampling – on the day of bidding which they call ticketing every man delivers in his written proposal signifying the price that he will give – these are all read aloud before the Company and the highest bidder is declared buyer'.

A few surviving records show that in 1771, the buyers were sent a sample of ore to test and then bid in writing what they wished to pay for the ore. As a comparison, the ticketed price per ton for ore in 1771 between Roe & Co of Macclesfield & Patten & Co of Cheadle was:

Date	Tons	Roe price	Patten price*	
15 March	80	£14.8s.6d	£15.12s.6d	
26 April	80	£14.12s.6d	£15.10s.9d	Bottom ore
26 April	20	£2.10s.6d	£3.0s.9d	Waste ore
7 June	80	£14.12s.6d	£15.10s.9d	
7 June	20	£2.3s.0d	£2.16s.9d	
30 August	94	£17.0s.0d	£16.8s.6d	

* Figure submitted by Robert Hurst for the 'Warrington Copper & Brass Company and Self'

The above indicates that although the Whiston Smelter was working in 1771, it could not cope with the available supply of ore and tonnages were still being sold to two of the three previous buyers (Cooper & Rotton having gone out of business in 1769).

Having been sold, the ore was transported by pack horse to the buyer (and to Whiston after 1779). Horses carried two hundredweight each, but there was 21 cwt to the ton in copper ore measurement. Thus the 374 tons sold to the above smelters between March and August 1771 would have taken 3,927 horse loads to clear it from the mine. On top of this, one has to consider all the other materials being delivered plus copper ore and metal going to Whiston, lead ore being smelted and the bars sold etc. It is thought that the payments by the smelters would have been to the mine, but this is not clear. Ecton ore was in demand by the smelters because it produced highly ductile metal which was used for boiler construction etc. (5)

The Cheadle works had built a copper smelter in 1768 on the Cheadle–Kingsley road near to the Woodhead Colliery. Although it was still receiving Ecton ore in 1771 as may be seen above, much of the clearly expected supply did not materialise and they had to rely on ore being brought from further afield at greater expense. Morten states (6) that the Warrington works did not receive Ecton copper prior to 1760 but this is incorrect (see page 28 on copper sales in the years before 1760).

In the 1780s, the mine started selling sieves to the women dressing the ore (e.g. February 1783 'scives to washer wimmen'). At this time the output of dressed ore must have risen to keep pace with the higher output being sent to Whiston. The mine purchased sieves from Alderwasley Iron Works, or at least sieve bottoms at 2s.0d each. (R.August 1780) and from Abney and Hathersage.

Workers on the Dressing Floor

The ore dressing account for August 1779 indicates that there were then 99 people dressing ore. This included 44 males (chiefly boys). The highest wages were paid to four men (6s.0d per week). The head women were paid 4s.6d per week. Most of the women employees were paid 3s.0d per week, some being paid 3s.0d for themselves and a child who was helping them. In the reckoning those in this category were paid for different numbers of weeks to other people, so it is not possible to tell if they were paid the same price per week as others or whether the time worked was equated to a weekly rate of 3s.0d per week.

The majority of the dressers earned 3s.0d or less – down to 1s.6d per week. Out of the 55 women, 51 are named. The most common name was Elizabeth and Mary (10 women with each name) and there were 7 each called Ann, Hannah and Sarah. Only four people did not sign for their wages with a 'X'. It would be easy to assume that those earning 3d per day were children, but the rate could apply to the work undertaken. In August 1782, Hannah Fogg was paid for 24 days at 3d per day and $7\frac{1}{2}$ days at 6d per day, but if 4p per day was to be taken as a child's wage rate, 24 of them were employed out of 125 dressers in all.

In 1783 Job White subcontracted some of the dressing floor activity, but precisely what is not clear. He paid 54 people (not 53 as stated by Pat Bromfield). Generally he paid less than the mine but no meaningful analysis can be drawn as the occupations are not known. He tended to employ females, Bromfield revealing that the ratio of women to men was 2:1. (7) Her detailed analysis shows that only about 12% of female labour at Ecton was likely to have been employed on anything like a regular basis. Of the rest, nearly 70% seem to have been employed as and when required.

It is a pity more is not known, as it seems strange that the mine seemed to be using a lot of casual labour at a time of rising ore output. Almost 75% of female workers seem to have been able to work for more than 66% of working days per reckoning, which suggests that they were attuned to the new regime of regularity of employment offered by the mine. Bromfield asserts that the flexibility of working was at the lower end of the scale – amongst children for instance – who may have been required at home and amongst girls who may have been less resilient to the work. In the December, 1783 Dressing Account is some evidence of this: at the rate of 3d a day, three were paid for 11 days; eight for 36 days; four for 17 days; five for 13 days; and six for 14 days. They were paid by George Crichlow, described as a 'dressing master'.

There is some evidence of children working with mothers but it would be nice to know if this was to assist the parent to get her work done or whether she was simply keeping a close watch on one of her youngest. The issue becomes more confusing, for payment by measure was introduced in 1782 when $3\frac{1}{2}$ times more female ore dressers than men were paid this way. (8) Unfortunately any changes in working practices this created are lost to us. In November 1786, three children were helping their parent to clean the slime pits (probably containing ground waste rock).

A further change to the method of payment occurs in the Dressing Account for May 1783. In excess of 57 people were paid by the barrow at 6d and $2,091\frac{1}{2}$ barrows were accounted for. There were in excess of 146 paid for dressing in all. There were also 110 labourers mentioned but some received payment for others working the same contract. Another 59 people were paid via Job White for dressing 'the lead and coper ore.' Consequently there were a minimum of 315 people employed plus Martha Rowland (for looking after the mine house) and the miners extracting ore on cope bargains, where they were paid for the volume of ore extracted.

The candle account for this period reveals that Thomas Austin and Co (12 men) received 38 candles which works out at one per man per week. Some 1,252 candles were issued to cope bargain men and at that rate, 179 men were extracting ore. However one candle per man per week seems odd. Nonetheless excluding the miners, the dressers amounted to approximately two thirds of the workforce.

Bromfield considers that the manual operations lasted as long as they did because a Stamps Yard needed water power and there may have been 'difficulties of maintaining a constant supply of water'. Mechanical crushing with the aid of a water powered stamps or crushing rollers was not introduced until 1818. Although prevalent in Cornwall, they were not so in the Derbyshire ore field until improved technology of the 19th century brought much improved crushing rates. (9) To this end, the Ecton Stamps Yard was the forerunner of many that were installed locally and in Derbyshire during the 19th century. It had nothing to do with water availability. Notwithstanding this, to suggest that circumstances must have changed in terms of river flow over thirty years or so, to enable the Swainsley Stamps Yard to be powered by the River Manifold simply cannot be sustained.

Children on the Dressing Floor

Efford's account of 1769 remains the best description of the mine in the 18th century (and perhaps of all). He stated that the women earned up to 4d–8d per day and were paid by measure. If this was so, there does not seem to have been much variation in their pay. Children were paid 2d–4d a day, some more, i.e., as much as their parents, and presumably therefore little difference was made between adolescent children and the adults. Efford stated that there was employment from 5–60 years of age. Girls aged from 8–12 years sorted the ore into three categories – best, second and worst. Efford remarked upon their 'astonishing dexterity'. The ore separation undertaken by the girls could have been different sorts of copper ore but may relate to the amount of impurities (rock and spar) associated with the ore. Bromfield (10) associates Efford's 'dexterity' of the girls with skill, but the separation of ore with differing levels of waste attached to it, or separating ores of a different colour hardly smacks of skill. More on this comes from Farey, who stated that:

> The Spar & Ore, as it is drawn and brought out of the mine in tram-waggons, is called Bowse: on the Hillock, this is separated into lumps of Spar & Stone, containing specks and strings of Ore; Goods, which are sizeable lumps of Ore: and Fell, which will pass thro' a riddle: these three sorts are separately knocked and buckered down by women and children; it is then washed and picked in sieves, and the very small from the buckering, is lued, that is, laved in water waving over the sides of the lue, and washing over the small spar etc., which goes to the Buddle-hole.'

By the time Farey visited Ecton, all the dressing may have been done on the hillside. Presumably when Efford in 1769 stated that little girls sorted the ore into three sorts, he was referring to Hannaway, Goods & Fell. The word 'Lue' has not been found in the mine accounts. It means a sieve with a coarse linen bottom.

The dressing account for December 1783 gives a little more detail than usual. It indicates that men, usually employed on other (unstated) tasks removed the stone. This would seem to indicate that more ore was being raised associated with rock and spar. There is a reference to another adult, Ralph Belfort, 'getting lead ore out of (the) Break House', i.e. the building where the ore was separated from rock and spar.

The same document records the payment to another adult, William Frost, 'for Getting Stone to the road, to repair, it from the children'. This indicates that children must have been doing more than separating ore as mentioned by Efford. It would seem that some manual separation was undertaken in the Break House prior to using the crushing wheel. This would involve breaking down the material; stone itself would have been removed via Apes Tor Shaft. The use of the expression 'the Break House' confirms that the dressing processes were under cover. John Byng, Viscount Torrington, creates the impression from his passing reference to Ecton that much of the separation was done out of doors. Just which building was the Break House is unknown.

Buddles

Ore was separated from rock or spar in water. Larger pieces were separated in a jig-tub where square or rectangular sieves were lifted up and down in a water filled trough. Smaller pieces of ore were separated by mixing with water and pouring down an inclined surface, called a buddle. The heavier ore did not travel as far as the lighter rock/spar which became separated. The very small particles, called slimes, were separated in a dolly tub (a barrel of water) with blades in it to agitate the water. The site of the early buddles is not known. The problem is that they may become covered with grass and quickly lost from view. They consisted of flat stones with a raised stone at the sides and ends to keep the water-borne material in the buddle. Joseph Billinge was paid for his man Solomon who spent a day 'at Willshaw's Buddle' on 16 April 1785. (Invoice 33, R May 1786)

The Burgoyne Dressing Floor

The 1755 agreement between the Duke and Thomas Gilbert resulted in the driving of the Clayton Adit level. This allowed drainage and haulage of ore and waste out to the Manifold Valley. The Clayton drawing shaft was effectively superfluous. The Burgoyne dressing floor was established close to the Clayton Adit entrance. Where the ore was dressed prior to this is far from clear, the priority being adequate water. Maybe it was down against the stream which now flows into the Fish Pond at Back Ecton. Even after the finishing of the adit level – and assuming the depth of the Clayton Mine working had reached that depth – the tramming of ore out to the Manifold still meant that water was below the site of the dressing floor, the River Manifold being 10–11 feet below.

This, of course, was the same for the Ecton Mine. Although the botham ores were dressed adjacent to the river, the coarse ores were dressed on the same horizon as Salts Level and the 19th century dressing floor. The dressing of ore wage costs include entries for 'attending to water' which was no doubt brought to the dressing floors in barrels. This must have been how the Burgoyne dressing floor faired too. The latter had a long building situated adjacent to Clayton Adit and after the completion of the Fish Pond launder or water channel in 1788, water was provided to this building and to the adjacent lead smelter (see the 1809 plan, page 13).

No details survive of the use of this building or its output of ore. All that is known is from the late 19th century Dale Mine litigation and a comment that the waste from the Burgoyne floor was dumped into the river, as at Ecton. So much waste was dumped in this way that it was possible to cross the river without getting your feet wet. The winter floods removed it and created the space for yet more waste the following year. The use of a building for dressing is confirmed in November 1782 (albeit at the Duke's dressing floor) when payment was made for walling in a 'dressing shade'.

Dressing Mixon and Fleet Green Ore

The December 1784 reckoning 'Charges of Dressing the copper ore upon wages' for the previous six weeks includes two entries for Aaron Millward. One entry (for 11 days) is endorsed 'Mixon' and the other, (for 1 day) is endorsed 'Shawfield'. He was paid 8d per day (4s.0d per week). This would appear to indicate that Mixon ore was being dressed at Ecton. Shawfield is on the Warslow–Newtown road and is adjacent to the copper mine at Fleet Green. It is suggested that copper ore was being raised here too and dressed at Ecton.

There is only the one reference for the Shawfield ore, but the Mixon must have been for a larger volume as dressing it covered 25 days in the February reckoning and 32 days, at the increased rate of 10d per day, in the March reckoning. Thereafter, references cease. There must have been a few tons accounted for in the 68 days that Aaron Millward was occupied by this work. These are the only specific references known for the workings of these two mines at this time. It seems that the Mixon ore may have been located above adit level. (12)

Raised Ore Volumes

In chapter 3, the annual ore figures in the 1750s ranged in the region of 500–550 tons, except in 1755 when it was only 205 tons. Presumably the miners were in between two of the large swellings of ore. As the lease comes to an end, we have seen that the lessees attempting to maximise their output and income, with the yield rising to 700 tons in 1759 and more than double that in 1760. The first year of the Duke's operation saw the output back at 576 tons, just above the 500–550 range. It rose to 1,160 tons in both 1763 and 1764 then slowly fell back to around 750 tons in 1767-68. There was little activity in 1769 as attention focussed on building the Whiston smelter. Yields during the 1770s were generally in the range of 700–800 tons, rising to just over 1,000 tons in 1778. Thereafter, the volumes rose annually to 1786, when they peaked.

Although figures fell after this year, they exceeded 2,000 tons per annum, falling significantly in 1791. The rot seems to have set in during late 1789 reckonings but output rallied. The renewed vigour was short lived, running at about 250 tons in the next two reckonings and not rising above this in the remainder of 1790 or in the first three quarters of 1791, when the remaining ore figures are missing for some time. For the full picture of raised ore volumes, see page 4.

References

1. Efford, Wm., *Gentleman's Magazine*, Feb., 1769, 'Description of famous Copper-Mine belonging to his Grace the Duke of Devonshire, at Ecton Hill in the County of Stafford,' pp 59-62

2. see Porter, L., & Kirkham, L., Ore Dressing in the Manifold Valley, *Mining History*, Vol 13, No 6, pp 40-48)

3. Dev. Coll., R March 1787

4. pers. comm., Dr J Rieuwerts

5. Mawe J., *The Minerals of Derbyshire, 1802,* pp 109 – 112

6. Morton J., *Thomas Bolton & Sons 1783 - 1983,* 1983, p13

7. Bromfield P., *Industrial workers in a Peasant Community: Manifold Valley parishes in the 18th century, with special reference to workers at Ecton Copper Mine c. 1760-1820* unpub. thesis, Keele University, Chapter 2, p 3

8. op. cit., Chapter 2, p 18

9. Rieuwerts, J., *Glossary of Derbyshire Mining Terms*, 1998, p 147

10. Bromfield, P., op.cit, Chapter1, p 6

11. Farey J., *General View of the Agriculture of Derbyshire*, 1811, Vol I, p 376

12. Porter, L., & Robey, J., *Copper and Lead Mines Around the Manifold Valley, Staffordshire*, 2000, p 152

WORKINGS AT THE MINE

The driving at the Boat level is given below and clearly this was a major achievement, but the main focus was of course on exploiting the ore deposit. The accounts give no details on work here, just payments to each team of miners working their 'contract', or cope -bargain, together with the tonnage raised and its cost to the mine. Other contractors pursued work elsewhere and some of those records are of guidance in determining what was done and where. There are many references to Chadwick Mine, where the location is usually given as 'ye lead sough'.

Work at Chadwick commenced at the beginning of the decade and continued throughout it. In 1764 work commenced in 'ye uper levl at lead sough' and what would appear to be the heightening of the sough itself: 'taking up ye sole of lead sough'. The latter is today virtually full of water, but displays some evidence of being formerly a coffin level. Much of this earlier work has been removed and these references in the 1760s tell us when this occurred. Shaped like a coffin in cross-section, they also have characteristic sweeping pick marks on each side.

The Mine House, later the home of the manager in the 19th century

Work in Ecton Sough

In September 1767, Samuel Pickering and his team were 'driving out of ye sough level' and previously had been raising ore. In the November Reckoning he was 'driving the level to New Shaft'. Not mentioned in December, he was back at the same work in February 1768, 'driving towards New Shaft'. The March payment indicated that a previous payment must have been missing as he was paid for 47 yds, indicating continuity of work, if nothing else. After driving 97 yards (48^1/$_2$ fms), in February 1769, they switched to 'cuting up ye sole of their gate

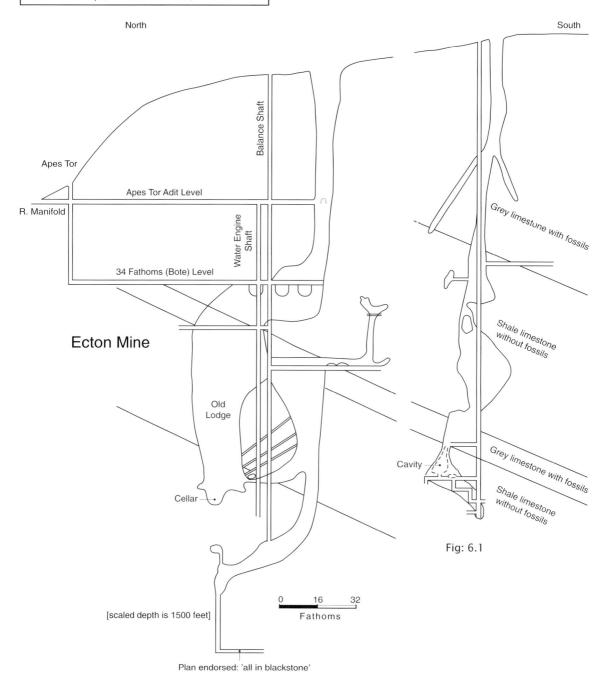

Clayton Mine

North

South

Apes Tor

Balance Shaft

Apes Tor Adit Level

R. Manifold

Water Engine Shaft

Grey limestone with fossils

34 Fathoms (Bote) Level

Ecton Mine

Shale limestone without fossils

Old Lodge

Cavity

Grey limestone with fossils

Cellar

Shale limestone without fossils

Fig: 6.1

[scaled depth is 1500 feet]

0	16	32

Fathoms

Plan endorsed: 'all in blackstone'

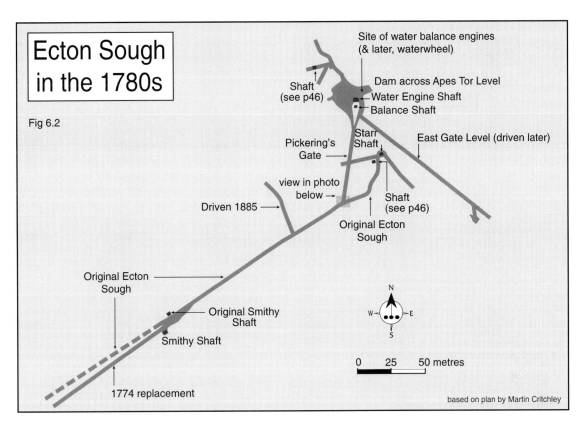

Ecton Sough in the 1780s

Fig 6.2

Site of water balance engines
(& later, waterwheel)

Shaft
(see p46)

Dam across Apes Tor Level
Water Engine Shaft
Balance Shaft

Pickering's
Gate

Starr
Shaft

East Gate Level (driven later)

view in photo
below →

Driven 1885

Shaft
(see p46)

Original Ecton
Sough

Original Ecton
Sough

Original Smithy
Shaft

Smithy Shaft

1774 replacement

N
W — E
S

0   25   50 metres

based on plan by Martin Critchley

Pickering's Gate (left) and the original sough to Starr Shaft (the pipe working) on the right. Note the narrow level section on the right behind the people

towards New Shaft' i.e. basically lowering the level of the floor. Pickering and his men must have moved to other work after 'cuting up ye sole' to a length of 55 yds and by March 1770 were raising ore (i.e. mining it, rather than lifting it).

In Deep Ecton adit level – the current name for the Ecton Deep Adit, formerly known as Ecton Sough, the passage branches with the left hand passage heading straight towards the engine chamber and the Balance Shaft and the large shaft known as the Water Engine Shaft. The right hand level, which is narrower and is not driven directly, goes to the pipe working. The distance driven by Pickering – 97 yds – approximates with the distance between the level at the junction of the two levels mentioned above and the Water Engine Shaft. The pipe working itself would appear to have been known as Starr Shaft. A reference to 'Driving for the New Shaft' (i.e. the Water Engine Shaft) is believed to relate to the crosscut at adit level between the pipe working (or Starr Shaft) and the level which leads straight to the engine chamber – and which was known as Pickering's Gate. The only doubt about this comes in November 1783, when William Millard was drawing water at the Sump Top in Pickering Gate. There is no shaft in this level, but if it extended beyond the Engine Chamber there are shafts just beyond and another in the original level near to Starr Shaft (see plan of Ecton Sough).

Payment to Joseph Gregory & Co for driving towards the New Shaft from Starr Shaft, from October 1768 until mid-1769, for a distance of 32 yds, roughly equates with the distance between the pipe and Pickering Gate. The difference can easily be allowed for in the extension south of the pipe working, for instance. It could relate to a level below the water line, but the short cut this crosscut afforded must have meant it would have been driven as soon as appropriate, alleviating quite a detour down the original sough to where Pickering Gate runs off, heading north towards the engine chamber.

The obvious problem with the above is that Pickering did not reach the site of the 'New Shaft' until February 1769. At this time the latter was 49 fms deep. How did the sinkers get there ahead of Pickering? The answer must lie in a connection between the engine chamber and the pipe working which gave access to the site of the shaft. A connection possibly does exist shortly below the surface (? 90 feet down) and was the site of the drowning of a cave diver in 1963. The sinking started in early summer 1768 (so Pickering's 'New Shaft' prior to this date was only proposed) at £2.5s.0d per yard, but the rate increased with depth. It reached £3.5s.0d per yard – the maximum paid to Josh Gregory & Co. In June 1770 a new team, Jos Mycock & Co was set on to continue the work at £2.10s.0d. Presumably the demands of the Gregory team took a step too far for Robert Shore and they were replaced.

By the end of 1770, the shaft was down 98 yds and had reached 161 yds by the end of 1771. It reached a bottom in November 1772 at 203 yds 1 ft and work was suspended until May the following year when a further 44 ft was sunk, presumably to create a sump. Sinking ended in November 1773 and the sinkers became drivers as they drove 6 yds at the 'shaft end'. Prior to Christmas, they were 'making two briging places at ye bottom of New Shaft'. Thus the final depth was 218 yds (654 ft) or 109 fms – just above where the celebrated double saddle exists at 110 fms and where the pipe deposit was so rich. It had taken $5^{1}/_{2}$ years to sink and cost in the order of £500.

This shaft was then used for draining water and may have been doing so prior to the completion of the sinking. In February 1773, there are payments for 'drawing out pumps at Apetor Shaft' and to William Newbold for 'making an Engon' (Engine, i.e. a gin or whim). The shaft was also used for lowering large objects into the lower parts of the mine (large pieces of timber, for example) and was available for raising ore. However, the boat level continued in use, for Edward Greenhough made a new boat in February 1772 at £4.9s.0d and a year prior to that, in February 1771, the 'Botegate' was widened for a distance of 264 yds, which roughly is the length of the 34 fms level (estimated from a mine section). Presumably having widened it, a wider boat was constructed to add to the small 'fleet' existing.

The shaft was used for pumping via the gin to the 34 fathoms level. Cast metal pumps for this came from Walker's foundry at Rotherham – their bill is in the May 1773 Reckoning and they cost £120.16s.4d. They had supplied another set of pumps about 12 months previously at £53.14s.6d. Where these were for is not indicated, but as water was lifted in stages to a lodge or cistern, the 1772 pumps may have been for one of these. The water, having reached the 34 fathoms level, ran into the Boat level. There was a choice here, either lifting the water in barrels at Apes Tor Shaft, or up the main shaft to run down the Ecton Sough. The 1772 pumps were quite possibly for this latter function. The 1773 pumps being for the shaft bottom.

At the end of the 1760s is the first reference to sinking Smithy Shaft in March 1769. Smithy Shaft's location can be determined reasonably easily: this is the shaft which existed on the dressing floor and is shown on the 1820 plan as being within a building – clearly the smithy. It drops to a location adjacent to the adit level and a cross cut was driven 18 ft to connect the shaft foot with the former adit. The latter was abandoned because of unstable conditions and this shaft replaced an earlier one located by John Barnatt which rose above the earlier level (see plan 59). When a new replacement adit level was driven it ran straight to this new shaft. In the mine account for June 1764 is an entry 'Mr Walker bills for castmeatle wheels, 16s.6d'. Geisler, (1) who visited the mine on his journey around the country in 1772-73 described and even drew a sketch of the tramway and its cast metal wheels. (1) Under the wagons were four small iron wheels which ran on square rails. The drawing (Fig 6.3) confirms the square nature of the rails and shows that flanged wheels were in use. The size of the rails is unusual. Whether the 1764 entry for wheels was the first purchase is not certain, but probably not, for there is a reference to 6 wagons in the 1760 inventory of materials in the mine.

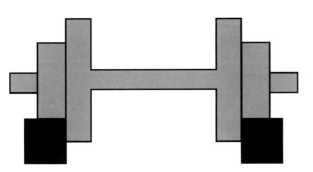

Fig 6.3 Based on Geisler's drawing of the cast metal wheels

The reference to 'cast metle wheels' in 1764 is an early one and some idea of the cross section may be gleaned from Geisler's drawing. He states that the rails were 5 in square. Going from that, it may be inferred that the wheels were something like 12 in. in diameter and 2½ in. wide. The width between the wheels is shown as being about 12 inches too, but that may have been shortened to reduce the size of the drawing in his diary.

However the remaining section of the original sough which runs to Star Shaft is not very wide (see p 59) and a 12 inch gauge may have been used. John Barnatt advises (pers. comm.) that the width of the accessible section of the original and replaced sough is 'very narrow', which also supports a narrow gauge between rails.

The first cast iron wheels appeared in Shropshire in 1729. Many early wheels were quite large in diameter. Some at Bath were 22 in. in diameter and weighed nearly 1¾ cwt. (2) Geisler did not comment upon the length of the rails. The inference from Lewis is that although cast metal wheels were not uncommon in 1764, they became more popular a decade or two later.

It is likely that the rails were made of wood. Geisler does not show an iron strip along the top of them (to reduce wear). Although the wheels had to be cast in Rotherham, more local suppliers were being established, plus better roads along which to deliver goods. Within a few years the mine could rely on its needs being serviced locally.

It is unclear when the change to metal rails was made. There are many references to the purchase of bars of iron which defy their ultimate use. However one reference is clear: in the December 1786 Reckoning is the purchase of 64 bars of Rail Iron from Pethills Forge. They weighed 15½ cwt and cost £17.1s.9d.

Geisler makes a further comment, which must be incorrect. He refers to the fact that Ecton Sough had boats in it. He even shows a water course on a crude plan and section of the mine. This did not exist at the time of Efford's visit about 3-4 years earlier and there is no evidence in the accounts to support this. Occasionally the 34 fms level was referred to as the 'sough' which is set to trip up the unwary, but why have boats on part only of the level? There is clearly no logic to it. Moreover, Geisler indicates that the boats went along for a distance of 150 fathoms which is about the length of the boat level. It is thought that he must have been confusing the mine water draining the sough with the boat level. It makes no sense to push tubs down the level, transfer the ore to a boat for part of the level and then transfer it back to tubs on rails for the rest of the journey down the sough.

Barnatt also falls into this trap concerning sough boats. (3)

Summary of Work

Thus the main work in this decade may be summarised:

Soon after the Duke took over, work started on sinking Apes Tor Shaft and driving the 'Deep Level', which became the Boat level. The winding nature of the inner end of the Ecton sough was replaced by a new level (Pickering Gate) running out of the old sough and heading north (approximately) to reach a new main shaft within the mine. Although descent by the miners was described by Efford as being dangerous – probably to the miners, let alone a visitor – this would no doubt have been attended to at some point. The main shaft or 'New Shaft' does not appear to have been used as a climbing road and the men are unlikely to have ridden a tub to the bottom – this too was dangerous, despite the speed of reaching one's place of work 660 ft below, which must have appealed to some of the men. It must have appealed to even more for the ascent after a six hour shift (the descent/ascent was in the miners' own time).

The site of the Water Balance Engine

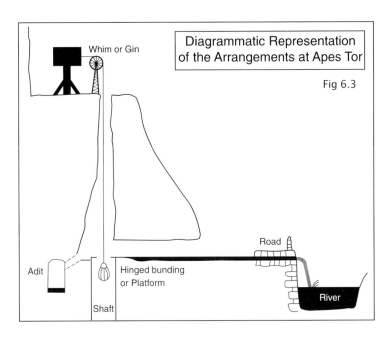

Whim or Gin

Diagrammatic Representation
of the Arrangements at Apes Tor

Fig 6.3

Adit

Hinged bunding
or Platform

Road

Shaft

River

Work on the Smithy Shaft in March, 1769 would seem to indicate that the poor quality of the strata near the sough entrance had finally forced the mine to sink a new drawing shaft from the hillside 'hillock' where waste was dumped and 'coarse ores' were reclaimed by 'pickers'. Smithy Shaft does not appear in the accounts again until the Reckoning of November 1780, when Joseph Barker was 'drawing stone up Smithy Shaft' and then in June 1786, when there is a payment for striking in the Smithy, i.e. landing the tubs which had been hauled up the shaft by a capstan, or stow, as they were called.

The Chadwick lead ore mine of on the east side of the hill seems to have been worked throughout the decade, although the ore raised was not very significant. Presumably it was dressed alongside the copper ore.

At the end of the 1760s, very little technical equipment existed at the mine. The water was raised by horses in barrels. Perhaps water was lifted from the boat level to a point nearer the Apes Tor Shaft foot. Blasting was by gunpowder in shot holes drilled by hand. Two-men teams, with a boy holding the drill while the men hit it with their hammers would have been a common sight.

The construction of the New Shaft – later known as the Water Engine Shaft – must have greatly improved the development of the mine as it entered the 1770s. With the new smelter at Whiston, the mine was entering into a new stage of its development becoming vertically integrated with two coal mines owned by the Duke, serving both the Whiston smelter along with the mine and its own calcining and smelting furnaces, plus a blast furnace for lead slag smelting (which was to be built in 1786).

Geisler on his visit to Britain in 1772-73 noted the existence of 'a vertical shaft from the top of the hill, from where in the future a steam engine is going'. If this was an early and serious intention to provide steam power, it was not realised until 1788.

Development of the Clayton Mine may have been proceeding too, but we have no details, unfortunately. Co-incidentally, the new Clayton Sough would have intersected the Clayton pipe deposit at about the same time as the Duke took over in the adjacent Ecton Mine. Working on a notional fathom per week, it would have taken some five years to reach its objective. Most of the ore raised in Ecton Mine came from the steadily deepening pipe working, but records show that 35 tons 6 cwt was raised in 1761 from 'Upper Starr Shaft' and 'Lower Starr Shaft'

Ecton Deep Adit (Ecton Sough) in 1963, Inset: Apes Tor Shaft flooded with water, taken prior to being capped with concrete, also in 1963

and 9 tons in 1762 came from 'Starr'. It is suggested that this is the pipe working, Upper Starr being above river level. A further 25 tons of ore is recorded as being from 'Starr' in 1767 which must have been from a vein in the working above the large deposits below river level.

This initially centred at Benit's Turn – presumably part of the pipe deposit – which today cannot be located.

In the early years of the following decade there are references to dressing and smelting 'Corse copper from Hamnook'. A 1/9th part was being accounted for, which must have been the royalty. This mine is situated high on the hill above Birch's Level and the site of the Lead Slag Mill, one of the most westerly workings on the hill. It was in the Burgoyne (later Blackett) royalty. The total tonnage of coarse copper metal smelted from Hamnook Mine between Autumn 1770 and Autumn 1772 was nearly 11 cwt.

Other work was centred on the Dutchman Mine, with work driving 8 yards (4 fms) from the Dutchman Engine Shaft foot in February 1761. Presumably later work driving from the hillside connected with this to create the Dutchman adit level – later much extended to link up with Bag and Good Hope Mines in the 19th century. There were later references to work at Dutchman in 1764 and 1767. Strangely, each reference was in a February.

A reference to work at the Smithy Shaft foot in August 1763 must relate to the old Smithy Shaft, later relocated adjacent the realigned Ecton Sough. This was first recorded as being the adit level in correspondence between Cornelius Flint and Boulton and Watt in July 1787 when Flint refers to the 'audit'.

The Installation of the Water Balance Engine

The need for a new pumping engine was recognised as early as February 1780, although its installation took some time to complete. Work to drive Apes Tor Adit level began by May 1780, but it took some time to complete (see below under Workings in the 1780s). The initial agreement on the project is confirmed in a letter dated 27 February 1780, from George Wild to John Heaton, the Duke's auditor:

'On Friday last I came from Ecton Mine where I had been with Mr Flint the Agent and Mr Newbold the Millwright who is to make the Engine we Levilled the Brook [River Manifold] as far as his Grace's land extends towards the mill above [West Side Mill] and found sufficient Levil to Erect a powerfull Machine and partly upon the Plan except anyone can hit upon something to make an Improvement we agreed in our Scheme and I believe understand each other well.' (4)

The overseer for the installation of the new pumping engine was George Wild, who was paid 10s.6d per week. He spent nine days at Ecton, one with Mr Heaton, the Duke's Land Agent and six days at Coalbrookdale ordering ironwork etc.

Their invoice, dated 31 March 1783, shows that the whole consisted of just over two tons of equipment. It included a double-tooth pinion and wheel plus wrought iron spindles fixed in it. The whole was shipped by canal to Stourport and then by the canal network to Froghall.

The beam was originally of wood and an oak tree of the necessary size was found near Derby and a 'drug' for carrying the huge piece of timber was hired. It would appear that six horses were needed to take it to Ecton and it took the best part of three days to get there. Responsible for getting it to Ecton was Joseph Ride of Compton, Ashbourne, whose warehouse received the copper metal cakes from Whiston. He charged £1.18s.0d. The trip seems to have been eventful, requiring repairs to the drug.

The double-tooth pinion and wheel may well be 'The Great Wheel' mentioned in the accounts. The beam itself had the pump rod on one end and a huge box on the other which filled with water, the whole being pivoted on a column which allowed a reciprocating motion. A downward movement of the (full) water box, thereby lifted the pump rod which fell as the box emptied, owing to the weight of the rods. This wheel would not seem to be required for the beam's principal purpose as a pump. The pumps were installed by Roger Mather, who was paid for 12 days at 2s.0d per day for 'putting in the pumps'. The Water Balance engine pumped water up from the 34 fathoms level. A horse gin lifted it to that height from the depths of the mine. (5)

The size of the water box has not been determined, but John Robey (6) states that he believes it to have been larger than 6 ft cube. The metal plates for its construction may have been made by Thomas Bassett at the Hanging Bridge Foundry, near Ashbourne. He invoiced for 12 plates weighing 17 cwt in May 1783. Alternatively, '32 plates of Rolled Iron cut to order' were supplied from Alderwasley Forge in March 1783, weighing 4 cwt, which could have been part of the project, but seem rather light for such a large box.

James Watt recorded some detail of the engine (7): The pump worked with a $4^{1}/_{2}$ feet stroke lifting water from the 34 fathoms level. The pump had a diameter of $9^{1}/_{2}$ inches. In 1788, the engine was drawing up gear (ore etc) and 'old spring water' in 17 to 18 hours per day. The weight of the copper ore raised per barrel was an average of 4 cwt and an average of 95 barrels of gear had been raised per day for 4 to 5 years back. The pumping engine was lifting 13.4 gallons per stroke at $12^{1}/_{2}$ strokes per minute, thereby raising 167 gallons per minute. This gave a capacity of 240,480 gallons per day. This was enough to drain the mine and at minimum expense – no costly coal was needed.

The engine leaves some detail unanswered! There was a single beam and the capstan would appear to have started work at about the same time as the pumps. The beam was associated with a cast metal wheel from Coalbrookdale. The wheel could have been on an axle which was turned by the motion of the beam. A crank on the end of a second motion shaft would then have coupled to a wooden axle which in turn worked the capstan. The reference in the Coalbrookdale invoice to a 'double tooth pinion and wheel' with wrought iron spindles indicates that a second motion shaft was intended.

Later, it appears that a second beam was installed (see below) and Dr Hatchet confirmed this in 1796: 'in this level is a machine or Balance Bob which is worked by a Tub which is filled with water and empties itself by a valve when it descends – this raises the ore in a barrel. There is a similar machine which works some Pump Rods'. (8) All in all, it seems likely that the original beam worked the pumps and the capstan, with a horizontal connecting rod turning the capstan's axle. The water for the beam came down the Apes Tor Adit from the River Manifold. The river was dammed just upstream from the bend adjacent to Apes Tor Shaft. At times of low water, a ripple across the width of the river marks the site of the dam. A leat led across the road – probably arched over to allow passage under the road – and into the adit. In June 1783, flood gates at Apes Tor are mentioned in the Reckoning. This enabled the mine to control the amount of water entering the hill. The use of water for power underground was a valuable commodity, but it had to be carefully controlled; a ranging flow in the river had to be kept out at all costs – hence the floodgates. As a reminder of what it was like, a flood gate exists at Consall Forge in the Churnet Valley, to keep excess water out of the Caldon Canal.

Once the engine commenced work, the Apes Tor Engine Shaft was used for raising stone, plus other specific tasks such as letting the hay down into the mine to feed the underground horses, together with a reduced amount of water.

In 1786, Robert Low, who provided a huge amount of miscellaneous items sent '6 Large Barrils for Apes Tor at 12s 6d each; 4 Kitts at 4s 0d each'; and charged for 'kitting one dozen of covers' at 2s 6d each and 'one dozn of Cover Rings at 4d each'. This would seem to indicate that the barrels had a lid capable of being fastened down.

The water, once landed at Apes Tor Shaft collar (or top) by the striker, could be led off to the river. On the west side of the shaft is a small passage which emerges at the roadside with a channel which runs along the roadside for a few yards (now often full of vegetation in the summer). It then was presumably culverted under the road to the river. See Fig 6.3

However the water had another use. A record in the Labourers & Smelters Account for 6 August 1785 reads 'Joseph Bonsell Co for Sundry Shifts pitching the Engine Case (sic) and Sludging A. Torr dam 24 shifts.' This dam existed at the inner end of Apes Tor adit level, behind the stone-built dam of 1823, erected for the waterwheel, when the water balance engine was replaced. The clay dam enclosed a wooden 'fence' across the width of the level to strengthen it. The clay was red, which indicates that it came from Newhaven.

Why was it built? The dam presumably created a head of water above the top of the upstroke of the bucket. The river must have provided most of this water. The water engine was worked daily, which was fine when there was plenty of river water. However in summer, the river level drops and presumably water flowing into the level would have dropped. Clearly it could be supplemented by the water from Apes Tor Shaft, although the precise working arrangement is unknown. For instance, was the water drawn up the shaft enough to cope with the engine without river water and if not, could the floodgates be shut and the water used to top up the dam with an outflow to the engine from below the top of the dam?

If so, it worked like a waterwheel below a reservoir or millpond. It worked until the water ran out. Mixon Mine had three reservoirs because of this problem. Consequently, it is possible that the efficiency of the engine could have failed during periods of dry weather. Alternatively, if the inner end of the level was lower than the outer (or out-bye) end, the dam could just be to allow for this. It is now no longer possible to walk through the level to sort out matters like this. The level is nearly full of clay (presumably from the river silt) and the roof has dropped near the inner end.

The connecting passage to Apes Tor Adit level from the the shaft chamber

A passage existed between the shaft top at Apes Tor and the level. Widened by the passage of inquisitive people in recent years (until the area was made secure), this passage had been reduced to what resembled a foxhole by the late 1960s when Peter Frost of Ecton, and, on a return trip, with myself disappeared down it to land in the level. It had been filled up with detritus from the shaft's upward extension to the horse whim site on the hillside above.

The Capstan

In June 1783, Samuel Naylor was paid for 'cutting the Roof for the Pump Roads to Rise & for the Capstan – 203 shifts'. This year saw more and more men moving over to a shift system of payment. In the same Reckoning, the men driving Apes Tor Gate were paid for 96 shifts. In the February Reckoning, 1781, Mr T Bird supplied two engine ropes 136 fms long each (816 ft) and five inches in circumference. They weighed over 8 cwt each and cost a total of £26. 9s. 2d. These must have been replacement ropes for the main shaft.

There would appear to have been a major alteration to the capstan in mid-summer 1784. The Reckoning of August 1784 refers to 'Expenses of the men assisting at the alteration of the Engine at the Capstan'. Forty nine men were involved, all paid one shilling a day. Most were paid for 1–1^1/$_2$ days but several were engaged for 3 days on the work. It is just a pity that no details of the work itself were recorded, but with 49 men involved, it sounds like a wholesale movement of the engine. At the same time, it would appear that two men were responsible for working the engine. They were given 21 candles each for a seven week period, so a candle lasted two days. John Harpur recorded on his visit in c.1776 that the pumps were not worked on Sundays. The Candle and Powder account for November, 1784 (it recorded the distribution of candles and powder to the men) stated that there were '8 Watter Drawers below the pumps'. The same account records for the first time that three men were engaged as 'Timberers'. The delivery of oak (and ash) trees was still a regular feature in the accounts, presumably for shoring up the huge workings. They would have been let down the main shaft by the capstan. Upon completion of the latter, the horse whim would have been made largely redundant.

The Chatsworth Water Engine Drawing

The drawing, endorsed in the hand of Cornelius Flint with the words 'The end of the Tub', undoubtedly is the Ecton engine. (9) The long beam, known to be 18 feet in length is seen pivoted upon a wooden frame, rather than on a stone structure. The chain carrying the pump rod is fastened to the arch head of the beam. Although the water seems to be discharging below the shaft collar, that was not the case. The fact that it is shown like it suggests that the drawing pre-dates the construction of the engine which was not off the floor as shown.

The water from Apes Tor level was fed by pipe to the bucket. Whether there was a cut off to the water supply is not clear. The bottom of the water tub, or bucket, opened automatically at the extent of the down-stroke. It was attached to a chain, which can be seen anchored at its upper end. The water left the mine down the adit level to reach the River Manifold. A model of this engine may be seen in the Peak District Mining Museum at Matlock Bath, based on how it is thought it would have looked. However the capstan on it is too small. Even a horse operated gin rarely hauled deeper than 400 feet.

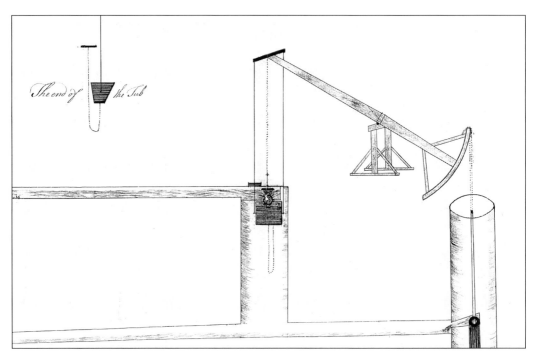

Workings in the 1770s

Robert Shore reported on the stock of ore at the mine at the end of 1770 (see pp 32-33). Appended thereto was a brief description of the pipe working at that time viz:

'The Copper Vein at Ecton goes down pretty near in a perpendicular direction at this time; is now sunk from the Sough or Levil which is taken from the River Manifold, upward of 70 fms, and all the conveniences completed to that depth And now ready for Sinking a fresh. The works upon the Sd Bothams is not so large a Compass as they have been nor able to raise such large quantities as they have here to fore But the Quality much Better'.

Clearly at the time of writing, exploration of the pipe working must have been either between the swellings of ore (John Harper's 'vaults') or they were in one of the smaller of these deposits.

Work continued at the lead sough to the end of the 1760s. It was referred to as Chadwick Sough for the first time in October 1772. The work by Jos Shenton & Co seems to have centred on the upper level at the sough and then in August 1772 occurs the first reference to 'sinking the forefield at the lead sough' by the same team. The upper level will be the level which runs off the main shaft approximately 50–70ft above the sough. It is now reached by climbing up the end of the working at the inner end of the sough. Presumably the shaft being sunk 'in forefield at the lead sough' eventually became widened out into the current excavation which drops down to Clayton Adit level, reached over a century later. Work commenced at £2 per yard, rising to £2.2s.6d and even more, to £2.4s.0d per yard as the sinking continued. However no sooner had this price been paid, when driving and sinking was reduced to £1.15s.0d per yard. The last reference to work in this mine was in May 1773, although this was the first reference since November 1772. If work continued at Chadwick Mine, it must have been by direct labour on wage rates rather than by contract. There are no further references in the 1770s.

In the 1960s, the late John Bonsall of Apes Tor Cottage told me of the existence of the Ape Tor Climbing Shaft and showed me its position (a sycamore seems to be growing out of the top of it now). At that time there was no documentary proof available of this, but confirmation was later found in the Ecton expense accounts. Work commenced sinking this shaft in March 1773 under William Barker & Co. He was a main contractor at Ecton, with several contracts working concurrently. Work was initially at £2 per yard, rising to £2.10s.0d. By November 1773 work has reached a depth of 104ft. There are then no further references until October and November 1774, when a further 35ft was sunk. Unfortunately, the accounts for 1775-76 would appear to be missing. Why there is a gap in the working both at Chadwick and here (i.e. prior to 1775) is not clear.

Much of the surviving accounts for the 1770s consist of summary accounts and many of these list the payments made, rather than give details of where the work was undertaken. Therefore the details of this decade are necessarily sketchy.

A major alteration was the realignment of Ecton Sough. It must have been giving problems of stability through the area from the entrance to where it reached solid rock. It was 'moved' slightly to the south and relined with stone including a stone arched roof. The capstone was dated 1774. The current one at the entrance is a copy and reads 'R.S. 1774'. Later the entrance was extended so that a branch of the narrow gauge railway could be built alongside the riverside of the Clockhouse smelter building. Because the level was on an angle to the embanked wall which included the level entrance, it required a skew-arch to be built in stone. As mentioned elsewhere, this realignment also required a new shaft to the dressing floor, the current Smithy Shaft.

Workings in the 1780s

The beginning of the 1780s saw work in driving Apes Tor adit level: 'Driving a Gate into the Hill at Apes Toor' (May 1780) and a few alterations such as 'driving a gate to the Ingine Lodge' – presumably in the area of the whim at the 34 tms level and 'Driving from Waggon Gate (presumably Ecton Deep Adit, or Sough) to the New Shaft'.

In May 1781 there was more work 'sinking in the Great Shaft, 38 ft,' which was the shaft later known as the Balance Shaft. There are also some perplexing references in 1780 to 'cutting the Engine Race'. This would seem to relate to the drainage channel in Ecton Deep Adit, for in May 1781 there was a payment for 'Cutting for the Gate from the Mouth of the level towards the River, 10 Roods at 8s.0d. £4.0s.0d'. The next Reckoning includes a payment for 'widening the coarse of the River, 6 Rood 17 foot at 16s pr Rood', no doubt to accommodate the egress of mine water from the level. Clearly water was to be removed from the mine by the adit but this must relate to water being lifted by barrels additional to the water drawing at Apes Tor.

Also in May 1781, the accounts reveal that there were 11 lots of men working cope bargains, i.e., there were 11 groups of men raising ore or doing other work in the ore deposit.

In 1782 work started on exploratory activity – driving towards the south end of the vein and activity in both the west and east skirts (sides) of the deposit, plus sinking a sump in the east skirt to assist drainage there. The Great Shaft was being deepened further and it continued through into 1783. In November 1784, payment was made for 'Expenses upon the Millwrights and upon the workmen at the time of the New Engine was put at Top of the Hill 10s.6d'. This must relate to the whim at the side of the later (1788) Boulton & Watt engine house and replaced men hauling the stone with a simple stow or capstan. The shaft was to accommodate the steam winding engine kibbles or tubs and took some seven years to construct. The Water Engine Shaft which descended from the adit level at that time is perhaps twice as big in cross section and took some five years to sink 600 ft or so. The new shaft was to be some 1,400ft in depth. In November 1783, work was sufficiently advanced on the new shaft that stone drawing was replaced by dumping it in the old workings: 'Samuel Adams & Rupert Marsh Carrying Stone from the shaft in to the old opens – 44 shifts at 1/- £2.4s.0d'.

A horse gin, or whim, for two horses from "The Mine" by Rev. Isaac Taylor, 1845 (6th edition)

Elsewhere in 1782, work continued in driving 'Ape Tor Gate'. Clearly a lot of stone was now being raised as development work progressed and some idea of the work it created at the time may be gained from two expense entries: 'Peter Hope striking and wheeling 15 draught & 59 barrels of stone at 3s.0d (with 90 barrels to a draught). Striking in this case refers to the receiving of barrels at the top of the shaft and moving the stone away. In this case, the 'top' would be the bunding or platform at the 34 fms level. 'Wheeling' would be pushing the wheelbarrows of stone to the shaft or from the shaft to the boats. Six weeks later, Wm Hillard & Co were paid for drawing 21 draught 11 barrels of stone at 7s.3d per draught, although the latter was 40 barrels, not 90. It clearly took longer to draw the barrels up the shaft. A later entry confirms that the shaft concerned was the 'Deep Shaft' or Water Engine Shaft as it became known (R. May 1783). The methods of payment become bewildering at times: in December 1783, John Barker was paid for filling barrels at 2s.4d. per Engine Shift with 120 barrels per shift. The Candle and Powder account for May 1783 indicates that Thomas Austin and Co. (12 men in all) received 38 candles for 3 weeks' work, which means each candle lasted a week, which seems unlikely. If it is true, then the total issued in that account to the cope bargain men (those getting the ore, by and large) – 1,252 candles – means there were 179 men involved. It all depends however, on how long a candle lasted!

In 1783 there seems to have been much more activity on development work. At the beginning of the year, Thomas Easting & Co started driving to meet Ape Tor Gate from the current inner end of the adit level. All this work was to accommodate a new method of water removal – the installation of the Water Balance Engine (see above). The engine needed more headroom for the pumps to rise and in May 1783 is a payment for cutting the roof away above the gaping hole of the 600ft plus deep main shaft; no doubt timbered over during progress of the work.

The first reference to the engine was also in March 1783, 'Driving & Cutting room for the Balance Beam', but the engine had been under consideration for some time. In December 1780, Cornelius Flint & James Newbold the millwright were paid their expenses of 'Going to view a Watter Engine upon Lord Ferreas land, £1.13s.8d'. This followed a visit by the two of them to 'Anglesee' (see p 77).

Flint went on further journeys: in March 1783 to Shropshire and Lancashire (a total cost of £4.13s.6d) and in 1767, he went with James Newbold 'to view the mines in Cornwall' at the significant cost of £40. Newbold was earning 14s.0d a week in 1782.

The beam for the Water Balance Engine must have taken some work and time to install. The June 1783 Reckoning includes 'Expenses to the Miners at John Marsdens [presumably a local pub] when the Great Beam was Got into the Mine'. Possibly there was some delay before the arrival of the pumping pipes for the first payment for installing them was not until November 1783. The same Reckoning mentions 'Thomas Hastin Co cutting room for the Engine Wheel'. In fact it was Hastin's team which was installing the pump pipes, or pitwork as it was called. What this 'Engine Wheel' was is not clear. Was it part of the capstan? – probably, as we have seen, see page 65-66.

The water was lifted to cisterns or lodges constructed at intervals up the shaft. There were at least three of them – the Balance & Nether cisterns plus the one at the shaft bottom. The beam was set to work early in 1784: 'Expenses at the time the Water Engine was set to work' probably including ale as well as final adjustments. Thereafter, the cost of drawing water from the mine (it had reached £2.16s.0d pr week per team) finished, although there were still water drawers at the very bottom of the mine lifting water to the bottom cistern. Thereafter, the expense account reveals hints of stoppages, when men were paid for being confined in the mine until the work was finished and payments to the man (called the tenter) who supervised the engine.

A major alteration to the engine was necessary early in 1785. The first hint of change was the record of the delivery of a single piece of oak by Edward Wooddisse in January. It was 18ft long and 21³/₄ inches square. It cost £8.2s.3d on the basis of 59ft at 2s.9d per foot. This calculation hopefully makes more sense to a timber merchant than to your author. The

February Reckoning contains a bill from James Newbold, the mine millwright which included his account for payment for four nights repairing the engine, at 2s.8d, the same rate as for day work. He worked the four nights instead of days, presumably so that the engine was able to be worked as needed during the day. The size of the beam (18ft x 21¾in square) is the only known measurement of the water balance engine known for this period. The Engine Man was Joseph Hall on 8s.0d per week. In 1786, there were two men doing this work perhaps indicating longer working, or the erection of the second engine (see below).

By the end of 1786, the two-man system used to work the water engine had changed to payments to three men. The wage had lifted from 8s.0d. per week to 9s.0d. In December, the work on the engine continued with 'labourers attending the alteration of the Water Engine and [perhaps crucially] the Capstan etc'.

While all this was going on, the mine still needed to be pumped and the February 1787 Candle account reveals the extra candles used by 'sundry People Employed Striking Barrels, dipping etc when ye engine was out of repair.' Striking and dipping would relate to the filling of the barrels (dipping) and landing them at the shaft top (striking).

At the same time, as the above work was done, a new 'Capstone Rope' was purchased as well as two Engine ropes (presumably for the whims, although three were in use – at Apes Tor; at the top of the new Balance Shaft for the steam engine; and at the 34 fathoms level on the Water Engine Shaft). The Labourers' wages account reveals that there were 29 men also assisting work 'at the Capstone and the Repairing of the Engine & Changing the Buckits etc'. In the same account, George Harvey & Co were paid for nine shifts 'repairing the Bunding and the Shade at the shaft foot & other work' at 1s.0d per shift. This must mean that some sort of shelter existed at the foot of the main shaft – perhaps for the men to eat in or keep them dry from falling water. The word 'shade' is peculiar to Ecton and was not used in Derbyshire except at Hillcarr (a 'shoad over the shaft' in 1770). In nearby Leek, the second floor of houses which were used for home work in the textile industry were also known as 'shades'.

At the same time, the Candle & Powder allocation account records two candles allocated to Thos. Fallows and Moses Kidd for 'Removeing some stone etc out of a Gate for a New road into the Mine. Also 2 cwt of powder was allocated to Sampson Hambleton & Co 'in Blasting some Crosild (sic) Lumps in side of the Hill'. The first entry has defied explanation; see Chapter 15 for possible explanation of the latter!

In March 1788 occurred a fall resulting in a 'loss of ore by a run in the Mine'. A payment was made to two lots of people of £3 and £2.10s respectively, indicating a loss of perhaps 1½ tones of ore. Not that much, but clearly sufficiently important to the men at the time.

In 1784, the engine shaft was 'laced' which means that the area around the cast-iron rising main (or pipe) of the pumps was divided vertically from the rest of the shaft for the purpose of inspection and maintenance. The provision of a ladderway for the purpose of inspection gave the miners a new and quicker way to work in the depths of the mine. Until then, a system of ladders, steps etc had to be used in the pipe working. The new footway would be quicker, safer and faster and perhaps less arduous.

Two Water Balance Engines

In 1786 comes the first confirmation that two engines were erected. In two Reckonings (September and November) there are references to cutting room for a balance beam. Dr Hatchet's diary (10) states: 'In this level is a machine or Balance Bob which is worked by a Tub which is filled with water at top and empties itself by a valve when it descends – this raises the ore in a barrel. There is a similar machine which works some Pump Rods'. Perhaps the arrangement postulated above, that the capstan was worked by a drive off the beam, did not work too well. Alternatively, the volume of water being raised perhaps meant that the additional load of drawing was too high, especially if one also considers the extra volume of ore being raised. Whatever the reason, it is clear that at some point a second water balance engine was added and this would appear to have been late in 1786. The Candle and Powder Account for September 1786 records that '32 candles and 44lbs of powder was given to 'Ben Twigg & Co 4 men Blasting room for a Balance Beam on wages.'

The engine would appear to have been commissioned during December, for Thomas Mather was paid 'To Ale & Meat to Pumps' (five days, 15-19 December). There was another bill to James Newbold (and his sons) for attending the 'masheen' for several days and nights. The work must have caused the stopping of the original Water Balance Engine, resulting in temporary arrangements to keep the water down by other means.

Farey confirms that the two engines existed: 'and large buckets fixed on the end of Beams are applied to work pumps in Ecton Mine.' (11)

Other Work: Underground

In December 1785, payment was made for 'driving a Trialgate at the foot of the Hill.' The work seems to have been successful for the following May, four men were working in wages 'Boreing and Cutting in the new vein in the levil' at 10s.0d each per week. There are few levels at the foot of the hill; this can only relate to Birch's Level, Swainsley or East Ecton Mines. The first and last named date from the 19th century. It therefore must relate to Swainsley.

Elsewhere work continued with the sinking of the new 'Great Shaft' and exploratory development work in the lower reaches of the mine.

The first Reckoning for 1786 (February) gives a hint that the mine was dealing with more water. The relevant part of the summary account is quoted in full as it gives a good indication of what the researcher can glean from this account and how frustratingly they always leave one with unanswered queries. If there was more water, it had not suddenly appeared, as payments for this type of work were by now common, if not as numerous:

	Fath	Price	£ S D
'Wm Birch & Co Sink'g a sump in the East skirt	4	£6/10	26. 0. 0
Josh Twigg & Co sink'g another sump in the same skirt	1yd1ft	£6/6	4. 4. 0
Do. drive'g a Gate in the North Vein	1 2ft	£4/10	6. 0. 0
Do. drive'g & sinking a Gate for Wind to the great shaft	2 1yd	£6	15. 0. 0
Do. Ore 2ton 3cwt @ £4.12s.6d			9.18.10
Jn (John) Heathcote & Co Sinking a Lodg at a sump foot	5ft	£1/1	5. 5. 0
Do Cutting room for the great shaft	22²/₃	14s	15.17.4
Do Sinking in the great shaft	2	£9/9	18.18.0
Do shooting room to fix the gage of the shaft & assisting in fixing the same. 12 men as wages 1 week each	10s		6. 0. 0
Josh Bonsall & Co cutt'g down a sump foot on the west skirt	2	£3/10	7. 0. 0
Do Lander'g the water at the sumphead 7 shifts	1s		0. 7. 0
Do ore 18 ton 9cwt at 52s.6d			48. 8. 7
Geo Gosling & Co cutting room for a Sumphead in the west skirt	11¹/₄ yd	14s	7.17.6
Do sink'g a sump	1	6s	6. 0. 0
Do ore 1 ton 3 cwt		50s	2.17.6'

A 'sump' was a short shaft where water was collected for removal from the mine. The 'great shaft' was the new shaft being sunk from the top of the hill to house the new ore drawing kibbles to be operated by a Boulton & Watt steam engine. In the way that a skirt surrounds a 'body', the 'skirt' of the mine was the outside of the body of the ore deposit. A 'gate' was a mine passage-way. Finally, 'wind' means ventilation! The employment of two engine tenters also indicates longer periods of pumping on a daily basis, or possibly two engines with a man at each, but this is unlikely. More water in the mine is clearly apparent.

Other Work on the Surface

Development work was not confined to underground activity however, for a new blast furnace was now needed. However for some reason power from the river clearly was not suited to the purposes of the mine and it had to be brought from the rear side of the hill. The blast furnace was situated on the flat ground close to Birch's Level and smelted lead slag. The reservoir was started in Autumn 1783. It was set out by Thomas Allen of Leek. The small dam was constructed and both a stream and Chadwick Mine supplied the water. The water was conveyed around the northern end of the hill in a gritstone launder (trough). The stone was brought from the quarry at Sheen. The launder was laid across the rear of the hillside dressing floor and descended down the hill roughly on the line later occupied by the wooden incline built from Clayton Mine entrance in 1884. In fact it had been removed during the excavation of the 'calcrete' scree bed, but the channel could be seen high on the side of the quarry face until the early 1970s when rubbish and grass blocked it from view. Coincidentally, the earliest reference to the removal of gravel from here is in R. December 1785, when John Godwin and two others were paid 1s.0d per day 'Cutting gravel at the hillside'.

It is traditionally held that this launder cost one guinea a yard to construct. Unfortunately, missing accounts prevent one from counting the actual cost. One specific invoice survives for the actual channel. William Gould was paid for carrying 262 yds of 'Hollod (hollowed) stone at Sheen pit', at 6d per yard. It confirms another traditional story that the stone came from Sheen which might therefore add credence perhaps to the story about the construction costs (R.December,1784). The bill related to work undertaken in carrying this stone between October 1783 & March 1784.

There are two lots of semi-detached houses built on the side of the launder and this must have been to provide a convenient supply of water from the launder. One is at East Ecton and the other nearer Apes Tor. The August 1785 account refers to the construction of one of these: 'work done at a Double House at Back of the Hill for Barker & Twig – plastering and glazing [?] 22 window lights.' As the Twiggs are known to have lived at the right hand house at East Ecton, this account probably relates to these two houses. Mr Wild's new house was being plastered at the same time.

In December 1785 James Ashton, a mason, was paid for 234 yards, 2ft 6in of water channel at 1 shilling per yard. At the same time he invoiced for 494ft 6in of 'Ashlours [ashlars] for a Furnice' at $2^{1}/_{2}$d per ft. Whether this was for a rebuild of one of the cupolas is not clear. He also claimed for time spent 'Building a shade at stone pitt' and also building a workshop at the mine, in the same Reckoning. Over the 25 years that the Duke had been working the mine, a whole complex of buildings had been erected: a calcining and two smelting furnaces for copper ore; the lead smelter and slagmill; a workshop; mine house; saw pit; smithy, break-house; in all probability additional buildings for the many more ore dressers who were now employed. In addition there was the house and depot at The Pen; and the smelter buildings and brick kiln at Whiston; the lime kiln at Apes Tor; and the brick kiln at Newhaven.

It would appear that the completion of this water channel was delayed for it features in the accounts of 1786. In fact the removal of the rock to create a shelf on which the gritstone channel was laid at Apes Tor appears in R.November 1786 when William Boam and six others were paid for 100 days work at 10d a day for 'cutt'g in the Rock for a water channel.'

An ore pen was also constructed during the early 1780s at the mine and dressed ore was stored there until moved to Whiston or smelted at the mine. Thereafter, there are many references to moving ore from The Pen to the Smilting House (sic) which could be confused with the High Moor Pen and Whiston smelter other than the cost of carriage being 3d-6d a ton! In other words it was at Ecton! A new road was levelled between The Pen and the Mine under Thomas Allen. He charged 3s.6d per day (i.e. one guinea per a six day week) for the three days he worked on the Reservoir launder plus £2.6s.6d for the new road, being 19 days (in 1785). This must relate to High Moor Pen and could be the current road from there to Butterton.

The movement of coal to the mine brought temptation and in February 1780 the mine paid 'expenses on apprehending three persons concerned in pilfering (sic) Coal £4.7s.6d.' They were named Francis, Byatt & Binns (Reckoning Feb.1780). This involved going to Grindon with the Constable and may therefore relate to the theft of coal from the High Moor Pen on Grindon Moor. There may well have been suspicion of theft a couple of years later too. In December 1783, the mine purchased a haystack off John Chadwick for £16. The following May, a Mr Johnstone was paid for 'measuring a Haystack purchased from John Chadwick for the Engine Horses – that was in the Mine'. He was paid 2s.6d, so some time was spent doing this, but the outcome is unrecorded.

During the 1780s it was felt that the mine needed a dwelling house – presumably for hospitality etc. In the 1870s, the wife of Richard Roscoe of Swainsley Hall stated that she was the grand-daughter of John Taylor, the famous Cornish mine engineer who became the Duke of Devonshire's mining agent in 1818. She could recall visiting Ecton in the early part of the 19th century and staying in the house at the mine. (12) The foundations of this house were commenced in mid-1780 and the building survives as a dwelling at the side of the road at Ecton. In the 19th century it was occupied by Samuel Bonsall, the mine manager. During the 1780s there are references to payments to Martha Rowland 'for her attendance upon the House at the Mine'. She was paid a guinea a year.

In the Reckoning of December 1779, Robert Low was paid for house furnishings, which were probably intended for the mine house. It included bed linen, Irish sheeting, 'making 6 sheets & 4 pillow cases, 2 Bolster cases and Lettering them, 3s 0d.'

The mine house probably also originally served as Cornelius Flint's office. In the summer of 1788 work seems to have started on the two houses behind the mine house – although another house existed on the west side of the road in the long range of buildings which occupied much of the frontage between the smelter and the mine house. At the same time, James Needham was paid for thatching a building at the Newhaven Brickworks. Potter's plan of 1809 (see p 12) shows one of the houses behind the mine house as the 'office', and it may have been built for this purpose.

Thatch Marsh & Goit Collieries and a Bucket Engine

There may well have been another water balance engine at the Duke's Colliery on Axe Edge, south west of Buxton. Thomas Wild, was the Duke's agent at his Thatch Marsh & Goit Collieries (? was he related to George Wild of Goits Moss?). One of the shafts was the Buckett Engine Pit. Roberts & Leach (13) suggest that it was some form of continuous system of coal removal using buckets. However they also say that there is no reference to the use of horses or engine and therefore it had no power source. The Ecton Water Balance engine was also called a Bucket Engine and this may have been what existed on Axe Edge if a water source was available.

Ecton miners were used in 1790 to sink the New Rise Pit and timber was fetched in that year from Barleyford Wood in the Dane Valley (14). See also end of this chapter for more on the Ecton miners at Thatch Marsh. Timber from this area was also sold to the Ecton Mine and Hazles Cross Colliery in the 1780s. The Accounts for this Colliery spell Wild as Wyld, but it is clearly the same.

Copper Precipitation

The precipitation of copper from the mine water in the presence of scrap iron was being practised at Parys Mountain as early as 1772-73 (15). There the water was saturated with copper sulphate. This does not appear to have occurred at Ecton, although the precipitation pans must have interested Messrs Flint & Newbold on their visit. Efford reported in 1769 that the water was sufficiently acidic to rot clothing, indicating perhaps the presence of a weak form of sulphuric acid. It is unlikely that there was copper-saturated water on the scale seen at Parys Mountain, but an invoice survives which makes one wonder whether a trial was in fact made. In the Reckoning for February, 1785 is an invoice for the sale of scrap iron to Francis Gosling of Pethills Forge, Winkhill, Staffs. There was 16 cwt sold at 9s.6d per cwt plus 'Old Do., [scrap iron] that had been in copper, 8 cwt at 5s.0d [i.e. £2]'. It does seem that it is possible that precipitation was tried but in the mining jargon of the time, 'failed to answer'. It is unlikely that old iron found under water in the depths of the mine would have been recovered because it was worth £2, or would it? See also p111.

Horses Underground

Once the mine decided to use horses underground, fresh responsibilities began. Hay and bran were needed and in the first few weeks seven cart loads of hay were delivered to Apes Tor. It was let down the shaft and boated into the mine. Joseph Sutton & Co., whose occupation was wheeling & boating stone and filling barrels, were also paid for 'Boating the Hay etc' in November 1783. The work probably took two days for there is a payment for 14 days and the team is thought to have consisted of seven men [on 1s.0d p.day]. The horse whim was situated at the 34 fms or Boat level and replaced the men who had previously raised the water. Each cart load cost 4s. 0d. Once a week Samuel Bonsall also went to Hartington Mill for bran. He went off to buy a horse, in Elkstones and then had to arrange for it to be lowered down the main shaft. The horse cost £5.9s.0d (R. February,1783).

Finding hay meant going in search of it; initially to Wetton, Stanhope and Warslow. One haystack in Wetton was thatched at a cost of 2s.0d. It seems that some of the horses were owned by the mine, but not all of them, for two or three were rented from Sam Bonsall.

He was also paid for 'Making New Pack Sheets, Repairing Old Ones and Drying them'. What did they cover? The ore seems to have been moved in bags. In January 1783, 22 bags for carriage of ore 'about the works' were made with cloth and twine purchased in Leek. These, when full, were ready with either small pieces of ore (up to nutmeg size) or fine particles (slimes) to be loaded onto pack mules or perhaps carts for the journey to Whiston. The pack sheets would keep the contents dry. Samuel Bonsall may have been the grandfather of Capt. Samuel Bonsall, born in 1799, who was the mine captain, or agent, for 33 years prior to his death in 1870.

In the period December 23 1782 – November 4th 1783, John Banks of Hartington Mill supplied 371 strikes of bran at 8d per strike and 4 quarters (1 cwt) of oats at 18s.0d per qtr – nearly 13cwt of fodder equating to about $^3/_4$ ton p.a. Like purchases of hay, it would have been lowered down Apes Tor Shaft and boated to the horses, working adjacent to the wharf at the inner end of the Boat level. In 1783, hay purchases from Winster seem to have been carried to the mine, rather than left until needed, the hay ricks reformed in the mine and covered with 'cloth' to keep the hay dry. Ten tons of hay cost £25 (R. November, 1783).

Horses of course, need feeding on Sundays, although the regularity of this does not feature in the accounts. An example to remind us of this important job occurs in February 1786. William Boam and John Goodwin '& two others' were paid for Sunday Work attending to the horses and 'in getting the water out of the Mine, 20 shifts at 1s.0d per shift'.

The purchase of 36 cwt of chain for letting horses down the main shaft indicates that they were secured well by men used to working with, and no doubt with a fondness for, these animals. Yet it must have been a stressful experience for the horses. A description of the raising and lowering of horses in shafts was obtained by Ken Howarth (16).

It related to coal mines in Lancashire and the book consists of oral reports gathered by the author. Former miners described how the horses squealed worse than a pig being slaughtered. At Wet Earth Colliery in 1900, a horse was brought down, had its legs tied together and was loaded onto an iron plate prior to lowering down the shaft. Another horse was bundled into a net and lifted up a shaft slung below the miners' cage, banging from side to side as it went up the shaft. One feels that the agricultural background of the Ecton men saw their horses being better treated.

In better circumstances, elsewhere, horses travelled up the shaft in the cage. On Saturdays, those that spent the weekend on the surface made their own way to the shaft bottom, jostling in the queue until it was their turn to go up to the day. This was unlikely at Ecton. There is no reference to a cage for the men, let alone the horses and so the latter probably stayed underground throughout their working life in the mine.

More fortunate would have been the horses used to pull the wagons along the Ecton Sough. These are referred to by Dr Hatchet in 1796 (17) and must have replaced the boys. They would have pulled the wagons from the Shaft to the dressing floor but a reference in the Reckoning of November 1780 Labourers' Account seems to suggest that they were in use at that time.

If the speculation regarding the feelings of the men towards the horses is considered a little presumptuous, backing for the view comes from an unexpected quarter – the 5th Duke. In dispensing his political seats, he made no demands upon how the candidates should vote with one exception. This was that they must be in favour of any Bill for the suppression of cruelty to animals. (18) If the Duke, whose lethargic attitude to life is well known, took this forthright view when handing down patronage, it's certain to have been his policy on his estates.

Regrettably, one of the horses was killed in 1798 'by an Accident in the Mine' and John Lownds was paid £4.14s.6d. Normally a dead horse had to be cut up to get it into the cage. The absence of one at the mine meant its removal up the large main shaft would be comparatively easy. It would be hauled by the capstan on the end of the rope (R. March 1789).

Flint's Journey to Anglesey

Why did Flint & Newbold go to Anglesey? (see above). Parys Mountain had only basic whims (called Whimseys in Anglesey) hauling ore and water barrels from the opencast and therefore it was not to examine steam or water power. Moreover, there were Newcomen engines in Flintshire which they passed in order to get to Anglesey (19), so they were not interested in steam power.

However what Thomas Williams had were smelting furnaces – lots of them – at Amlwch, although their precise location is no longer known. It seems more likely that they came to view these ahead of the expansion of the Whiston Works in 1780. Williams also had 'titles' (as they were called) at the mine which burnt ore continually for some six months in order to drive off an excess of sulphur. The Ecton ores did not have this encumbrance and were not subject to this treatment as a result. Therefore it would have been the ore reduction furnaces at Amlwch which were probably of interest to the Ecton men more than anything else.

The Boulton & Watt Winding Engine

Documents in the Boulton & Watt Collection (20) shed light on the drawing and pumping arrangements, (see above). James Watt also made calculations on possible changes to the water engine. He confirms that a rotative drive off one of the two water engines existed, producing calculations based on adding a two feet diameter wheel to the rotative shaft. This was to work upon a crank shaft of eight feet length and a four feet stroke working the $9^{1}/_{2}$ inch pump at the 34 fathoms level and lifting the water as was existing to the Ecton Sough. This would lift 12 gallons per stroke, less than the 13.4 gallons already being lifted. However, the two feet diameter wheel could be made to produce 15 strokes per minute, thereby raising 180 gallons per minute. This was an improvement of nearly 19,000 gallons per day.

Ecton Engine House between the Wars

Flint wrote to Watt on 30th July 1787, after reflecting on his journey home the day before, after visiting Watt. His letter indicates that prior to the installation of the Water Engine, 110 barrels of 80 gallons each were raised by horses per 6 hour shift, giving a daily capacity of 35,200 gallons. The letter reiterated what Flint was hoping to achieve:

> 'The Business that will be wanted to be done is to raise about 40 tons of gear a day in 8 hours time or thereabouts from certain depths that you have noted, the Greatest part of which to be raised to the level of the Audit [Ecton sough] and the rest to a level where there is a Boat Gate 34 fathoms below the Audit, and also 7,680 gallons of water out of the vein to the present Water Engine Lodge.' (Boulton & Watt Coll., Birmingham Central Library)

The 7,680 gallons represented excess water from the wettest season in the mine bottom. Water Engine Lodge is considered to be the 34 fathoms level reservoir. Watt referred to this as 'The Long Lodge', indicating perhaps that the water entering the pump was flowing in from the underground canal. In the event the new steam engine was only used for winding and pumping house water up to the boiler in the engine house at the top of the shaft. Other notes state that three horses at a time were used for drawing at the 34 fathoms level gin. The difference in weight of copper compared with lead was highlighted: 'when they draw that ore which contains Lead ore they draw abt 7c [cwt] or 6 but in copper they drew 5c in a Kibble.' There appears to be a section through the ore deposit then being worked indicating that the pipe working (or 'vein' as Cornelius Flint referred to it) was 80–90 yards in height (40–45 fms) by 6–8 yards wide (3–4 fms).

Watt did not often go to visit the site of proposed engines (21) and a letter from Flint recommends that Watt or some other person visit the mine (letter of 26 December 1788). In the event, the plan for the layout of the engine house was found to cut into the building housing the horse gin. In fact the corner of the engine house was in the middle of the 'race' where the horse walked. If Boulton & Watt were not that bothered about going to the mine, the latter was not sitting on its laurels. In Spring 1788, George Wild was despatched 'to view the steam engine at Measham' This was a Boulton & Watt engine erected in 1778 and altered for winding, using a spiral balancing drum in 1787. Flint & Newbold also went down to Cornwall presumably to see the winding engine at Wheal Maid Mine near Camborne.

Down in the Shaft, men were experiencing poor ventilation in the sinking and others were 'driving for wind for the Shaft' in midsummer in 1788. Water for the boiler was to be pumped up the shaft and 'House Water Lodge' was made to accommodate the pumps and the cistern in which they sat. This cannot be seen at sough level and must now be under water. A cistern was constructed in the engine house for this water. Samuel Travis was busy making a boiler and other materials started to arrive.

The January 1789 Reckoning reveals that Boulton & Watt's engineer was paid five guineas and his board (11 weeks at 10s 0d). The same document makes the first reference to the current name of the new winding shaft – the Balance Shaft. An early problem must have been within this shaft, for this Reckoning also includes details of payment to Wm Sheldon & 15 other workmen 'cutting and widening the deepe shaft where Barrels meet, 60 shifts at 3s.0d each'. Despite this ability to draw water from the mine, a mere or reservoir was constructed just to the south of the engine house to collect rain water. It is still there – the only depression on a pockmarked hillside which is not a shaft or working. The actual engine was a 16-inch cylinder, double acting engine with sun and planet gear, using a double spiral balancing drum. It was not used for pumping mine water and the Water Balance engine continued to be used for this. The engine raised kibbles to the sough level. In 1804, Salts Level was driven higher up the hillside and ore dressed upon the hillside dressing floor thereafter.

With the original plan sitting in the middle of the gin, the engine house was placed 4–5 feet away from the position on the plan, situated so that the length of the pump rod remained the same (letter 4th March 1788). There were other misgivings too. The plan made no allowance for a possible replacement of the boiler. The 12 feet diameter fly wheel could not be got into the building, unless cast in parts, there being no 'sufficient open to admit it'. Further, the proposed 'gin barrel' (the double spiral balancing drum) was drawn on the plans to a width of 16 feet, in diameter. This was the same diameter as the horse gin adjacent, yet substantially more rope would be needed to be carried on the new drum.

Flint therefore proposed that the diameter be increased to 18 or 20 feet. There were other reasons why Flint felt the increased size to be desirable. One gets the impression that the men understood the practical problems at the mine far better than Boulton & Watt. They also knew the solutions despite some of the complications and challenges of the new technology. One of Boulton & Watt's men desired to stay on at the end of the work. Flint wrote to advise that 'Mr Isaac Perrins [of Boulton & Watt] asks to let his assistant John Varley continue to take care of the engine if he can be spared ... there is nobody about the Workes fit to be intrusted'. Varley must have been released, for he stayed for six years before moving on. Flint described him as being 'a very good young man'.

The difficulties of the plans being drawn without knowledge of the works continued. Flint wrote in March 1788 to comment that the plans showed the:

'fixing [of] the Injection Pump and Rod in the Middle and on one side of the Pit – we have had a good deal of consideration about this matter, indeed you have fixed the Pumps there in the same side of the Pit the Gear [ore etc] is now discharged. It is true, I do not wonder at such a mistake happening, it is very possible and probable too that a stranger might consider the Gear discharged differently to what it is.'

This was only one of several diplomatically written letters Flint wrote during this period to his engine maker.

Another such letter concerned the double spiral balancing drum Watt used to counter balance the weight of the rope in the shaft. Flint wrote that an alternative system (and a much simpler, cheaper one) was in use in 'this neighbourhood' which Flint had seen at different places. However, Watt preferred his own solution. Flint even sent James Newbold to Birmingham to explain how the alternative solution worked in March 1788. Regrettably, a month later, Flint was advising that 'Poor Newbold who was lately with you has had part of 2 fingers of his left hand totally severed by the coggs of a wheel at the Works at Ecton'.

In 1788, the accounts start to reflect the activity going on around the arrival of the engine parts and other items associated with it.

Hugh Henshall and Co. (a carrying company owned by the proprietors of the Trent and Mersey Canal) sent their invoice 30 April 1788 for 75 items sent from Stourport to Froghall. The goods weighed 4 tons 2¹/₂ cwt. The invoice is endorsed 'the Rate of Goods from Stourport not Perishable is 18s [p.ton].' These items – all parts of the pumps, had been delivered to Stourport on the 18 April. Fifty seven of the items were plain pipes, each 6 feet long and 3 inches in diameter. They had been made on behalf of Boulton and Watt by Joseph Rathbone and Dale Company of Coalbrookdale and cost £83.8s.0d. Mark Gilpin of Rathbones calculated his bill on 4 tons 8 cwt!

The mine wasted no time in fetching the pumps which were to be used to supply the engine with water. William Blower made four journeys from Froghall to the engine house. This seems strange until one realises that the haulage system within the mine itself was on the Water Engine Shaft, not the new Balance Shaft, so they would need to be lowered by the horse gin to the new water lodge where they would be installed. Blower charged 10s. 0d. per ton to deliver the 75 items.

The 57 lengths of 6 feet long pipes when connected would be 342 feet long. The shaft was 312 feet deep according to James Watt, (317 ft per a mid-19th century miner's notebook) to adit level. Exactly where the pumps were situated and how water reached them from the nearby water engine shaft is not clear.

Laurence Follows' team of pack horses was busy in the spring of 1788 carrying 737 loads of lime from the kiln to the mine. He charged only 1¹/₂d per load and one wonders whether this was therefore from Apes Tor lime kiln. He delivered another 397 loads (at 2d) 'to the Engine at the top of the Hill' and more to Mr Wild's new house at Lower Lee (Ecton Lee) and the 'Gutter at Ape Tar' (both at 2d per load). He charged 6s. 0d. per day for 4 days' work with 6 horses 'carrying sand to the Engine'. The expression 'Ape Tar' for Apes Tor may still be heard today.

Mathew Fearn (? of Bakewell) supplied 17 beams up to 23 ft 6in long x 9in x 9in for a 'Stove Ingin Frame' plus timber for a wheel for the engine, which sounds like parts for the spiral balancing drum. Much of it was 8 ft in length, the radius of the drum. The latter delivery took five loads and the price included turn-pike charges. It was fetched by William Mellor of West Side Mill, Bakewell and he charged 19s. 3d.

Soon, even bigger baulks of timber for the main engine frame, the pulley frame at the shaft collar, or edge, the beam for the pump rod etc. were on their way. Daniel Whillock invoiced for the carriage of 6 pieces of Riga timber measuring 134 feet, plus another 25 dales 20 feet long each and 24 measuring 14 feet long. He also bought the boiler from

Apes Tor Limekiln

Ashbourne. Kenwrights in Stoke-on-Trent also sent to Froghall by the canal '7 Dantzick Balks' ranging from 14–40 feet long (R. June 1788).

Other deliveries included 14 gallons 'of the best Cod oil' at 2s 8d per gallon in two casks, from Wm Hurd and what would appear to be 36,500 nails from Abram (sic) Harrison of Belper. The boiler (mentioned above) was made by Samuel Treavis (? Travis) and weighed a little over 9 cwt. It cost £15.8s.7d and may have been made of copper. In 1790, the mine was using 'sweet oil' purchased from Joseph Bradley of Ashbourne (R. February 1790). His invoice stated that 'we have good oil at 21d to 2/-.' In the next Reckoning, it is clear that the mine had followed this up and had purchased Rape Oil, Linseed Oil, Fine Pale Whale Oil and a keg of 'sope.'

Curiously, the invoice for the casting of the steam engine itself came later – or at least it is to be found in the September 1788 Reckoning. It was receipted following payment on 22 December 1788. The date on the invoice is 27 February and is from John Wilkinson of Brosely. It went in 9 lots of packaging with ten small items in a cask. Other small items were made locally. Walter Bassett of Mayfield supplied gudgeons and brasses to the 'fire engine' late in 1788, presumably for necessary alterations.

From Boulton & Watt's invoice, it would appear that the Wilkinson castings went to Boulton & Watt's works in Birmingham for the engine to be built up. They invoiced for hundreds of items (literally) on 6 September and that month Izaak Perrins arrived at Ecton to erect the engine along with John Varley. Perrins stayed for 11 weeks and the mine was charged 24s 0d. a week for his services, plus 30s. 0d. for travelling to and from the mine. John Varley came to the mine with Perrins but as is mentioned above, stayed on. His wages varied between 12s. 0d. and then 13s. 0d. per week. In the 6 weeks ending December 1790, he was paid £1. 6s. 0d. per week, a considerable sum of money.

Boulton & Watt's invoice was dated 5 March 1789 and was paid the following May. It amounted to £397. 6s. 5d. and payment was made by six separate bankers' drafts. In the September 1788 Reckoning is a bill for carriage of two wagon loads of cast iron 'from Froghall to Top of hill Ingin' which would appear to be part of the engine, on the same invoice, William Mellor charged for the delivery of 'Two Drug Load of beams and Rods to Top of Hill Ingin', which will be the wooden engine beams, connecting rods etc.

Another invoice for the supply (unusually) of timber balks from Derby may indicate where they were purchased. The beam for the first Water Engine also came from Derby. A late bill from Wm Bloor and John Wardle of the carriage of 'Cast Iron and Engine Meterials from Froghall Wharf to Top of Ecton Hill', weighing $7\frac{1}{2}$ tons would probably account for the bulk of the engine.

At the end of November 1788, the whole system was tried for the first time (on the 29th). Flint wrote to Watt 'every part thereof was put in motion and seems to act in every respect agreeable to the wishes of everyone concerned with it'. Problems soon appeared. Within a month the pump rod broke 'from water being froze in the pumps'. This was resolved by allowing warm air in the mine to rise up the shaft.

More dramatically, the system of counterbalancing the weight of the ropes involved a heavy weight in the shaft on the end of a rope. It moved up and down depending upon where the kibble was. This broke loose 'being perfectly wore by the friction of the weight that connects the Roap and Chain to the Pin that goes through the Spiral Shaft' (i.e. the Balancing drum). It was replaced by a stronger pin 'made of Steel & Iron'. However the weight, allowed to drop down the shaft, caused much consternation. Three men were employed at that time in deepening the shaft. Flint must have been a cautious man for he had arranged for staging to be placed in the shaft at different places to protect the men. The weight went through the lot, close to the shaft side, where for some reason the protection was weakest. The men had left the shaft '2 or 3 minutes before'.

Flint decided to sink a separate shaft to contain the weight. It may be seen today. Below the Engine House is a large semi-circular stone wall raising above the valley side. This was to raise the level of the ground to the same level as the Balance Shaft Collar (i.e. the one containing

Invoice of Sundry Engine Materials, sent to Preston Brook 27 Feby 1788, by Mr John Wilkinson, to be forwarded to Soho, for the Account & Risk of his Grace the Duke of Devonshire...

D
1 Cylinder 16 Inches Diameter — — 11 — —
2 Inner bottom — — — — — — 1 2 7
3 Outer do — — — — — — — 1 1 10
4 Top — — — — — — — — 1 3 12
a 5 Piston & Cover — — — — — 2 1 24
6 Air Pump — — — — — — 7 — 15
a Bucket for do — — — — — — — 35
7 Round Cover — — — — — — 1 — 4
a Gland for Cylinder — — — — — — 24
a Do for Air Pump — — — 10 27 29 30 Al 74
Gunborings — — — — — — 2 — 5/. — 26
a Middle brass for Cylinder — — — — 6
a Bottom do — — — — — — 5
a Bush for Gland of do — — — — 3
a Brass for Air Pump — — — — 3
a Bush for Gland of do — — — — 3
a False Face — — — — 26 1 20 16 34 —
Fitting Piston with Furniture &c. — — — 2 6 2
Fitting Air Pump, turning Top &
Bottom facing the Cylinder &c. } — — — 2 13 6
Box No 8 — Cask No 9 — — — — — 46

£ 49 18

NB. The Articles to Which a is prefixed are in the Cask ——

The invoice from John Wilkinson, February 1788

the kibbles. Thereafter the weight wound on/unwound off the spiral drum and went up and down its own shaft.

In 1795, there was talk of increasing the size of the engine, which would have involved a new boiler. Flint wrote to Watt (9 August, 1795) that there were two boilers, 5 feet in diameter in the neighbourhood. One of them had never been used and they were made 'of iron', 'but we suppose neither of them are likely to be considered by you fit for the purpose of an increased power of the engine' Flint was again being more diplomatic than perhaps he should have been to his illustrious engine maker.

These two boilers were on the Dale and Hayesbrook mines in Warslow parish – the Dale Mine being literally opposite Ecton Mine. They are believed to have been Newcomen boilers and at 5 feet diameter one would have gone in the existing engine house. The new Watt boiler, which was, in the event, never purchased, would have required an extension of the building. (22)

The Ecton Engine House Site

The original engine house had a different roof profile than now. The roof kept losing tiles in high winds and was lowered in the 1930s. It had an off-centre ridge, causing one side to be a lot longer than the other. This appears to have been adopted by Watt at other sites, for example, in 1788 a similar engine house was built for John Christian (or J C Curwen) of Workington, Cumbria. The engine house here was similar to the Ecton Engine. It was a 14-inch cylinder, with a 4ft stroke. It was double-acting (i.e. steam pressure applied to both sides of the piston), with parallel motion, sun and planet gear and a double spiral balancing drum. (23)

The road to the engine house, described as 'a carriage road' was made at the beginning of 1788. This allowed coal to be carried up to the engine. The initial ropes may have been supplied by William Bird. On 17 December 1787, he supplied two pairs of engine ropes, 110 and 114 fathoms each, $5^1/_2$ inches in circumference. They weighed $29^1/_2$ cwt., (just under $1^1/_2$ tons and cost 45s 6d per cwt (£67. 3s. 0d) (Dev. Coll., R February 1788). This would seem to suggest that they were spliced together. In November 1789 Samuel Goodwin, already a rope supplier to the mine and based in Leek, supplied two tapered ropes weighing just under 33 cwt at $6^1/_2$d per lb (£99. 11s. 2d) which would appear to be replacement ropes for the Balance Shaft. In November 1788 he had supplied various ropes which do not appear to be for the Balance Shaft plus two bells, which might have been for a form of communication at the shaft. By a comparison of the weight of the ropes in the Balance Shaft, Goodwin also supplied a rope for the capstan in September 1789. It weighed $5^1/_2$ cwt. The Victoria County History states that he was a grocer and also made sacks. If he was like Robert Low, of Warslow, he stocked or obtained almost anything. (24) He must have been making some of the longest ropes employed in mining or indeed in any other trade.

The size was later changed, for in 1794 Flint advised Boulton & Watt that the mine was using ropes 7 inches in circumference at the shaft top and 5 inches at the bottom (i.e. tapered ropes). They were therefore 2 inches in diameter down to $1^1/_2$ inches. The supplier had been John Hall of Leek but in 1794 they were using Samuel Goodwin, also of Leek, who charged $5^1/_2$d per lb. It would seem that there was some initial difficulty obtaining tapered ropes. In 1794 the depth of the Balance Shaft was 202 fms (1,212 feet).

The balance weight was on the end of a 15 fms length of rope. Hence the majority of the winding drum was used to receive the shaft rope as a kibble rose from the bottom. It simply wrapped around the drum. The balance rope wound on and off the inverted spiral above.

From left to right: the reservoir (in shadow) with the balance weight shaft behind it; the engine house; the top of the pipe working (fenced off) and another shaft on a north-south vein. This field is called The 'Om.

The top of the Balance shaft and the adjacent Engine house with the rear wall of the gin house (there is evidence of holes for roof timbers)

The balance weight shaft raised above ground level to the height of the Balance Shaft

The first Boulton & Watt balancing drum was erected at Wheal Maid Mine in Cornwall in 1785 on an older Boulton & Watt engine. This had a diameter of 15 feet. However an earlier one was erected by John Wilkinson at his coal mine at Bradley in Staffordshire in 1782 or 1783. It also had a 15 feet diameter drum.

Although the intention was to construct the drum with a diameter of 16 feet, Flint considered that a diameter of 18 feet to 20 feet would be preferable. No shaft existed as deep as the Ecton Balance Shaft. A wider diameter drum, meant less windings and consequently less friction (and wear and tear) as the rope wound on and off the barrel. This arrangement seems to have been accepted by Boulton and Watt and the plans were altered accordingly although as noted above, the mine appears to have originally ordered timber for a 16ft diameter barrel. The upright shaft supporting the drum or barrel (as Flint called it) was hollow cast iron. Flint wrote in February 1788: 'Mr Watt's recommending of it is a sufficient reason for us approving it.' The two pulley wheels, which let the rope down into the shaft were 6 feet in diameter and made of cast iron. The wheels on the gins were smaller and although some were of cast iron, others were of wood.

The Ecton winding engine would appear to have been the first Boulton & Watt example in the Midlands and either the third or fourth they supplied to anyone. It appears to have been the first with a drum over 15 feet in diameter. Boulton & Watt must have been keen to supply a winding engine to Ecton. It probably worked the deepest shaft in the country.

Despite the large expense of work connected with the new engine, the accounts give some indication that the main ore deposit may have begun to fail. There are many references in the December 1789 Reckoning to trials being pursued; no doubt to find the 'next' large deposit, or sidewards extensions of it. Unfortunately no other major deposit was to be found. The irony is that the new winding arrangement was installed as the mine began to fail.

Although the mine was usually not unduly troubled by water, in 1795 Flint reported that a spring had been located 22 fathoms below the sough. This was being allowed to drop to the 34 fathoms boat level. The inrush was 80 gallons per minute. As each barrel carried 80 gallons, the Apes Tor gin could not cope with this extra volume. Other arrangements must have been made to improve pumping or water lifting by barrel. This would have included running the Water Balance Engine at maximum capacity. Eventually, the flow diminished without the need to alter the Boulton & Watt engine to provide additional assistance.

It was normal to pay an annuity to Boulton & Watt based upon the amount of cost saving achieved by the engine. In 1789, agreement was reached by Mr Heaton for the purchase of this annuity.

The Engine House Today

The engine house, as built in 1788 survives but its distinctive roof profile was lost when the roof was lowered. The stone chimney with its brick lining – the bricks presumably from the Newhaven brick kiln – has been a stump since at least the 1920s, but recently has been reduced still further for no apparent reason.

On the south side of the building an open fronted small room on a lower level is where the ashes were raked out from beneath the boiler (removed c.1856). They remain nearby, mostly grass covered. The entrance to the barn is original and the area outside it, now covered with a manure-based soil, consists of slag block paving. Slag blocks were used elsewhere – a quantity was sent to Wetton Mill in the late 1780s – but this is the only known survivor using blocks made at Ecton (a lot exist at Whiston, where the Stable House and an adjacent building (now a dwelling) are built of slag blocks. More exist in Black Lane – named after the broken slag surface of days gone by – near to the abandoned tramway which went under the road).

The surrounding circular shaped stone wall of the covered gin also survives on its east side. Covered gins are not usual in this area – at least not permanent ones built of stone – and reflects the exposed nature of the site. Water was pumped up the shaft to supply the boiler, but the rainwater mere exists close by on the south side of the building. Presumably rain water was used when it was available. The stone work, which built the balance-weight shaft up into the air to match the collar of the main shaft, also survives, it is shaped like an inverted cone.

All the machinery was scrapped in the mid-1850s when the water supply to a waterwheel driven set of pumps (the replacement of the Water Balance Engine) was lost. (25)

When last inspected, this important building, worthy of preservation, built on the deepest shaft in the country at the time and maybe the deepest of all shafts in 1788, was about to lose a significant number of tiles on the east span of the roof close to the ridge.

Adjacent to the building is the enclosure containing the shaft and site of the balancing drum. On no account should this enclosure be entered.

The Boat (Bote) Level

In 1755, the Duke of Devonshire entered into an agreement with Thomas & John Gilbert relating to a sough company draining Clayton Mine through the Duke's land. The Duke took a 1/12th share in the company. (26).

The Gilberts may have met the Duke at Chatsworth – they were after all not without influence (John as agent to the Duke of Bridgewater and Thomas as land agent to the Duke of Sutherland) and they were minor gentry in their own right. However, whichever way was used, it is most likely that the underground canal at the Duke of Bridgewater's Worseley coal mines – which connected with the Bridgewater Canal – was known to the Duke and the idea for the construction of a canal at Ecton came from John Gilbert. The diary of James Brindley, the canal engineer indicates that he came to Ecton with the Gilberts in May 1759, but the reason is not stated. Perhaps it was then that the idea of the Boat level was promulgated.

The Gilberts were possibly still active at Ecton in 1795. An advert for the newly erected Warslow Mill states that the mill (it was partly a cotton business for Mules or Jenneys) 'was near to the Ecton Mine and another Mine adjoining, belonging to – Gilbert Esq and Company.' However a document (undated, but between 1774-76) suggests that the Duke had taken an assignment of the Gilbert lease of 'Clayton's Mine and other mines in Ecton Hill.' (27)

The idea for a similar underground canal as at Worsley at Ecton must have been confirmed shortly after the Duke took control at Ecton. In the Reckoning of 13 February 1762 is the first reference to John Hall and partners sinking 'the New Shaft' (being paid £12.10s.0d for sinking 10 yards). The same Reckoning records the first reference to 'driving in ye deep level'.

At the end of 1763 is the last reference to the sinking of the New Shaft, by Wm. Butler & Co. This team of contractors then commenced 'driving the deep level at the New Shaft.' The following March Reckoning confirms that they were 'driving Ape Tor Levil'. A calculation of the depth of the shaft from the Reckonings indicates that the New Shaft had been sunk 235 feet. The water level at the Water Engine shaft is at the same horizon as the Ecton Sough (or Ecton Deep Adit). The boat level is 34 fms level below sough level (i.e. 204 ft). The water level in Apes Tor Shaft is perhaps 5 ft below the shaft collar – where the concrete capping is now – and the shaft rose even higher up to where the horse whim was situated making up the difference between 204 and 235 ft. The evidence is compelling that this 'New Shaft' is Apes Tor Shaft.

It is clear that the deep level, started simultaneously with the shaft, is the 34 fms level, being driven from the pipe workings. In February 1764, Wm Butler & Co were 'driving deep levl at New Shaft' and 'Saml. Picering [was] driving deep level on vein side' i.e from the vein side of the level, rather than driving a level into the side of the vein. Sam signed his name Pickring. Confirmation that this deep level is the 34 fms level rather than the later Apes Tor adit level is provided in June 1764, when Wm. Butler was driving at the 'Engine Shaft foot'. Thereafter, the level from the shaft was referred to as 'Ape Tor Gate' and the level from the inner end as 'the deep level'.

As early as October 1762, the deep level was being railed 'for carts' and by Feb 1764 it was being 'fanged'. Fanging was a practice of constructing a conduit below the floor for the passage of air or, as in the case of Ecton Sough, water. By June 1765, Apes Tor Gate and the deep level together had been driven 193 yds. Thereafter work was started on a 'cross from Deep Level Turn head'. Work in the level seems to have finished by May 1766 and it is suggested that the level would have been flooded at about this time.

The first reference to a boat is in 1769, so the earliest boats would seem to have been made by the mine carpenter and not invoiced separately as a result; quite an achievement by a land-locked rural carpenter. Boats were in use before this, however. In the autumn of 1767 are references to driving in the 'old Bote gate' and driving in the Bote gate in the spring of that year for a distance of some 86 yds. This suggests that the boats were in use prior to 1767 and that a realignment of the level was made for some reason. The 'cross from the Deep Level Turn head' can now only be speculated. However it is suggested that it may relate to the construction of a wharf at the bottom of the shaft with the canal coming in at an angle to the shaft having been driven in a straight line from the pipe. Presumably the wharf would be large enough to stockpile at least two boat loads of ore and the landing point for the ore-kibble.

A query arises from Efford's description of 1769. He states that ore was trammed out of the sough level by boys pushing wagons running on rails etc. If the ore was being floated down the Boat level, why was it also being raised to the adit/sough level?

As there was only one whim, presumably ore and water were not raised simultaneously. Were there periods of the day when water was raised manually to the 34 fms level and then removed in barrels up the shaft, ore being raised at other times? This could mean that while pumping was underway, i.e. in the daytime, the ore was raised to Ecton Sough and then trammed out by the boys, which seems unlikely. Perhaps it relates to ore won from above the boat level. If water was lifted out of Apes Tor Shaft, presumably the canal, or a cut from it took water to a sump at the bottom of the shaft which was used to fill the barrels. If so, the arrangements must have allowed for the loading of kibbles also at the shaft base to remove the ore. It is unlikely that this was achieved in a manner similar to that used on the Bridgewater Canal system – where containers of coal were lifted directly from the boats.

Perhaps the water and ore were raised on demand. If a boat arrived, its contents were lifted and emptied and then the lifting of the water barrels was then resumed. None of this addresses the point referred to above concerning pumps at the shaft. Too little is known today to be certain of day to day arrangements. The horse whim at Apes Tor seems to have been worked daily by four six-hour shifts.

Despite the advantages of the new arrangement, ore tonnages did not change by much in the years of the next decade. However one presumes that the costs, which remained fairly static, reflected the ability to pump more as the mine deepened without much difference in expenses. What would affect this state of affairs would be the mine depth. Gins were operable down to about 400 feet. Beyond this, other gins would be needed. Eventually three lifts were needed at Ecton prior to the introduction of the Water Balance Engine. In May 1769 Edward Greenhough was paid £3.8s.0d for 'Making New Bote etc' and £4.9s.0d for another one in February 1772. These could have been replacements or even larger boats following later work on the level mentioned above. The level also appears to have been heightened, for there are references to removing rock from the level roof.

The surviving records in the Boulton & Watt Collection housed in Birmingham Library include letters and calculations concerning the winding engine provided by that firm in 1788. Amongst all the technical data and letters from Cornelius Flint are a few details relating to water removal prior to that date. The water is confirmed as having been pumped up to the 34 fms level. It was usual to pump water up to a certain height and hold it at the top in a cistern or 'lodge' prior to pumping it by a second lift to a higher level. The 34 fms level was regarded as a lodge. James Watt referred to it as the 'long lodge', and indeed it was.

A horse gin existed at the inner end of the 34 fms level and the cistern here was called the Engine Lodge (Reckoning Aug 1780). Presumably it was fed from here into the boat level.

It would appear that there is a strong case for arguing that the Ecton Boat level was the first to be developed after the Worsley scheme. For work to start in mid-1762, plans must have been mooted in 1761 and clearly the Boat level represents the first major investment at the mine by the Duke.

Roberts, (28) states that Worsley's underground system started in 1759 and by the end of 1760, '137 metres of navigable level had been driven', so the sinking of Apes Tor Shaft and driving of the 34 fms level had commenced some 18 months later. Roberts points out that Worsley was not the first mine to use boats: Nantymwyn Lead Mine, north of Llandovery and the Gwauncaegurwen Colliery in the Tawe Valley (both in South Wales) did so from 1747 and 1757 respectively. Worsley brought the principle into major practice with different levels of canals connected by an incline underground.

In addition to the Speedwell Mine (see below) at Castleton in Derbyshire, there was another boat level near Ecton and it was also owned by the Duke of Devonshire. This was the 'Duke's level' at Thatch Marsh Colliery on Axe Edge, south west of Buxton. In fact the entrance (now sealed) is off Level Lane in the Buxton suburb of Burbage. It would appear to be over two miles in length. (29) There were other Derbyshire boat levels such as at Blackclough Colliery (30), plus Hillcarr & Magpie Soughs.

Mining mariners will find three articles by Roberts of interest. (31) Other early schemes recorded by Roberts include the Donnington Wood Canal formed by John & Thomas Gilbert and Lord Gower (brother-in-law of the Duke of Bridgewater) in South Shropshire. The boat level here was in use shortly before October 1766. (32) The Gilberts were also partners with James and John Brindley and Hugh Henshall from March 1760 in a scheme to work Goldenhill Colliery, which was later connected to Harecastle Tunnel. (33) Ivor Brown has investigated the underground canals in Shropshire, where there appears to have been at least eight. (34) Later, John Gilbert was involved with Speedwell Mine at Castleton under an agreement of 1771 (35) and a boat level here is now a tourist attraction.

The Worsley boats were flat bottomed and made from oak and elm. (36) They were 45ft 6in long and 4 ft wide, drawing 2 ft of water and with a capacity of 10 tons. The coal was containerised in metal coal boxes, with lugs for lifting and there were 12 to a boat. There were smaller boats where local conditions demanded. (37) It is persuasive to think that the Ecton boats used barrels, which were then lifted up Apes Tor Shaft, but we cannot be sure.

The dimensions of the Ecton boats were not given by Harpur (38) when he visited the mine in the late 1760s but he stated that 'the water in ye carriage' (i.e. the width of water in the level) was 2–3 feet and 4 feet where the boats passed. James Watt's notes of calculations at the time of installing the steam engine in 1788 state that a barrel of water at Ecton lifted 80 gallons. A similar barrel would therefore lift approximately 7 cwt of ore (a gallon weighs 10lbs). However it is known that although they took 7cwt of lead ore, they were only loaded with 5cwt of copper ore. If the boats were modelled on the Worsley boats, and assuming a 2ft 16ins diameter for the barrels, each boat would have a capacity of 18 barrels, with a total cargo of about $4^{1}/_{2}$-5 tons, allowing for void around lumps of ore etc. It is likely that the Speedwell Mine boat level was not too dissimilar to the Ecton boat level. A visitor to the former in 1796 (39) stated that the boats were flat bottomed and that the boat was 'worked thro the canal by pieces of wood fixed in the sides of the rock by which the Boatmen held so as to pull the Boat forwards. In this manner we went for about 700 yards...'. Probably the Ecton boats were moved in a similar fashion. In 1772-73, the Ecton boats were described by Geisler, a Swedish visitor as being 'long & narrow' which may be a clue that they were similar to the Worsley 'starvationer' boats. (40)

Drainage of the Speedwell Mine Boat level revealed the remains of a former oreboat. (41) The Speedwell Mine boat was flat bottomed and the width of the boat appears to be about 2ft 6in – rather narrow considering the width of the level. The tonnage of 5 tons is probably about right, with the boats flat bottomed and made of hardwood.

The tonnage of ore raised in 1767 was 788 tons of copper ore. If the boats were moving 5 tons at a time, or perhaps less, the number of journeys were clearly less than one a day, in fact there were little more than three journeys per week. This had risen to 7–8 journeys per week by 1786. On this basis, the principal function of the boat level would have to be for pumping, with Gilbert cleverly suggesting that the subordinate use of ore transportation by boat be incorporated into the project. By the 1780s there are specific references to the removal of stone by the boat level, but not ore, which probably means that the latter was removed via 'The New Shaft' and trammed out along Ecton Sough. Water continued to be removed via Apes Tor Shaft. In November 1779, William Bagnall was paid for 36 men drawing water at 7s.0d per week. Presumably this was from various 'ends' to a central point for lifting up to the Boat level. In February 1781 Wm Birch & Co were paid 7s.0d per shift which probably equates to seven men employed for 'Wheeling & Boating'. Presumably a major job of the Capstan was ore haulage.

Drainage and Haulage via the Boat level

Efford stated that horses, six hours at a time, at a common wem (whim) or engine were sufficient to keep the mine clear and indeed, the accounts for 1769 record the payment of £1.6s.10d per week to Wm Hambleton, John Marsh, Jonathan Prime and John Chadwick for working with 'engine horses'.

However the payments include for 220 weeks 2 days of work in a seven week period by 'Watermen' and we know that the mine purchased their candles (i.e. they were not working a cope-bargain). The total time paid for would seem to be for eight men per shift over the seven weeks of the 12 August Reckoning period, with 4 days not worked by various men (perhaps because of haymaking distractions). These men would have been working in the mine pumping water by hand to the 34 fms level. The volume of water may well have increased for it seems that more men were at work at Apes Tor Shaft a few years later. By the 1780s there were eight men employed 'below the pumps', but by May 1786, this had increased to 12 men, with three men to a six hour shift indicating that the volume of water had increased.

In the Reckoning for 23 December 1780, Samuel Bonsall was paid for his team for 'Drawing the Watter in the Mine with 4 Horses and Drivers', 6 weeks at 56s.0d. Additionally, Richard Birch was paid for 3 horses and drivers at 26s.10d per week. Paid similarly were John Lownds, John Marsh and John Chadwick. A further note states 'N.B. the weekly payment for Drawing Water in the mine for the future will be £2.16s.0d p. week'. The next Reckoning expense account shows Samuel Bonsall still drawing this amount (i.e. 56s.0d p.week) and the four other teams doing the same. Fortunately, it also makes it clear that these four teams were drawing at Apes Tor Shaft, confirming round the clock pumping (four shifts of six hours each). Presumably there were two men at the horse whim and one at the shaft bottom. But why three horses? Were they replaced after two hours or were they all employed on the whim together? Probably the latter.

In November 1783 there is confirmation that the Apes Tor horses were owned by the mine, when Joseph Sutton was paid 11d per day for seven weeks' daily 'attendance upon the Dukes Horses A. Torr & driving the same'. At the same time, those driving the horses underground were paid 5d a day for what appears to have been a six day week; why the work at Apes Tor was considered to have been so much more important is not clear.

The reference to Samuel Bonsall's four horses underground is probably the first reference to the use of horses underground at Ecton. It fits in with the acquisition of chains, to let horses down into the mine, a few weeks earlier. Some delay in the introduction of the horses seems likely for the horse whim was being made in Spring of that year. William Bassett spent two days making ironwork for the horse gin in April. At the same time he was 'making iron work for ye mesheen' (six days) plus another six days on iron work 'for ye waggon' indicating that the mine had a four wheeled vehicle from 1780.

Although the Water Balance engine drew water to the sough level after 1784 the accounts for May 1784 clearly indicate that water was still being drawn at Apes Tor. The same account refers to the drawing of stone as Apes Tor – 36 shifts in seven weeks, indicating a five day week plus one Saturday shift for Daniel Cantrell and Wm Sheldon and their horses. This account would seem to indicate that three shifts were devoted to pumping and one to raising stone.

This situation had not changed at the beginning of 1786 (R. February 1786 Labourers' Account) so far as the emphasis of stone was concerned: 35 shifts of stone was drawn up the shaft and 14 shifts of water (= 49 shifts in 49 days). The accounts do not specifically refer to the other teams who worked at Apes Tor around the clock and Wm Sheldon had died. The payment was to 'Widow Sheldon and Daniel Cantrell... 2 Horses and a driver'.

Possibly the two employed the horse driver, for John Sutton was paid for striking the barrels (landing them at the shaft top) and it is hard to imagine anyone else involved. The accounts always used Christian and surnames (plus the village, if two people had the same name). The only exception was in the case of a widow. Her Christian name was replaced by 'widow' and presumably that was how she was addressed.

The following Reckoning in March 1786 gives an idea of what work was undertaken by the widow and her partner at Apes Tor, although this was for six not seven weeks. They drew out of the mine 36 draughts of stone and 6 draughts of water (40 barrels to a draught). This was one draught a day, or 280 barrels per week, working six hours per day. This equates to the boats bringing 240 barrels of stone to Apes Tor per week. At 7 cwt per barrel (see above), this equates to 84 tons per week, or between seven to eight boats per week.

However, the 1784 accounts clearly state that stone, not ore, was being raised at Apes Tor Shaft. Sir Joseph Banks's report of his visit in 1767 refers to 'a navigable drift... by which the ore is convey'd with scarce any trouble from the Farfield to a convenient shaft where it is drawn up with horses to the day'. Efford's report in 1769 is equally clear, stating that: 'the ore is carried out by boys and thrown into a heap'; he also states: 'Trucks have cast brass wheels and run on grooves through the adit by boys of 12-14 years old'. He is clearly telling us that the ore was removed straight onto the dressing floor, by the river, by boys using a tramway system, not boats. It is more likely that the wheels were made of cast iron, not brass, however.

Was this a result of the changes to the Boat level recorded above, or was that to allow more pumping? Was the coarse ore raised to adit level, trammed to the Smithy Shaft and lifted onto the coarse ore dressing floor, while Botham ore was removed by the Boat level and then carted around the hill to the Botham ore dressing floor at river level. We cannot be sure but this may well be the case. The stone, which was later lifted up Apes Tor was no doubt used in the lime kiln which existed close to the shaft. By mid-1785 up to four kilns of lime were being made per Reckoning. There is of course a further explanation for using the sough for removing ore and not boats. On occasions the need to extract more water than usual occurred and at such times the use of the boat level by boats may have been suspended.

In September 1780, payment was made for enlarging the Boat Gate. Payment was made for 64 fathoms – about two thirds of its length, the bulk of it on day rates, rather than the work let on contract. Presumably this was to allow the passage of larger boats, which must have been forward planning ahead of the expansion of ore production. Further alteration followed eighteen months later: 'Ripping the roof to fill the Boat and making a dam etc £2.0s.0d.' However the last entry for the 1780s occurs in November 1784 and is much more interesting: 'Cutting the Boat Gate to Apes Tor Shaft foot & Room to lodge the stone there, 61 yards at 8/6d £25.18s.6d.'

So the Boat Level had been used for over twenty years with the need to manhandle ore barrels from the canal to the shaft. It would seem clear that the shaft was being used for removal of stone and not ore too. This reference would seem to support the contention made above that the amount of ore previously removed down the canal per week did not amount to many journeys. Consequently, the need for a wharf adjacent to the shaft may have been realised as an improvement but not imperative. The extra volumes of stone in the 1780s seem to have made the extension of the canal and a new wharf desirable to improve output.

The extra volume of stone also begs the question 'was the ore body changing its character' or was the additional stone coming from exploitation of veins? Some of it must have come from the work mentioned above of extending the Balance Shaft and the sumps as the mine became deeper and the drainage had to keep pace with it. However it is also known that in the 1780s there were several teams driving trials and 'gates' which must have increased the volume of stone being 'produced'.

The interesting point is that having been landed at Apes Tor, it has all subsequently been removed. Whether it was carted around the hillside to the front of the hill is doubtful: there is no reference to this in the accounts. There is also no resolution to the point about containerisation. Even though the original wharf was at a distance from the shaft, it would be easy enough to put the barrels from the boat onto a railed flat wagon to push it to the shaft. It is just frustrating that points such as this remain speculation.

The alterations to the Bote Level continued: in the December 1786 and February 1787 Reckonings, are records of the provision of gun powder 'to ye canal'. The men were therefore blasting the boat level once again.

In 1783, the first reference to the payment for filling the lime kiln is found. This was at Apes Tor and still survives. No doubt much stone from the mine was used up in this manner. For further information on the significance of this lime kiln and ore at Wetton, see Chapter 11, Agricultural Improvements. Despite the 'production' of stone, a 'stone pit' was established. This was the quarry by the roadside between Ecton and Ecton Lea. Presumably building stone was extracted for the new buildings which were constructed around the mine. Potter's map marks a round building at this quarry. It is suggested that this housed an edge runner breaking down stone, as a 'grinding wheel' in 'a Round House' existed in a chattel inventory of the mine of 1760. Clearly this was similar. This quarry was still being worked in the 1950s by Manifold Quarries, under Mr Alf Ilett, who lived in the former mine house. The stone pit was allocated one pound of gunpowder per Reckoning in the 1780s.

One final query regarding stone removed also remains unanswered. It is known that in the 1780s some stone was dumped in the worked out 'opens' or chambers. Was this done extensively and only stone removed as required by the lime kiln once it had been built ? It seems likely.

In September 1780 it would appear that the 'Ecton Men' had an agreeable excursion attending 'the Derby Election'. Their expenses amounted to £190. One can imagine the 18th century equivalent of the men being 'bussed' to the election (on the new mine wagon and various carts). It must have involved an early start (or a night in Derby) and one can also imagine the cajouling and presumably the bribery of voters that must have been behind the visit. (42)

The Mine Fails

In 1788, the raised ore volume fell and the decrease continued. In two years – 1788 to 1790 – the volume fell from 3,200 tons to virtually 2,200 tons, a substantial drop back to the level of production in 1781. In a similar period (1787-90), metal production (based upon the weight of cake copper dressed) fell from 468 tons to 347 tons in 1788 and then dropped to 261 tons in 1789. The effect on profitability was sudden – in 1787, it was of the order of £24,700. By 1789 it had dropped to nil. (These figures are based on a notional sale price of £77 per ton and Mr Heaton's summary (Dev. Coll., L/60/20)

Problems had clearly arisen in 1788 with the fall back in metal production. This could have been through a collapse in yield, or a loss of market. Mathew Boulton was complaining about difficulties of obtaining supplies from Anglesey in 1789. Thomas Williams blamed it upon a huge contract to supply the East India Company and others overseas with over 4,000 tons of metal. In reality, the latter seems to have been a convenient guise to mask the falling yield from Parys Mountain.

So if the Duke had lost a part of the East India business it is surprising that other opportunities to fill demand caused by short comings from Anglesey were not realised. (43) Either the Duke's copper was not being marketed properly, or the yield was dropping and it seems, on balance, that the latter may well have been the problem, associated with a contraction of the ore deposit.

Metal production remained steady throughout 1789 and 1790 but ore yields showed signs of slowing in mid-summer 1788. The drop was not too great and there was a rally in the Reckonings for December 1789–March 1790 to over 400 tons per Reckoning. However it then dropped significantly to getting on for 50% of this volume. If the mine was considered to have 'failed' in 1790, it happened in spring 1790 so far as ore volumes were concerned. The output of ore for 1790 was about 2,260 tons, but in the period to September 1791 (for six out of eight Reckonings) the output was only 882 tons. The yearly total could well have been only 50% of the 1790 total.

The redundancy payments made in 1790 (see below) were made in the March, May and June Reckonings, with 45% of the total in March. The payments seem to have been made by George Wild who had received a total of £610 including a sum from the Duke. The effect of the redundancies on George Wild may have been profound. Within a year he was dead and his widow was in arrears with the rent to the sum of 10s. 0d. at Lady Day 1791. (44)

The contraction of the ore deposit had been known for some time and significant work had been done in trying to locate another (the ninth) deposit below the huge one then being worked out. Many trial shafts were sunk on side veins and five are shown on a section of the mine, together with the Balance Shaft. The mine's deposit continued, but it was substantially smaller than the mine had become used to and cuts in the work force were necessary. The mine section shows the deposit pinching out at about 170 fathoms below river level (1,020 feet) or 1,337 feet below the engine house. A visitor to the mine in 1838 (45) states that the depth at that time was 1,650 feet to the lowest working.

On 12 June 1790, *The Times* reported 'The Duke of Devonshire's hitherto very productive copper mine, in Derbyshire (sic), is almost expended of its rich ore, and threatens to deprive its noble owner of a very considerable revenue.' Two days later it also reported 'The Devonshire *Copper* Mines have failed – the party must now make up the deficiency from their inexhaustible store of *brass*'!

In 1790, £547 was issued as redundancy pay including £114. 3s. 0d. donated by His Grace with a further group of 57 men and 21 women leaving in 1797. This second group received £1.1s.0d (a guinea) each (to the men) and 10s. 6d. to the ore dressers. The remaining workforce included 14 companies of copers (the groups of men raising ore) and 68 other workers. The lower output saw production reduced not only at the smelter but also at the coal mines. Equally important, the demands on suppliers reduced too, as less timber, furnace stone and bricks, clay and sand was needed, together with fewer candles, gun powder, utensils and much more. It is clear that the Duke continued to employ an over capacity of employees as production fell, for despite the reduction in revenue, the expense account was fairly steady to the end of the decade. *The Times* had in fact reported incorrectly: the Duke's 'considerable revenue' had fallen substantially in 1788 and in 1789 had gone. Moreover, the cost of the Hazles Cross Colliery had far to go before the purchase price was redeemed without having to risk a sale on much depleted coal reserves.

The expansion of the local economy had a marked effect on the way of life of the community. Regular working patterns brought regular wages and a higher standard of living (and perhaps more dependent children). Many families were employed *en bloc* at the mine, although some had additional income from small-holdings. The impact on domestic budgets was to be severe.

In 1795 following the redundancies at the mine, the loss of the income previously enjoyed was producing a severe problem in Wetton. An account of 10 February 1795 indicates the extent of the poverty being experienced and perhaps the hunger too. Eighteen households involving 76 people received 456 lb of oatmeal per week from Wetton Mill. John Redfern, the miller, charged £13.6s.0d for 7 loads and 144 lb of meal. Additionally, 32 households received 1 cwt of coal a week. The document covers four weeks and appears to be a 'one-off'. A bill survives for the delivery of 10 tons 10 cwt of coal from Kingsley Colliery, charged at 5s 0d per ton for the benefit of the Colliery's accounts. (46) Just how long this situation prevailed is not clear but it was certainly serious. The oatmeal would be used to make oatcakes. The latter are still eaten widely in North Staffordshire.

The Duke's intervention at Wetton would not have been replicated in other villages not on the Devonshire estate; at least by the Duke. However the small number of pensions continued to be paid and it would appear that positions elsewhere were offered.

Although the evidence is circumstantial, the Duke may have deliberately tried to create work for the Ecton miners. In March 1790, a new shaft was begun on the Goyt Colliery, known as the New Rise Pit. (47) It became operational the following October. Ecton miners were employed on this and the coal mine account refers to 'Liquor given to the Ecton Miners and mason 14s. 0d.' This mine was being substantially expanded and four additional shafts were sunk in 1790. (48) These shafts were shallow, although the New Rise Shaft reached 32 fathoms (192 feet).

John Taylor, the Duke's mineral agent who was appointed in 1818, wrote of the Duke that 'He continued to work his mines in Staffordshire long after all profit had ceased, and with actual for a considerable time, out of mere consideration for the labourers, and many old persons are still maintained there by pensions out of his pocket.' (49)

The Duke eventually closed the Ecton mine in 1825, the smelter in 1818 and the Clayton Mine lease terminated in 1822. There were speculators who wanted to continue all of these, but the profits were never to be the same again. Not only had he continued operations but reorganised the dressing floor entirely to the hillside as the demand for more tipping area increased. This followed the start of driving of Salts Level in 1804 which enabled ore to be lifted to the level of the hillside dressing floor without having to use the Smithy Shaft.

The smelter was sold to the three Sneyd brothers, William, Clement and Thomas, the sons of John Sneyd of Basford Hall, near Leek, Staffs. They owned the Mixon Copper Mine, south west of Ecton. The purchase had gone through by 1821. In 1828, John Keys was taken into partnership and he purchased the Sneyd interest in 1846. (50)

The village pub in Whiston is still called The Sneyd Arms. A further pub existed in the row of cottages opposite Whiston Hall in Black Lane. One wonders if this pub (it closed about 30 years ago), known as The Ship, was named after *The Ecton*, which took Whiston Copper to London from Gainsborough.

After Effects on Devonshire Revenues

The loss of revenue from Ecton to the Chatsworth coffers seems to have resulted in renewed vigour on the Devonshire Estate. Mention has been made above about increased activity at the coal mines on the Axe Edge moors. It seems strange that this was not evident at Hazles Cross unless the reserves were in fact failing. Certainly John Heaton wrote that the areas being drained by the Duke's level were exhausted in 1811, but that was two decades later (see Chapter 11 re this).

The Duke had a large Yorkshire Dales estate and mines at Grassington and there is definite evidence that mines here were extended during the 1790s under Cornelius Flint. This included a reorganisation of the mines under the direction of Cornish Mine captains brought in to manage them. (51) There is an interesting research project here for someone to determine how the Devonshire Estate responded to the loss of the Ecton income.

It is known that the Estate spent £613,646 on purchasing landed property in the period 1773-1810. Of this, £393,000 was spent in 1791 onwards, i.e., 64% of the total. Moreover, much of the pre-1791 expenditure was at Buxton (£94,000), the purchase of Estates at Chesterfield and Staveley at nearly £91,500 and the Kingsley Colliery for £21,500. This amounted to over £207,000, leaving only another £13,600 spent anywhere else in this period. Moreover, during the 1780s, after the purchase of Kingsley Colliery, the only major expense was at Buxton, building The Crescent etc. (52)

In Chapter 14 there is a further reference to this capital expenditure examining how successful it was in terms of revenue generation. It is not considered appropriate to continue with this aspect in this chapter.

Depths of Workings

Depth of shaft to sough 317ft (James Watt states 312ft)

	Source				Total Depth
1759	J Roose	45 fms	=	270 feet below sough	587ft
1767	Sir J Banks	160 fms	=	'below crown of hill'	960ft
1769	Wm Efford	80 fms	=	480 feet below sough	797ft
1772	Accounts	101 fms 4 ft		610 feet below sough	927ft
1773	Accounts	109 fms	=	654 feet below sough	971ft
1781	Two ropes bought	136 fms	=	816feet below sough	1133ft
1788	Balance Shaft	172 fms total			–
1788	Total depth	213 fms per J Watt			1278 ft
1794	Balance Shaft	202 fms			
1838	*Ashbourne & the Valley of the Dove*				*1,650ft*

The mine would have appeared to have reached 1,000 feet deep in the early 1770s perhaps 1774, the figures quoted above at that time are to the bottom of the main shaft. Banks must be referring to the top of the hill and even then it seems to be an exaggeration.

The Clayton Mine

Perhaps the biggest mystery at the Ecton Mines concerns the exploitation of the Ecton Pipe Working. Who was responsible for its discovery, how much ore it yielded and where it was smelted remains unknown. It is held locally that the money for Buxton Crescent came from Smacker's Open – one of the largest single deposits, so rich that miners were only allowed to work it for three days a week, working from hammocks suspended across the face of the deposit. The miners were paid according to the ore they won and the difference in their pay and the rest of the work force was worrying to the management.

Buxton Crescent was built by the Duke of Devonshire. Smackers Open is in Clayton Mine. It is known that the Duke took a lease of Clayton but the Crescent was built by then and it is also reasonably sure that that lease – dated 1804 – did not result in much profit for anyone. This would seem to indicate that the profit – and it must have been huge – predates 1804. But who smiled all the way to the bank?

The Duke did not have an interest in Clayton Mine during the involvement of the Gilberts. On 17 December 1753, Thomas Gilbert took a 30-year lease from Sir Roger Burgoyne, at a rent of £3 per annum, covering his lands on Ecton Hill. The royalty was to be 1/8th of all ores obtained except for Clayton's (sic) Mine where a more generous 1/10th was agreed – presumably because the much greater depth of working incurred higher production costs. On 27 September 1755, the Duke allowed Gilbert to Drive Clayton Adit through his land to unwater Clayton's Mine and also to provide a horizontal level to remove ore and waste. It included the right to work veins in the Duke's land within 100 yards of the sough (Clayton Adit). The consideration for the lease (of 21 years) was a 1/12th part of the benefit of the 1753 lease. So, if it was Gilbert who exploited the main reserve of ore, the Duke would have made 1/12th of it.

Perhaps more telling, was Smacker's Open being worked by the partnership which involved the Duke at the same time as he made a fortune in his own mine, linking folk tradition about Smacker's Open with the Buxton Crescent. Part of the answer must be the indication that the Duke took an assignment of the Gilbert lease (see Chapter 6, 'The Boat (Bote) level'), but it doesn't answer the question of why are the records not at Chatsworth.

Another puzzle is the quoted ore statistics. They all seem to relate to the ore extracted from Ecton. The ore from Clayton must have been equivalent to Ecton at times, but why does Clayton

Clayton adit level entrance

Clayton pipe working at the surface above the Reservoir of 1783

never feature in the details of the ore extracted? Why does it never feature in the descriptions of visitors? Perhaps pointedly, why is the upper large deposit called Chatsworth Open?

There is a serious gap in our current knowledge concerning this mine. It would not be so bad if it was similar to the dozens of small mines which characterise the North Staffordshire ore field. But Clayton, like Ecton, is different; hugely different. Yet in terms of historical detail it is as though the richness of the ore pipe below adit level never existed. Our only descriptions of it are Kitto's report during the 1883-4 dewatering and the fact that miners worked in hammocks. (53)

Something somewhere is not quite right; initial thinking was that the original records had been lost, but if the Duke was working the mine, and it is traditionally held that he was, where are the records in the Devonshire Collection? One would expect them to form part of the Ecton Mine accounts – one finds, occasionally, the inclusion of items not directly relating to Ecton Mine, but the mine account was a convenient cost base to which it could be attached. Why then not Clayton? Further, where was the ore smelted and by whom? The tonnage would have been substantial.

If Whiston could not handle the capacity despite being extended in 1780, was the ore handled by the Cheadle Copper Smelter built by Pattens (the term is used loosely, the company had a variety of names) in 1768 and worked until 1792 (54)? To date it has been thought that the works was built to smelt Ecton ore but found its potential supplies going to Whiston. The possibility that it was built for the Clayton ore has not been mooted previously. Morton (55) states that the widespread story that the copper and brass industry of Cheadle came as a result of the need to smelt Ecton ores 'may be discounted'. Indeed, but it may well have been sustained by Clayton ores and the closure date of 1792 for the Cheadle Copper Works could be due to the loss of local ore at a time when other supplies were tied to the monopolistic controls of Thomas Williams at Parys Mountain.

Further, where are the waste hillocks for this mine? It is likely that the road to Ecton Lee is built on a hillock down stream of Clayton Adit but the tipped waste between the road and river is not substantial. If Ecton hillock waste was drawn up to the top of the current hillocks i.e. to the 1880s dressing floor level, where did the Clayton waste go? One wonders whether the waste deposited in the south end of the field behind the old Ecton Station building came from Clayton. Dumping it on Devonshire soil would not be a problem if it was the Duke who wanted to do the dumping. There, currently, seems to be more questions than answers.

On balance, an educated guess (and it is stressed that this is only a guess) is that the exploitation of the Clayton reserves were probably made by a partnership which included the Duke and may have had the two Gilbert brothers (Thomas and John) as principal partners. The Gilbert brothers had interests in the Clayton Mine inherited from their father in 1742 and later extended by subsequent leases (56). At some point the Duke seems to have taken on the mine himself, (pre-1776) by assignment of the Gilbert's interests. (57) Herein probably lies the answer to the Chatsworth connection, but why is there no mention of Clayton revenues or expenses in the Ecton accounts?

It seem likely that the exploitation occurred after 1755 and may have been completed by 1792. The ore would have been dressed on the 'Burgoyne Dressing Floor' – the flat ground outside the Clayton Adit entrance – and sold by ticketing to either Roe & Co or to Cheadle, where the brass works or the copper works could have used it. The impact of not one, but two huge deposits being worked at once would have had a significant impact on the locality, especially in the movement of ore.

Finally, why on earth is the celebrated ore deposit at Clayton known as "Smacker's Open"? The term has defied all attempts at explanation, but it possibly comes down to the nickname of the miner who discovered it.

Neighbours

Roger Flindall has found a letter which survives which would seem to date the beginning of the Gilbert brothers involvement on Ecton Hill, but in the land adjoining that of the Duke of Devonshire, probably at the Clayton Mine. (58) The letter is from John Gilbert to Leeke Okeover dated 30 September 1734, viz:

'Dear Srs
I have made inquiry about Sr. Rog: Borgoins Mineral affairs in Staffordshire and find they are likely to turn out well, provided any person had them that could afford to lay out a Sum of Money, ye persons that clames under the Lease from Sr. Roger not being in cercumstancies to attempt a Sough which must be brought up before any good can be done so that ye work must be Idle or at least so wrought that it will not turn to any advantage to Sr. Roger, now was he clear of them I would engage a Set of Partners that would discover in a Year or twos time what ye ground would produce, if he thinks fit to turn ye Winster people off, if he pleases to let me hear from him, and let me have the same terms as Reding & partners has, I will enter into Covenants with him, pray let me hear from you, I am Dear Sr Your Affectionate Kinsman & Servt

John Gilbert'

It would seem that Gilbert set up the partnership, for when his father died, he left his shares in several mines on the Burgoyne royalty to his two sons John and Thomas. This was eight years later, in 1742. (59) This Company was working Clayton and other mines on the hill at the same time as the Ecton Mine was being worked under the 1739 lease and became neighbours of the Duke in 1760.

References

1 Althin, T., 'Eric Geisler and his Tour Abroad 1772-73', *Med Hammare och Fackla*, Vol XXVI, 1971

2 Lewis, M.J.T., *Early Wooden Railways*, 1970, p 195

3 Barnatt J., The Development of Deep Ecton Mine, Staffordshire 1723 - 1760, *Mining History*, Vol. 15, No. 1, 2002 pp 10-23
   This article consists of two parts: a historical account and a survey of accessible workings linked to an assessment of archaeological remains. The latter is most welcome

and is recommended to those interested in knowing what exists below ground to this day above water level. Regrettably the first part is stated to have been written without regard to the many invoices which survive or perhaps a detailed assessment of the summary account sheets. Some of the assumptions reached are therefore at a variance from those suggested in this book. A reassessment of these issues has been made, but no changes introduced. The detail is not reproduced here. Interested readers should refer to *Mining History*, the Bulletin of Peak District Mines Historical Society, in press

4   University of Nottingham, Dept. of Manuscripts and Special Collections, P/C 11/17) George Wild's address was Goits Moss. This letter also contains details about Norbriggs Colliery and mining in Chesterfield. Thanks to Roger Flindall for finding this reference and checking it out for me

5   In the same Reckoning (November 1783) Thomas Mather was paid 6d per day for 8 days work labouring and in the June 1783 Reckoning, Roger is recorded along with Ben Mather (working for Job White, the dressing or washing master, at 4d per day) and George Mather, on 10s per week. In 1868, the mine was taken over by Colin Mather, known as 'Cast Iron Colin', of the Salford, Manchester based firm Mather & Platt, who were iron founders. (Porter, L., & Robey, J., *Copper and Lead Mines Around the Manifold Valley, Staffordshire*, pp 86-87). Did his family originally work at Ecton? Mather & Platt currently manufacture sprinkler systems etc. The November 1783 payments record six people – all apparently women – paid 9d per day for washing (excluding any in Job White's team). One was Silence Mather, whose wages were collected by George Mather. All six worked between 8 & 11 days only each. There were also a lot of Mathers in the Monyash and Flagg area.

6   Porter, L., & Robey, J., *The Copper & Lead Mines around the Manifold Valley, Staffordshire*, 2000, p 55

7   B & W Coll., Birmingham Central Library

8   Hatchet Dr., *A tour through the counties of England and Scotland in 1796 visiting mines and manufactories*, edited by A Raistrick,1967, p 66

9   Dev. Coll., Devonshire Mining Collection, Bundle 123

10 Hatchet, op cit., p 66

11 Farey, J., *General View of the Agriculture of Derbyshire*, 1811, Vol 1, p 339

12 Deposition Papers, *Roscoe v. New Dale Mining Co Ltd and Niness*, 1871, author's collection

13 Roberts, A.F., & Leach, J.R., *The Coal Mines of Buxton*, 1985, p 40

14 op.cit., pp 50-51

15 Rowlands, J., *Copper Mountain*, 1966 p 45

16 Howarth, K., *Dark Days,* privately printed, Llanrwst

17 Hatchet, op.cit., p 66

18 Lees–Milne, J., *The Batchelor Duke*, 1990, p 16

19 Rolt T., & Allen J., *The Steam Engine of Newcomen*, 3rd Edition, 1997, pp 146-54

20 B&W Coll. Birmingham Central Library

21 pers. comm. Rev. Dr. R. Hills

22 see Porter & Robey. op. cit., p 116, for more on these boilers, albeit their fascination for stone-throwing boys on their way to the Ecton School from Warslow

23 Dickinson, H.W. & Jenkins, R., *James Watt & The Steam Engine*, 1927, new edition 1981, p251 and illustration plate XCIII

24 Victoria County History: Staffordshire, Vol 7., *The Staffordshire Moorlands,* p118

25 see Porter, L. & Robey J., op. cit., pp 82-83

26 op.cit., p 68

27 *Derby Mercury*, 24th December, 1795 p1 col 3 & Dev. Coll., AS/1053

28 Roberts, P.K., Boat levels Associated with Mining1: Coal Mining, *Ind., Archy., Review*, Vol 2, 1981, p 86. Also, Hughes, S, *Copperopolis*, 2000, pp 98-103

29 Roberts, A.F., & Leach, J.R., The Coal Mines of Buxton, 1985, p 42

30 op.cit., p 43 quoting Farey, 1811, p 191

31 Roberts, P.K., '2: Metal Mining', *Ind., Archy., Review*, vol 3, 1981 and 'Coal Tunnels Associated with Mineral Exploration, *Ind., Archy., Review*, Vol 1, No 1, 1980/81

32 op. cit. Vol 2, p 93

33 op. cit. Vol 2, p 93

34 Brown, I.J., Underground Canals in Shropshire Mines, 1997, *Bull. PDMHS*, Vol 13, No.4, pp 17-23

35 Roberts, P.K., op cit Vol 3, p 209

36 op.cit., Vol 2, p 91

37 op. cit. Vol. 2, p 91

38 D.R.O., J. Harpur's Jottings

39 Hatchet, op.cit.,

40 Althin, T., op. cit.,

41 see photograph in Ford & Rieuwerts (editors), *Lead Mining in the Peak District*, 2000, p.63

42 Dev.Coll. AS/1717

43 Harris, J.R., *The Copper King*, 2003, pp 92-93.

44 Dev. Coll., Wetton Rentals AS/943

45 the anonymous author of *Ashbourne and the Valley of the Dove*, 1839

46 Dev. Coll., Wetton Rentals, 1795

47 Roberts, A.F., & Leach, J.R., op.cit., p 46

48 op. cit., p 39

49 *Derby Mercury*, 19 January 1831, p 3 col 4

50 see Porter, L., & Robey, J.A., op.cit., p 242

51 Raistrick, A., & Jennings, B., *A History of Lead Mining in the Pennines*, 1965, p 215

52 Dev. Coll., Account Book of the 5th Duke's Expenditure 1773-1810

53 Porter, L., & Robey, J.A., op.cit., pp 92&100

54 Morton, J., *Thomas Bolton & Sons 1783 - 1983*, 1983

55 op. cit., p 13

56 Porter & Robey, pp 67/68

57 Dev.Coll., (AS/1053)

58 Derbyshire Record Office, Document 231 M, Okeover MSS, bundle of letters 4433-55

59 For more on this see Porter, L., & Robey, J.A., op. cit., pp 67-71

In 1759, the engine shaft had been sunk to a depth of 270 ft below the Ecton Sough (See chapter 3) i.e. it had passed the 34 fathoms (fms) level where the 'double saddle' was found. Here, a vein running east-west cut another orientated north-south.

Weakness in the strata at this point had been exploited by mineral bearing solutions creating a large deposit of ore. At the 34 fms level the pipe increased from 18ft across, so that a heading 45 ft high by 24 ft wide was driven horizontally for 126ft. (1) John Harpur described the workings in 1767 or thereabouts. He stated that the roof in the chamber above the 34 fms level was 90 ft high. (2) Indeed it may be, but caution must be drawn for he states that the 34 fms level 'boat level' was at the 3rd chamber some 300 ft from the surface end of Apes Tor Shaft, which actually rises up from the boat level 34 fms (204ft) below adit. Harpur states that the 3rd chamber, was one of the largest openings. At the time of his visit the miners were working on the 8th chamber, all being one below the other. The 4th Duke of Devonshire descended to the 4th chamber according to Harpur.

Sir Joseph Banks describes in his Journal (3) a visit to Ecton on 9th December 1767 stating the depth to be 160 fms 'below the crown of the hill'. In 1769, Efford (4) was more precise. He stated that the depth of the mine was 160yds (80 fms) below the river. Efford also gave a good description of the workings at that time. In fact, despite the richness of the workings, it remains the most complete description of the mine and its dressing floor throughout its history. Even when the mine was at its greatest profitability, no fuller description was attempted and no drawings of the mine were made – or at least none have survived.

The descriptions given by some of the visitors form the basis of this chapter. They are quoted verbatim, except where some sentences have been created by the use of a few full stops etc to aid understanding.

The Journal of Sir Joseph Banks, 1767:

'Went to see Ecton a Copper mine belonging to the duke of devonshire probably the richest in the Island this year, it will clear about 11 thousand pounds besides doing the whole years work at a navigable drift which is worked in deadstone without a spark of oar [sic]. Every Circumstance of this mine and the hill it is in are so wonderfull that they merit a very particular description. The hill itself is situate upon the Banks of the river manyfold & shews wherever the water or any other cause has bar'd the strata of the Earth, a Confustion scarce to be described. In one place by the river side the strata make an appearance not unlike this: the first is an arch of about forty ft diameter; as it goes Lower the bedds get more & more pointed till they are quite sharp. By the side of these stand two or three bedds of limestone set right upon their heads so that till they are examined they appear like a vein beyond these the beds are bent but in an inverted arch so that more variety of Positions in the space of 60 or 70 ft can scarcely be conceivd, but irregular as this may appear to be, the inside of the mine is still more so what they are working on seems to be a pipe which instead of going horizontal is set upon its head and goes directly perpendicular. It is of an immense size and very irregular figure so that the chambers of the mine are /of a size/ so magnificent as scarcely to be equald by the finest buildings.

The Contents of this pipe are full as irregular as the rest of the hill Limestone Chirt Spar Copper (tho much the Largest Quantity are of the Latter) Jumbled together in a confused mass, now a lump of Copper half a ton weight, sometimes a lump of Limestone as big but the Pieces are generaly of a size much inferior to this nor do these lay at all regular but turning winding & twisting all manner of ways as if barrows full of these materials had been thrown irregularly into a hole made to receive them.

The depth of the mine is 160 fms from the Crown of the hill from which place it has been brought down by shafts began about King Williams time but never very rich till within these ten years. At the depth of 96 fms I found plenty of fungi of two different Kinds neither of which I had ever observed before. One was branchd the stalk compressed & indented. At the end of Every branch a brush of exceeding fine milk white filaments perfectly like Cotton. The other was reddish Consisting of a number of filaments standing all manner of different ways making a Kind of turfy Covering sometimes two inches deep upon any kind of timber upon which also the other always grew chiefly upon pump stocks &c. In one of the drifts also at a great depth issued a small quantity of Bitumen tho but a drop the Miners seemed Quite una[c]quainted with it asking me whether I had Ever seen such a thing before & what it was.

Here is also found a Small quantity of a whitish ore much resembling if not realy antimony but this in such small Quantities that is little bit now & then which is Kept as a Curiosity is all that they can get.

The Measures at the walls of the pipe are as Extraordinary as any part of it indeed they are so all through the rock you very often meet with what the workmen call saddles which are where 5 or 6 heads of stone incline downwards making a very acute angle as in one place I describd above this Case. The workmen tell me that the uppermost of these distorted measures is always chirt.

The workmanship of this mine is at [sic] wonderfull for its boldness & Cleverness as any other part of it particularly a navigable drift much under Level by which the ore is conveyd with scarce any trouble from the Farfield to a convenient shaft where it is drawn up with horses to the day.

Its Profits have been an increasing fund solely belonging to the Duke of Devonshire in Less then ten years they have increased from 3 thousand a year to Last years receiving which made ten [thousand]. This years account the director Mr Shore tells me will be near twelve & this appears more likely to Last & increase than Ever.

The method of Selling ore here is worth observing. The ore is all beat down small before it is weighed which is done when certain people who are bidders are present. Two hundred at a time is what their Scales weigh. A man stands by for the purpose takes from Every one of these a small Quantity upon the point of a trowel which he puts into a tub for that purpose. A great deal of Labour is bestowd upon this that it may be mixd together as much as possible as many sorts of Copper come from this mine & the value of all are to be judged of from an assay of these. The buyers take every one a small quantity of this mixture & declare themselves bidders for the quantity of ore on a certain day then fixed about six weeks or thereabouts This they call Sampling. On the day of Bidding which they call ticketing, every man delivers in his written proposals signifying the price that he will pay.'

The Journal of John Harpur, c. 1767-70

He refers to the Dale Mine as being a zinc mine and a reference to a lead mine probably refers to Clayton Mine, as he draws the level on a crude plan which also shows Ecton Sough. He does describe the lead mine as being upstream of Ecton Sough. If this is a reference to the Dale Mine, then the Zinc mine (lapis calamin) must be somewhere else nearby, which is unlikely.

His description (2) is as under:

'Went in ye mouth of the sough which is abt 20 feet above surface of the Manifold. No abt 60 yards – about 160 yards water carri[age] boarded Strait line southwards

Then abt 70 yards further on a boarded passage winding first to ye east then south again

Then come to a large circular opening or vault or chamber abt 30yds wide ye sides and roof of it all stone and spar with holes or places in it from whence ore taken away pretty much alike, from all parts of ye circular vault.

The floor of this opening or chamber is rock at ye southern end there is an opening or trap door down into another opening vault or chamber abt 80 yards below ye first.

Ye descent down to this an other chambers is by ladders aside the mine(?) rocks and there are a kind of landing places called by ye miners bundings and this 2nd in a circular form like ye lst.

So ye roof of this 2nd chamber appears to be near 30 yards high over head.

In ye walls or sides of this vault in some parts more in some fewer holes or places dug into ye rock than others. Most holes appear to be on ye south side or south east side.

In all there are 7 of these vaults or chambers including ye first and an eighth now sinking abt 20 yds and which had a good deal of water in it (being Sunday when seen and pumps not working for ye miners can work only as ye water pumped out from some of the vaults from time to time, but some of ye vaults are quite dry – in others springs break in.

[*Margin note:* Some holes a yard or two high and (?) yards obliquely as ye ore is dug in (?) past. Ye miners go with ye(?) of ye circular vault. These holes are some of them near as big as a room of 10 or 12 feet, some smaller like cupboards].

The 3rd like ye second but some of ye seven vaults are cut more oval and one or two nearly triangular. This 3rd one of ye largest.

[Note some of these vaults are 30, 20 and ye lower ones not above 15 yards high. Some appear to be 30 yards wide across and some much larger, near 60 – The 3rd appears to be one of ye largest]

To all appearances ye vaults lye partly nearly one under another and no great of appearance of varying or Hading to any point of ye Compass any way equal to one or two hundred feet but of keeping a kind of circular form. Late Duke went down to part of ye 4th Chamber.

From ye 3rd floor a sough or water carr for boats which goes eastward to ye place where ye engine (horse engine) is worked – which is abt 50 fathom high (abt 300 ft) It is cutted abt 100 yards from ye sough up to ye engine.

Water in ye carriages about 2:3 and in some places where boats pass near 4 feet [?] pumps and winlasses with 2 handles which draw ye water up into troughs.

Lapis Calamin Mine [?] in Warslow N side of Manifold.

It is tho[ugh]t ye copper mine near it but a little further up ye river now working again.

But tho' this mine appears to be circular, yet by ye greater number of holes So east and Lap Calam NW it may be only a Broad Vein of 60 or 70 yards wide, ye lesser chambers or cupboards in ye sides may be narrower parts of this great broad vein.

There is also a new shaft digging in ye direction in ye (?) written sketch.'

William Efford's Visit of 1769

Less confusing than Harpur is the description by Efford:

Ecton-Hill, that part of it, in which the mine is situated, is of a conical figure; its perpendicular height, next the River Dove, which runs close by, is about 700 feet; its diameter from the same, quite through, about half a mile; the upper strata, or mould is about fifteen inches thick, and produces exceeding fine herbage, for sheep, and other cattle, who constantly graze on the top and sides, and where the declivity will permit the plough, very fine wheat, barley, and oats are produced in great plenty.

This copper-mine was discovered about thirty years ago, by a Cornish Miner, who in passing over the Hill accidentally picked up a bit of ore, annexed to some fine spar, which that metal usually adhered to. On viewing the situation, and considering the great height of the Hill, he concluded that vast quantities of copper-ore might be found there; and if that should be the case, no place could be more convenient for working it; and therefore he communicated his sentiments and discoveries to some adventurers at Ashburn, who approving the project applied to the then Duke of Devonshire (grandfather of His Present Grace) for a lease to search for copper on that Hill. It appears by the most authentic accounts, that more than 13,000L. were expended, before any returns were made, and several of the original adventurers despairing of success, sold out their shares at a considerable loss. But the second adventurers were more fortunate. After sinking a shaft of about 200 yards deep and driving in an Adit, immense quantities of Copper Ore were found, which continued to increase, the lower they descended, till the termination of the lease, by which very considerable fortunes were acquired.

About 6 months before the decease of the late Duke (father of His Present Grace) the lease expired, and the whole undertaking fell into His Grace's hands, and has ever since continued working to great advantage.

To take a view of this stupendous Copper-Mine, you must enter at an Adit at the base of the hill by the River Dove, and proceed about 400 yards, almost in a direct line. At your entrance, for about sixty yards, 'tis four feet and a half high, walled up on each side with good stone masonry; but afterwards it varies in its height, and rises in some places to six feet. When you arrive at the centre, there is a spacious lodgment of timber, for landing and receiving the ore from below, which is drawn up by a man at a winch, who generally works naked, and is put into four-wheel waggons that will hold about a ton and a half each. These waggons have cast brass wheels, and are run in grooves, through the Adit, by boys from 12 to 14 years of age, with great facility.

When on the lodgment, you behold a large hollow overhead, at least 250 yards high, by the sides of which there is a passage to the summit, but dangerous to attempt, as the timber-works seem in a decayed state.

Thus far into the Mountain, with the aid of lights, 'tis easy enough of access. The late Duke of Devonshire ventured to this platform, took a cursory view of the works, gave the miners ten guineas to drink, but returned immediately not choosing to descend below. Indeed, such a horrid gloom, such rattling of waggons, noise of workmen boring of rocks under your feet, such explosions in blasting and such a dreadful gulph to descend, present a scene of terror, that few people, who are not versed in mining, care to pass through.

From the platform the descent is about 160 yards, through different lodgments, by ladders, lobs (1), and cross-pieces of timber let into the rock, to the place of action, where a new scene, ten thousand times more astonishing than that above, presents itself; a place as horrible to view, as imagination can conceive. On the passage down, the constant blasting of the rocks, ten times louder than the loudest thunder, seems to roll and shake the whole body of the mountain. When at the bottom, strangers are obliged to take shelter in a nitch cut in the rock, to avoid the effects of blasting the rocks, as the miners generally give a salute of a half dozen blasts, in quick succession, by way of welcome to those diabolical mansions.

At the bottom of this amazing work, the monstrous cavern of vacuum above, the glimmering light of candles and nasty suffocating smell of sulphur and gunpowder, all conspire to increase your surprise, and heighten your apprehensions.

This singular mine, in its position, situation, and inclination is different from any yet discovered, in Europe, Asia, Africa, or America. The wonderful mass of Copper-Ore, with which the mountain is impregnated runs not in regular veins or courses; but sinks perpendicular down, widening and Swelling out at the bottom, in form like a bell.

Suppose yourself now upwards of 200 fathoms deep in the bowels of a large mountain, in a great hollow of immense diameter; then suppose around you an impenetrable wall of limestone rock, interspersed with small veins of Copper-Ore, yellow, black and some brown, intermixed with spar, marcasite, mundic, and other sulphurous compositions, of all colours; and at the same time figure to yourself the sooty complexions of the miners, their labour and miserable way of living in those subterraneous regions and you will then be apt to fancy yourself in another world. Yet these inhabitants being trained up in darkness and slavery, are not perhaps less happy, or less contented than those who possess the more flattering enjoyments of light and liberty.

Hence the wisdom of providence is conspicuous, which, as Pope says, has placed happiness nowhere to be had, or everywhere.

There is no timber made use of, except for lodgments, or platforms, ladders or steps set into the rocks, for ascending or descending into the mine; neither is there any quantity of water to retard the works, notwithstanding it is at least 150 yards below the bed of the river; four horses, six hours each at a common wem or engine, are sufficient to keep the Mine clear.

The timber-works about the Mines are very ill contrived and worse executed. In descending from the principle lodgment you pass thirty ladders, some half broken, others not half staved; in some places by half-cut noches, or steps in the rock, in others you must almost slide on your breech, and often in imminent danger of tumbling topsy-turvy into the Mine; nor are the shores which support the lodgement below in better condition.

Notwithstanding the great depth of the Mine, (which is the deepest in Great Britain) a little expence, judiciously applied, would render the approaches to the lower-most part, easy to the miners; but however troublesome the descent may be, above sixty stout, well-made fellows, work here night and day, six hours at a time, for one shilling each man; and although the major part work naked (a pair of coarse canvas drawers excepted) they are as merry and jovial a set of mortals, as ever inhabited such infernal abodes. So much for the internal parts; we now come to the methods of dressing, cleansing and fitting the Ore for sale.

The Ore, as before observed, when conveyed out by the boyes is thrown together in a heap, and two men with large hammers, or sledges are employed to break it into small pieces. This done, it is carried in small hand-barrows by little boys, to a place under a shed, erected on purpose to be picked and sorted, and is then laid by in different parcels, best, second, and worst; this operation is performed by little girls from eight to twelve years of age, who are surprisingly quick at the work, separating the various kinds with astonishing dexterity. From this place, the Ore is carried to another large and convenient shed, where about fifty women sit back to back, on benches to buck or beat it with flat hammers still keeping every particular sort separate, from each other. The Ore, now reduced to a small sand, is again removed to the buddles, for washing, where an old experienced Cornish man has the superintendency of it, as a great deal of the finest ore would be lost, if this operation is not properly performed. Here then it is curiously washed and cleansed, and afterwards exposed for sale in the open air, in various heaps, ticketed according to the different qualities and quantities. When all is ready, notice is given to the Smelting-Houses, whose proprietors or managers attend, and each bids what price he thinks proper, (generally from 7L. to 16L. per ton) the highest bidder being the buyer; it is then fetched away at the buyer's expence. The refuse part of the Ore, which is not fit for sale, is beat down small, and carried to the Smelting-House on the premises, erected by His Grace, and there run into a Regulus, in large pigs or bars, and is then sold from 70L to 90L per ton. Upon the whole, nothing is lost.

The great advantage to the country around, arises from the number of hands employed, and the circulation of between three and four thousand pounds in cash annually, in a place poor and thinly inhabited before this mine was discovered, but now quite improved, and more than 300 men, women and children employed winter and summer, who have proper overseers for every department, where everything goes on with the utmost harmony and cheerfulness.

The Miners, as before hinted, work at two pence per hour, six hours at a time; women, by task, earn from four-pence to eight-pence per day, and are paid by measure according to the quantity of Ore they can buck, girls and boys, from two pence to four pence per day, some more; thus there is a constant employment for both sexes, and all ages, from five to sixty years old. The Carpenter's shop, the Smith's forge, the Cooperage, with the neat dwelling houses, of the superintendents, little kitchen gardens and out-houses annexed are all singular in their kind, and happily adapted to make life agreeable in that solitary place, which lies between two monstrous hills, separated at least two miles from any other inhabitants.

This Copper-Mine in the state described, clears annually between 8 and 10,000L. and if worked with that spirit, which usually accompanies large returns, double that sume might be made of it; but His Grace, it seems, is content that it employs all the labouring poor who present themselves for work, from the neighbouring parishes.

On the Opposite side of Ecton-Hill is a lead Mine, which is likely to turn out to great advantage; the veins of lead approaching very near to the Copper; and they are driving in an Adit parallel with the other.

Thus have I given a faint idea of this valuable Copper-Mine; a perfect description, I am sensible, would require a much abler hand, A draught, section, and perspective view of its internal parts are much wanted, things constantly supplied by the ingenious Germans and Hungarians, who delineate to a proper scale, every shaft, stade, groove and course of the veins throught the Mine, together with a description and narrative of their discoveries, the appearances, and various strata cut through in sinking down, and in driving their adits. This method would, I must own, serve as a future guide to other discoveries and a saving of large sums to Mine-Adventurers, many of whom expend considerable fortunes, without the least rational sign of companion to Minerals, being led (through a mistaken zeal) into airy schemes of that nature, by the over-persuasion of ignorant, yet cunning, and designing men!

A Visit in 1838

The final description is by an unknown author and although of a later date, is considered worth including. (5)

'Since the mine has ceased to yield that enormous amount of mineral riches for which in past days it was so famous, public curiosity has died away, and of late years but little has been made known, respecting it. The scene described by the writer just quoted (6) cannot now be witnessed, the operations of the few remaining adventurers being conducted on a limited scale; to the lover of enterprise, however, a visit to the mine in its present state will be amply gratifying, though the descent is a task of difficulty, not unattended with danger.

In the autumn of the present year (1838) we (the writer and a friend) determined upon exploring it. On reaching the entrance we prepared for the adventure by enveloping ourselves in coarse miners' frocks; thus equipped, and being furnished with lights, we entered the horizontal shaft, or level, accompanied by two or three of the most experienced miners. The passage for some distance is floored with boards, placed across sleepers, beneath which flows a current of water, a few inches deep. Proceeding along this level for about three hundred yards, we arrived at the point of descent, which is accomplished by the ladders before mentioned. Their sides are formed of wood, and the staves chiefly of iron, some of which are loose, and others so worn away by the repeated treading of the miners, as to convey a fearful sense of insecurity to those who were unaccustomed daily to make trial of their strength. We now found out the utility of the miners' substitute for a candlestick, (a lump of moist adhesive clay into which the candle is thrust;) this we could place securely against the side of the shaft, while the hand that held it was at liberty firmly to grasp the iron hooks and stays, which in the most hazardous situations have been driven into the rocks to assist descent.

After descending what appeared to us an almost interminable number of ladders, and after groping our way through several cavernous passages, hewn out of the solid rock, and scarcely high enough in some places, to admit of our standing erect, we landed, within forty yards of the bottom of the mine, in a gloomy excavation of great extent, and very considerable height. In the dense and overwhelming obscurity which reigned around us, scarcely broken by the feeble glimmer of our lights, we were unable to form any probable estimate of its proportions; if we state its altitude to be in some parts not less than fifty or sixty feet, it is certainly not overrated. We were now buried, as it were, in the very bowels of a mountain, at the depth of at least fifteen hundred feet beneath its summit. The situation itself is one of appalling loneliness, and even in the company of the miners, who, from the force of habit, beheld the scene with careless indifference, it is hardly possible to shake off the apprehensions which it is so well calculated to inspire. But these imaginary dangers vanished before a real one.

Just before our arrival the miners had effected a blast, the shock of which had loosened some pieces of rock, suspended, and almost detached from the roof. Some of these now fell within a few feet of the spot in which we were resting, causing us, it is needless to say, to make a hasty and precipitate retreat. The reverberation through the cavern occasioned by these falling fragments of rock, was loud and startling, what it would be in the case of an explosion, we had not then an opportunity of discovering. The rich bed of ore, in excavating which this vast chasm has been formed, is now exhausted; and thin leafy veins are all that remain for the miners to work upon; as one of them remarked to us, (rather expressively) "the trunk and the branches were exhausted – they were then at work on the twigs." The air of the mine is close, but to those who are accustomed to it, not inconveniently so.

We were informed that the workmen are subject to no more disease, and perhaps even less, than those who are exposed to every change of temperature in the open air. That this was the fact, their muscular frames and healthy appearance clearly indicated. One of our guides however stated, that in the course of forty years' experience as a miner, he had seen many of his fellow workmen drawn up to the entrance in a mangled and often lifeless state, arising from falls, or from injuries received in the dangerous process of blasting. Our guides next led us through a narrow passage on one side of the cavern, to the mouth of a shaft leading to the bottom of the mine; but being told that the passage was insecure, we did not risk a further descent. Proceeding a short distance, we arrived at the great perpendicular shaft; on looking upwards the sky at the summit of the mountain was distinctly visible. Having gratified our curiosity to its full extent, we prepared to retrace our steps.

The miners, in number perhaps a dozen, now left their labour, and each with his feeble light, defiled up the ladders before us. The effect produced by the motion of their dark forms, brought into strong relief amid the thick gloom in which all beside was enshrouded, was striking, almost unearthly, and we lingered some moments to observe it. On reaching the upper level, we heard the sound of running water, and turning off to one side were suddenly conducted to an immense water-wheel, of extraordinary power; its diameter being thirty-two feet, and its width across the staves about six. By a singular exercise of ingenuity, this wheel is put into motion by the water collected in the upper parts of the mine, while its power is employed in drawing off that which would otherwise accumulate in the lower.

Nothing we had hitherto beheld surpassed, for startling effect, the scene now before us. The revolution of this enormous wheel, and the action of its appendant machinery over a dark and apparently unfathomable abyss, added to the deafening roar of waters, increased in a ten-fold degree by the echo of the cavern, might serve for the reality of some one of those scenes deemed to exist only in the imagination of the poet. It must be witnessed to be appreciated, to describe or to paint it is almost impossible. Near the wheel there is a capstan, with a rope equal in strength to a ship's cable, used for raising heavy weights. To preserve the rope from the effects of damp, fires are sometimes kept burning, often for months together. Passing along the level by which we entered, we emerged into the light of day, after an absence of about an hour and a half.

The actual depth of Ecton mine is stated to be 1,650 feet. In the year 1835 an assertion, perhaps never yet contradicted, was put forth in a newspaper, and from it copied into other publications, that a shaft at Monkwearmouth colliery in Sunderland was the deepest in the kingdom, being then extended to 1,600 feet below the surface of the ground. This statement must have been made in ignorance of the Ecton shaft, which then exceeded it by fifty feet, and has now it is believed, for aught that yet appeals, a perpendicular depth surpassing that of any mine in Great Britain.

The supposition, founded on the existence of volcanic fires and hot water springs, that the internal heat of the globe becomes more intense, in proportion to the depth we penetrate from its surface, has in Ecton as well as other mines, received strengthening testimony. Under the direction of Mr. Hopkins, the able geologist, who has bestowed so much labour in surveying the strata of Derbyshire and the adjoining counties, some experiments by means of thermometers, are now being conducted in different parts of the mine. The results already ascertained are decidedly favourable to the truth of the supposition. These results may be regarded as more conclusive than those obtained from the like observations in coal-mines, in which other causes have been assigned for an increase of temperature, independently of the presumed subterranean heat.

The miners now engaged here have a lease from the Duke of Devonshire, by which they are empowered to work the mine for their own benefit, on paying to him a tribute amounting to one-tenth of the ore procured.'

References

1. Note on an undated cross-section of the pipeworking, Dev. Coll. box of Ecton papers of 1770s. See page 27

2. Jottings of J. Harpur, Derbys Record Office, 2375/M, No.63-65

3. Banks, J., Journal of an Excursion to Wales and the Midlands began 13 August 1767 ending 29 January 1768, University Library, Cambridge. Ad MS 6294

4. Efford. W., *Gentleman's Magazine*, Reprinted in Bull. PDMHS, 1961, Vol 1, No 5, pp 37-40

5. Anon, *Ashbourne and the Valley of the Dove*, 1839, pp 152-155

6. The author is quoting William Efford

Commodities

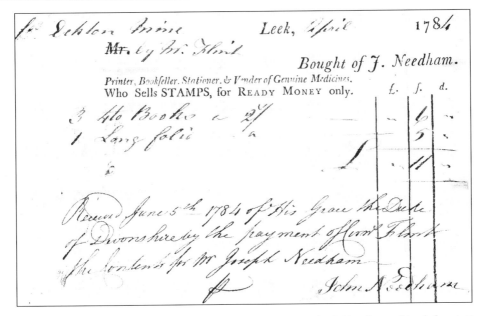

The oldest printed invoice in the Ecton Accounts. It was sent by J. Needham of Leek for stationery

The remaining records of the mine, despite their completeness, give little away concerning the day to day activity around an important contributor to the local economy. However, a careful study and analysis does allow one to appreciate more than was intended by the 18th century book keeper. The provision of sundry goods relied on carts and packhorses for transport and there must have been a continual activity as materials were brought to the mine and dressed copper ore and metal was carried away. Because only summary sheets of the accounts survive for the years under Robert Shore's management, less may be gleaned than for the years under Cornelius Flint.

Ale

Separate from the refreshments for weigh days and the Christmas party, ale seems to have been purchased, at least initially, for the 'pumpers'. These payments last until February 1764. During this period, bills from John Critchlow probably included ale, but the summary sheets do not mention details. He was paid in May 1762 for 12 gallons (£0.16.6d) – approximately 2d per pint delivered to the mine) and again in December 1762. A bill for Feb 1764 (£0.18.6d) from him is the last specific entry. These must have ceased once pumping was changed from a manual system to a horse-operated whim, if not before. In the 1780s, there are references to the purchase of 'custom ale', plus hops and malt which were regularly purchased at both Ecton and Whiston.

Bricks

The purchase of bricks became important, once the decision to smelt ore at the mine was taken, although in later decades the volumes were much higher than in the 1760s. Most of the supplies came from George Bacon from 1765-69. Purchases were in the order of £8-£13 per annum. In 1764, the cost was £20.18s.6d but this would have included the cost of the calcining furnace built with brick like a potter's bottle kiln. Construction of other furnaces and repairs in 1767 clearly placed a demand on local brick makers.

Far fewer were ordered in 1769, reflecting the reduced use of the smelters as ore was stockpiled ahead of the construction of the Whiston smelter. In 1769 William Hillard supplied 16 cwt of bricks at 1s.9d per cwt. In the 1780s, bricks and tiles were purchased by the quantity, rather than by weight. There was a brickyard at Reapsmoor, between Warslow and Longnor (which traditionally is held to have supplied bricks for the Crewe & Harpur Arms Hotel in Longnor). Whether it was supplying the mine at this time is not clear. The only current detail on this brickyard dates from the mid-19th century. There was clay at Newhaven and much of it was to find its way to Ecton later, so perhaps this was also a source in the 1760s.

There were regular supplies of bricks and tiles from the Froghall and Ipstones area in the 1780s. Brick production started at Whiston in 1782, but it is not clear if much of this found its way to Ecton. However in March 1786, two consignments of bricks went to the mine from Whiston, totalling 8½ tons and sent at the same rate as the ore and coal. Most of the bricks needed by the mine (fire bricks particularly) were delivered from Newhaven, especially after a brick kiln was built by the Duke there in 1786. From 1 September 1784 a tax was introduced on bricks and tiles, the rates being 2s.6d on all bricks and 3s.0d on most sorts of tile. Ridge or pantiles were taxed at 8s.0d a thousand. This was based upon unburnt bricks and there was some allowance for wastage. The rate of tax was increased in 1794 and 1803. (1)

Brick deliveries were recorded both by the volume of bricks and by the ton. It is also difficult to determine whether a delivery was bound for Ecton or Whiston in lots of instances. This makes it difficult to assess the volumes being delivered. An indication of the figures can be gauged from the deliveries to Ecton and Whiston in the period August 1779 to the end of 1780. Whiston received 126,500 bricks and 50,531 tiles, whilst 13,330 bricks went to Ecton, plus 39,577 tiles. Some of these were made at Froghall Wharf by Williamson and Henshall.

The completion of the Newhaven brick kiln did not mean that all the bricks bound for Ecton were subsequently produced there. In the September 1786 Reckoning, William Mellor brought 3 tons 13 cwt of brick back to Ecton from Whiston as back carriage for instance. The Newhaven oven was fired with coal from the Duke's own collieries at Hazles Cross and Foxt Wood.

Moreover, the production of fire brick prior to the building of the Newhaven brick oven indicates that many unburnt bricks were being sent to the Ecton furnaces. They would have been used unburnt, being fired as the smelter was used for ore calcining or smelting etc. Adam Young produced 25 tons 5 cwt of fire bricks at Newhaven between 18 June and 25 August, 1783 for instance. Additional to clay bricks were white bricks, thought to be silica bricks, which are still made at Newhaven's Friden brick works. There are also specific references to red bricks. This must have been from red clay and some of this exists to this day at the inner end of Apes Tor Adit level behind the remains of the 1823 dam.

See under chapter 10 for further details on purchases in 1780 for both Whiston & Ecton Smelters.

Clay

At 2s 6d per cart load, 5 loads were purchased in 1760. Clay or bricks were to become a significant item later. Clay was presumably used for sealing parts of the mine from water ingress (or egress). For instance, water pumped up to Ecton Sough left the mine by flowing along the level. Quantities of clay were used to create dams (e.g. in the Boat level at its inner end). In the 1870s it was used in an attempt to stop water from entering the Dale Mine from the River Manifold and it could have been used in the Boat level, for instance.

Fire clay for Whiston came from Cauldon Lowe and Milkhillgate Green. The location of the Cauldon Lowe deposit is not clear. Joseph Ratcliff was delivering clay in each of the first four Reckonings of 1781. The last four Reckonings for the year have not survived, but it would appear that about 580 tons might have been delivered during the year. For 1782, 597 tons were delivered and this was probably the pattern in 1783 too. Until the mid-1780s, Ratcliff (his name is spelt with and without a final 'e') delivered c. 600 tons per annum. Thereafter the volume dropped to about 450 tons in 1785 and 530 tons for both 1786-87. After that, the volume dropped rapidly – to 355 tons in 1788 and to 180 tons in 1789. At the end of 1789, clay deliveries from Cauldon Lowe ceased and thereafter they were made from Farley Ribden. Clay pits existed mainly on the south side of the B5417 at Ribden, on the Oakamoor – Cauldon Road, south of Cauldon Lowe village and just north of Tenement Farm. The word 'Farley' has since been dropped.

Previous deliveries may have come from either side of the former Cauldon Lowe School where there is a considerable amount of disturbed ground close to the A52 between Hoftens Cross and Rue Hill. Confirmation of the use of Ribden clay for refractory bricks (made at Oakamoor), albeit in the 20th century was made by Dodd & Dodd. (2) Additionally, in 1783, there are deliveries recorded from Thomas Langford of Milkhillgate Green which is between Cauldon and Calton. His clay pit seems to have been at SK096490 and is marked on old large scale OS maps. It is just down the lane to the west of Huddale Farm. The Reckonings for 1783 are incomplete, but it is known that he delivered 142 tons in three Reckonings. He charged 7s.0d per ton compared with 4s.0d from Joseph Ratcliff who was nearer to Whiston. The fireclay would have been used in making fire bricks for furnace linings and also for bonding bricks or stone in the fire hearth. Today, the Milkhillgate Clay pit may be seen, partly infilled, the view impaired by bushes and vegetation. It appears to have been roughly 20 feet deep and perhaps 20 feet or more in width.

The Milkhillgate Green Clay Pit

Langford would have been able to have avoided tolls at Stanton Dale and Rue Hill on the Blythe Marsh – Thorpe turnpike road (the A52 from Stanton Dale to the turn for Oakamoor at Rue Hill). The Stanton Dale tollhouse was not built until 1790 and although Rue Hill was planned at the same time, it did not open until 1792. (3) The date of the now demolished toll house built on the A52 near Lanehead (west of Windy Harbour) is unknown. This would appear to have been the only other barrier on the turnpike before reaching Whiston.

Langford delivered 238 tons in 1783 and he continued supplying clay until 1787 when the invoices cease. He probably delivered about 1,000 tons between 1783 and 1787.

In February 1786 (invoice no 10, R. February, 1786), four people were paid for 27-29 days [it was a 7 week reckoning] for getting clay and sand at 'Newhaven Brickhill'. It seems to have been a family concern, for the four were John and James Buxton & William and Joseph Slater. William Slater Jnr turned up for $1\frac{1}{2}$ days work (all the above at 1s.3d per day); and Mary Buxton and Ann Slater for 2 and 1 days respectively at 8d per day. The sand and clay must have been carried to the cart in wiskits for 6 were bought at $4\frac{1}{2}$d each and included in the same bill. To round things off, William Slater used his horse and cart for $1\frac{1}{2}$ days at 1s.6d per day. This may have been to move the sand to the mine, for Wm. Mellor of West Side Mill moved 8 tons of clay (invoice 33; same Reckoning). The need for clay was not as great as at Whiston, but substantial deliveries of bricks were made to the mine.

Iron

Purchases of iron commence in June 1762 with 'Mr Bulex $22\frac{1}{2}$ of rowld iron £0.6s.0d'. It is unclear whether some of the suppliers were wholesalers or foundries/ironworks. Two references to 'Mr Evans bill for rooled iron' at £6. 17s.1d and £29.18s.10d probably relate to Thomas Evans of Derby. Additionally are the following: May 1765 'John Whelldon bill for Steel £1. 12s. 0d'; August 1766 'Josh Horobin bill for Steel £3.13.10d'; March 1768 'James Benit bill for iron and steel £8.16s.0d'; August 1768 'Wm Hellifield bill for Files £0.10s.9d'. There are several early references to purchases of iron items from 'Mr Walker' – Walker's Ironworks at Rotherham.

Bills for iron from Robert Longden relate to his Ashbourne foundry (some of the Whiston deliveries after 1770 were simply marked 'from Ashbourne'). Between 1763 and 1768, he supplied £130.17s.1d. worth of iron, but as usual, details are unknown. The account, in two instances, made payment for two trips by a messenger who incurred the expense of one shilling on each occasion travelling on the turnpike road. His destination was Ashbourne and Mayfield. There were in fact two foundries at Mayfield, one at Middle Mayfield and another at Hanging Bridge. (4) However it is the Bassett foundry which regularly supplied items to the mine and smelter. Ashbourne had a smith's forge as early as 1595 and there was another at Snelston at this date. (5)

The Bassett's Hanging Bridge foundry may have been rebuilt at some point, or moved. In May, 1833, the *Staffordshire Advertiser* carried an advert for the sale of 'a newly erected iron foundry, with models, blowing machine, bellows etc with good yard well supplied with water, and house, now occupied as a beer-house, known by the sign of the Anchor' in Mayfield parish. (6) Included in the sale were various houses, including the Rock Houses, all in the area of Hanging Bridge. A former foundry existed adjacent to the bridge, on its north west side, until the road and bridge were widened in the 1930s. The sale was by auction at the Marquis of Granby Inn, Ashbourne on 26th May 1833.

After June 1768, Francis Hurt's Alderwasley Foundry (it was situated on the site of the ironworks near Ambergate), became a regular supplier. There are three entries for 1768, totalling £24.0s.11d. One was for 'Cast Mettle Boxes' and another for 'Cast metal wheels'. The latter reference is interesting, but not the earliest, for in the Reckoning of 23 June 1764 is this reference: 'Mr Walker bill for castmeatle wheels, 16s.6d'.

Alderwasley Foundry was a regular supplier for decades of iron bars and 'brewers squares'

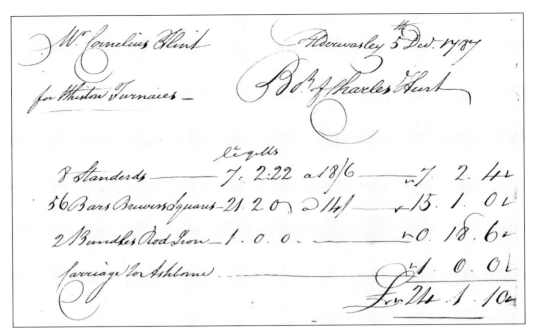

One of the invoices (for Dec 1787) for Alderwasley Forge, owned by Charles Hurt. The iron goods were for Whiston. It is in the handwriting of James Croft who worked for Wilkinsons who managed the works

– large square vats; were these used as pans for precipitation of copper? (see also p 76) – plus other specific requirements of the mine and Whiston Smelter. In November 1783 is an invoice from Smith, Clarke, Brunton, Bales & Smith of the Griffin Foundry, Chesterfield for 20 tons of 'brew house squares' which cost £12.12.10d. Smith, Clarke, Brunton and Baker (of the Chesterfield foundry) sent to Ecton '1 extra good anvil' weighing 4 cwt plus a smith's vice (R December 1780). Presumably this was the same firm. They cost £7.3s.7½d plus 7s 0d carriage. Presumably this was the same foundry.

Throughout the 1760s another regular supplier was Thomas Bird who supplied 'iron' and 'iron and steel'. Two bills are a little more helpful, indicating that iron was supplied at just over £1 per cwt. The total invoice value for 1761 to 1769 is £181.13s.1d. According to Glover (7), an iron forge at Killamarsh, in the parish of Eckington, near Chesterfield, was run by John Bird. Was this the foundry supplying Ecton? From later invoices, it seems likely.

Iron Hoops came from various suppliers and presumably were used to strengthen barrels. In 1761, James Wolley supplied 56lbs of iron hoops at 3d per lb. Mr Thomas Evans was the principal supplier, being paid £54.13s.6d for hoops. These were supplied in 1762, 1766 and 1769. Mr 'Longdin' supplied a few more in 1766 (£2.4s.0d) and became a regular supplier of them.

There are three early entries for the task of ironing a cart (one is described as a 'wagon' in 1761, two in 1764, at £1.11s.4d, £1.15s.0d and £1.11s.11d. Only slightly cheaper was the payment of £1.6s.0d in November 1765 to John Rhodes for 'ironing a Watter Barrel', presumably for draining workings.

One item which was specifically recorded in the accounts was in August 1761 'Mr Balm for a large Iron Weigh beam £1.16s.0d' – presumably scales for weighing ore, which Sir Joseph Banks stated weighed up to 2 cwt. This was the weight carried by each pack mule.

Throughout the 1780s, deliveries of iron goods were ongoing features of the accounts, with the main suppliers being Alderwasley Forge at Ambergate, Pethills Forge, Bassett's Forge at Hanging Bridge, Mayfield and Robert Longden of Ashbourne. Bar iron, hoop iron and 'brewer's squares' featured frequently, plus spades, shovels etc, these often being supplied by Pethill's Forge (see below).

His Grace the Duke of Devonshire.
To John Bingham Dr

9th June 1787   £ s d

One Dozen of Bottoms - 1 "12" 0
at same times one Doz Riddles 0 "13 - 0
7th July one Dozen of Bottoms - - 1 "12" 0
at same times two Doz, Riddles - 1 " 6" 0
paid Carriage - - - - - 0 " 1" 0
the same times one Doz Blind Boys 3 " 6" 0

                                        8 "10 " 0

John Bingham's invoice for Riddles and 1 Dozen of 'Blind Boys'

It seems that special castings were usually made by Bassetts (Thomas & William) and there are many charges for making 'models'. It would have been interesting to have had more detail on these. An example was 12 pots supplied in 1780. They weighed 189 lbs each on average – (i.e., over 1½ cwts). Were they casting pots or for something else?

A most unusual item supplied in June 1787 by John Bingham of Abney were 'blind boys,' which remain unidentified. This particular invoice is reproduced above.

Pethills Forge, near Winkhill, Staffs

This forge was situated adjacent to the River Hamps upstream from Winkhill on the A53, between Leek and Ashbourne. Other than the Ecton accounts, the only known product from this foundry was the weathercock on St Edwards Church at Leek. (8)

Most of the early accounts only mention George Critchlow and do not state the name of the foundry, but one does! Additional proof is that George Critchlow, the proprietor, died in late 1780 and his bill for November 1780, was receipted by his wife Elizabeth when she was paid in February 1781. There were four accounts for 1765; one for 1766; two for 1767, and two for 1768, to a total value of £52.18s.5d. The summary sheets, simply state that the bills were for 'iron etc' or 'Ironwork'.

The foundry used ironstone which outcropped locally. It had commenced by 1758. George Critchlow was succeeded by his son, also George, but he died in 1782. It was then taken over by Francis Gosling who continued supplying the mine. A foundry had existed here in the 16th century and a reference of this period survives, referring to Pethills pool, no doubt a mill pool for a water powered set of bellows (9). It was still supplying iron items to Ecton and Whiston in 1790. These included spades, shovels, rail iron (to Ecton), and other items made to order. See also in Chapter 11 for more on this foundry.

Mine Implements

Boreing Hammers

'John Whieldon' (he signed himself 'Wheldon) was paid £1.16s.0d for 'Boreinghamers'. In March 1764 he is recorded supplying ten dozen more at 6s.0d per dozen and he completed his total order for 13 dozen (132 hammers) in May.

Candles and Gun Powder

Candles were purchased at 6s.6d or 6s.8d per dozen for a dozen pack, the price dropping down to 5s.6d or 5s.9d per dozen by 1762. Thereafter they were purchased with powder up until 1764 when the mine only purchased candles for the pumpers or watermen as they were sometimes called. From September 1764 to the end of the decade, these were purchased from John Beastall (or Bestall). These cost £51.9s.5d in 1765, but the price fell to £45 in 1766 and to £43.4s.4d in 1767 where it remained until the end of the decade. This would seem to reflect less hours spent pumping.

An account survives which summarises the amount of candles and powder purchased between the end of May 1780 and 21 September 1782 (say 28 months). In this period, 23,172 candles were purchased at $6^{1}/_{2}$d each plus 16,626 lbs of black powder, at 11d-12d per pound. This equates to a yearly purchase of 10,000 candles and 3 tons 4cwt of powder. Without doubt, the mine must have had a pronounced influence on local candle production. Powder was delivered chiefly from Messrs Wilkinson of Chesterfield who delivered 600 lbs at a time. It was delivered in barrels and probably their barrels weighed 120 lbs each. Other suppliers of powder delivered smaller quantities, frequently, but not always, in multiplications of 120 e.g. 240 or 360 lbs at a time. Ecton usually purchased 'F' type powder from Wilkinsons.

At $6^{1}/_{2}$d per candle, each one cost over 25% of the daily wage rate for one of the mine's labourers. Powder consumption at this period resulted in some 60-120 lb barrels being purchased per annum. There was a deposit on each barrel sent.

Wilkinsons were wholesalers. It seems likely that they were used as a supplier because of other connections – the mine banked with them and fetched the mine cash from their Chesterfield office. The mine also purchased lead metal from their Shacklow smelter a few years later. Wilkinsons also ran the Alderwasley Foundry for the Hurts. There was a gunpowder works at Fernilee on the River Goyt, strangely omitted by Cocroft. (10) However it opened early on the 19th century. The manufacture of gunpowder was restricted to sites in use for that purpose in 1772, by Act of Parliament. Others had to obtain a licence. (11) As Wilkinsons were wholesalers, it is likely that the powder came from quite a distance. The site of the Fernilee works is now below Errwood reservoir. The number of gunpowder works in the British Isles was only 16 in 1700 and 25 in 1800. There were no other Midlands area works noted by Cocroft. (12)

For September 1785 – August 1786, 12,540 candles were purchased at $7^{1}/_{4}$d or $7^{1}/_{2}$d each. They came from:

Mr Armstrong of Ashbourne	-	4,320
Mr Roberts of Winster	-	4,554
Mr Cresswell of Ashford	-	3,666

Purchases of powder amounted to 10,192 lbs at $9^1/_2$d per lb. This amounted to 4 tons 11 cwt and came from two suppliers – two-thirds of it from Wilkinsons of Chesterfield and the rest from Mr Cresswell who was also supplying candles. Mr Cresswell also supplied candles to Chatsworth. Additional supplies came from Fogg and Sterndale, Manchester, but it is not known why it was needed.

In the Account for March 1781, Foxt Wood Colliery purchased six candles which cost 6s. 8d. per dozen and weighed 1 lb each.

Cart and Horse Hire

In the Reckoning for December 1762, Ben Aston was paid £2.3s.0d for a cart and £1.17s.6d for another one in March 1764. Three years later, he was paid the same sum for a handcart. Efford refers to hand carts on the dressing floor, in 1769. These would be little handcarts used by boys and additional to railed wagons used in the sough. An example of a handcart from Royledge Mine may be seen in the Lead Mining Museum at Matlock Bath, recreated by and from pieces found by Len Kirkham.

In December 1779, a cart and two horses cost 5s.0d. to hire per day. Two carts and four horses cost 8s.0d. Usually a horse cost a 1s.0d. a day to hire. In the Reckoning for August 1780 is an invoice dated 25 July for the purchase of accessories for the cart horse at the mine:

'Cartsadle and gurtle	6s 0d
to a croper	3s 0d
to a brechband	8s 6d
to a coller	5s 0d
to a backband	1s 2d
to a halm straps & sackstring	1s 3d'

Chairs & Bowls

John Bestall, in addition to candles, also supplied chairs and bowls in August 1761 at 5s.6d and more. 'Chairs etc' were purchased in May 1763 at 10s.5d.

Corves

In March 1762, Sam. Boden was paid £0.12s.0d for 18 corves and John Twigg was paid £0.1s.0d for taking them to the mine. The mine purchased them regularly and they are also regularly recorded in the coal mine accounts.

Feathers

In December 1762, Robt. Bowring was paid £0.12s.0d for feathers. They were pieces of iron either side of an iron wedge which was hammered into cracks to split the rock. Examples may be seen at the Mining Museum in Matlock Bath.

Freys

In November 1766, Richard Clay had a bill for a pair of these at a cost of ten shillings, but the term is unknown.

Kibbles

In November 1761, John Hole was paid £2.11s.0d for 'Cibles'. They were frequently bought along with barrels.

Lanthorns

Probably lanterns, bought in 1766-68 and supplied by John Billings.

Nails

In 1761, £21.4s.0d was spent on nails and generally costs were about £5 p.a. for this, although £30.14s.0d was spent in 1764. There were various suppliers, but Ed. Fowley and John Shaw were the main suppliers.

In 1780, John Shaw sent no less than 186,500 nails to Ecton. They were described as being plating stubs; lat (lathe) nails; Tingle nails and dubles. In the same year Thomas Getliffe supplied 24,700 nails and Thomas Hewson 2,500 more. However, where they were based or where they sent the nails to is not clear. In the 1780s, most nails seem to have been made in Belper. The huge volume of nails used gives some idea of the amount of timber, which must have also been used at the mine.

Riddles or Sieves

In the 1760s, there are not many entries and details are not very specific, being for 'Ridles'; 'Sieves' and 'Sive Bottoms'. In the 1780s it becomes clear that the mine purchased riddles (at that time) from the Hathersage area.

An example is James Hodgkinson's invoice of December 1779: 'I have completed your order and sent them to the Red Lion at Tidswall [Tideswell].' It consisted of '24 Sive bottoms of No 48 wires £12.16.0d; 12 Wire brooms £4.18.3d [and] 12 Ridles at 1s 2d per Ridle 14s 0d.' His address was not stated, but further supplies came from John Bingham and some of his invoices are endorsed Abney or Hathersage.

Ropes

After 1761, rope costs averaged £62 p.a. Principal suppliers were Caleb Wilcock of Winster, Samuel Ellam of Ashbourne and a Mr Balm. Generally the summary nature of the accounts give little away. The ropes seem, however, to have been purchased by weight. In 1763, fine spun rope cost $5^{1}/_{2}$d per lb and coarse $4^{1}/_{4}$d per lb. This was to change by the 1780s when ropes were purchased by the fathom. An invoice in the Reckoning of November 1786 from Caleb Willcock was endorsed 'Hemp is now advanced to £40 a Tun – extraordinary indeed; as we have no war no [r any] charge of convoy – shall send you some more, as soon as is convenient.' See also under Boulton & Watt in Chapter 6 for more on ropes.

Spades & Picks

In 1762, 6 picks cost £0.10s.4d. They were purchased by weight rather than per item (e.g. 31 lb at 4d). In September 1761, Geo More was paid 12s.0d for 6 spades (2s.0d) each. Many were made by Pethills Forge in the 1780s. An unusual item was the purchase of 'Fishing spades'.

Coals

Smithy coals were purchased from 1760, but tonnages were not great. In 1761, some 18 tons were purchased and the total quantity of coal thereafter was: 1762 – 31 tons; 1763 – 43 tons; 1764 – 53 tons; 1765 – 22 tons; 1766 – 28 tons; 1767 – 12 tons. One gets a feeling that the coal tonnages are understated after 1764. The accounts include no coal figures at all for 1768 and most of 1769.

In March 1761, Joseph Bassett supplied 54 loads of 'Coals' at 1s.5d per load. In 1765 coal was costing 12s. 0d per ton. On this basis, a load was 2 cwt 40lb, indicating that it was brought by packhorse with just over 1 cwt per pannier. The coal pit was not indicated. One is also

Suppliers to Ecton and Whiston Mines

1 Manchester — ropes
2 Hathersage — sieves/ridddlcs
3 Sheffield — Iron goods
4 Chesterfield — iron goods, gunpowder
5 Tideswell — collection point for sieves from Hathersage
6 Shacklow lead mill — pigs of lead
7 Ashford — candles, gunpowder
8 Bakewell — candles
9 Winster — candles, ropes
10 Matlock Bath — fluorspar
11 Alderwasley Forge — Iron goods
12 Belper — nails and iron goods
13 Ashbourne — candles, iron goods, oil
14 Mayfield — iron goods
15 Oakamoor — tinplate, rolled copper sheets
16 Whiston Smelter — coal
17 Stoke-on-Trent — timber
18 Hazles Cross Colliery — coal
19 Foxt Wood — coal
20 Ipstones— brick and tile
21 Shaw — timber, coal
22 Ross Colliery — coal
23 Froghall— brick, tile, canal goods lime
24 Cauldon — clay
25 Milkhillgate Green — clay
26 Pethills Forge — iron goods
27 Castern — timber
28 Wetton Mill — horse feed
29 Biggin— timber
30 Newhaven— clay, sand, bricks
31 Hartington Mill — horse feed
32 Sheen— stone
33 Warslow Common — stone
34 Leek — surveyor, stationary, ropes
35 Danebridge — timber
36 Goldsitch— coal

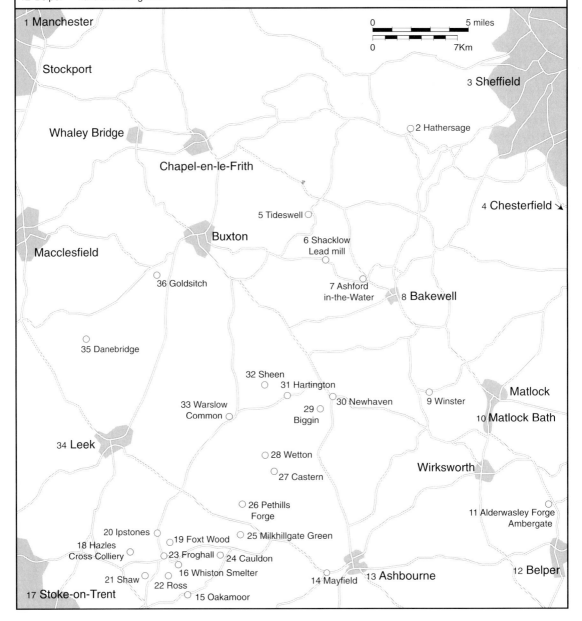

tempted to suggest that he had six horses and made nine journeys. At that time, it is difficult to conceive where the demand would come from to justify a packhorse carrier in that area maintaining twelve horses, even if he doubled up as a farmer; most farms might have justified up to six horses, but not twelve. Six horses would also have brought the equivalent of a cart pulled by one horse. After February 1766, such deliveries were referred to as 'smithy coal', but there is only the one specific reference to 'loads'.

At the end of 1769, regular coal movements commence presumably between coal pits and Whiston, indicating that the furnaces at the smelter had been lit: $22^1/_2$ tons were included in the 18th November reckoning and $40^1/_2$ tons in the 31st December reckoning perhaps indicating that the fires were lit towards late October. See Chapter 11 for more on coal production.

Cooper (also known as the Cowper)

Payments in the 1760s were chiefly to Robert Low and John Hole. Payments in total by the mine were in the order of £25-30 p.a. Barrels were needed for water drawing and presumably ore and waste, prior to the purchase of metal kibbles.

Clock

In January, 1761, Peter Simpson was paid £1.5s.0d for 'a Grove watch'. In June, 1767, Samuel Carrington received £4.10s.0d for 'a Clock and Deal Plate'. It was repaired by James Brown in 1770 at a cost of £1.16s.6d The mine clock was situated on the north side of the smelter, which became known as the 'clockhouse smelter' It is likely that the clock confirmed the starting and ending of the working day. This was usually six hours in the adjacent lead mining area of Derbyshire, where work at the mine had to be fitted in with agricultural activities. (13) However the dressing floor hands may have had a longer working day.

Leather

There were occasional payments for the purchase of leather and one, in June 1763 'Josh. Smith for Bucetleathers' perhaps indicates why it was purchased. In November 1762, Godfrey Webster supplied 84 lb at $6^1/_2$d per lb. Generally about £3 p.a. was spent buying leather, chiefly from Godfrey Webster. Bucket leathers were for the pumps.

Lime

In the 1760s, lime seems to have been purchased principally by the packhorse load at $10^1/_2$d per load. It was probably used for building work and extra quantities were paid for in November 1764 (for 104 loads) and a similar amount a year later. There were various people bringing it to the mine, but no confirmation that the price was for the lime and carriage, but this is likely, nonetheless.

In September 1785 Ralph Belfoot was paid for 'two kilns full of Lime, getting stone and preparing cinders' at £1 per kiln full. He was paid separately for drawing the lime out. However, such references are not many and the tonnage of stone not great. The removal of the continual volume of stone being drawn up Apes Tor Shaft started shortly afterwards. There is a reference to the 'Apes Tor hillock' in the 1790s.

Quantities of lime were also in regular demand for the making of lime mortar. From July 26-November 11 1780, Thomas Malkin delivered 136 loads at 7d per load to Whiston, which is likely to be for building work, although most of the buildings are likely to have been erected by this date. If this relates to packhorse delivery, it equates to 70d (5s 10d) per ton, indicating a delivery from Cauldon Lowe. It may have been by cart but 7d for delivery from Froghall to Whiston seems too low per ton.

Oats, Hay Straw and Thatch

There are various annual items for oats, oat straw and hay which would have been for the mine horses which were used for water pumping, both on the surface at Apes Tor and, later, in the mine. Hay, including old hay, which some farmers prefer for their horses, cost 4s.0d per cwt in 1762 and 1763. In 1761, oat straw cost 12s.6d per cwt and in 1762, oats were costing 12s. 0d a quarter (cwt).

In August 1789, 40 thrave of straw cost 5d per thrave. The almost bewildering array of measurements may be gauged from George Locker's carriage bill at Whiston. He charged for 2¹/₂ cwt of hay at 3s 6d per cwt, '3 pecks of Otes' and 'won (one) Thrave of wheat crow' at 3s 0d (R. February 1786).

From time to time, thatch was fetched by Gervase Wood, thought to be of Pikehall, east of Newhaven. Whether it was straw stems or reeds is not known, but there is no obvious water source at Pikehall. In December 1787, he charged for '600 of Thatch'. It was supplied by the thrave. He delivered 400 thraves to Ecton and 200 to Wetton Hill, where a building must have been constructed at the quarry. Wood delivered coal to Newhaven (September 1786 account), so whether he also lived at Pikehall isn't clear. He charged for the thatch as well as delivered it.

The grass around the mine was cut for hay annually. In the September 1786 Reckoning, Elizabeth Lovet and three others were paid for a total of 14 days work, at 8d per day for making hay. Despite the fact that Wetton Mill was on the Devonshire Estate, supplies from there were rare. The first one from 'Wetton Mills (sic)', was in the late 1780s and 17 strikes of oats, priced variably at 2s. 0d; 2s. 6d; 3s. 1¹/₂d and 3s. 4d per strike. The miller was John Redfern. Bran for the mine horses came from Hartington Mill. The hay was also cut at Hazles Cross Colliery.

Oil

'Oyle and cloth' were to become regular purchases. A small quantity was bought in 1761 and although other purchases may be hidden in the summary of invoices, specific references occur in 1764: 'Mr Smith bill of Oyle etc £3. 4s .7d'. The only other references occur in 1768 and 69 when 'Oyle & Cloth' cost £7-£8 on each occasion. Presumably it lubricated horse whims, pumps etc. Train oil was regularly purchased in the 1780s. It was made from pilchards (pers. comm. Stuart Band). Different types of oil were tried in 1790 from Joseph Bradley of Ashbourne including whale oil.

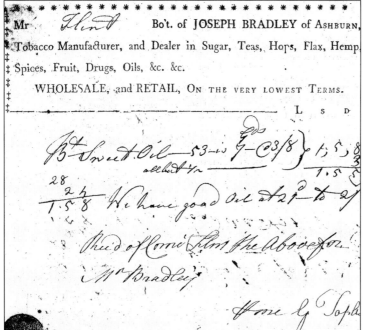

Joseph Bradley's invoice for Sweet Oil from 1790. See also p 81

Timber

Considerable amounts of timber were purchased by the mine and later, additional purchases were made by Hazles Cross Colliery. One of the principal woods was at Castern, sometimes spelt Casterne. It must have been of a significant size, far greater than the wood which survives to this day on the slopes of the River Manifold, south of Wetton. Similarly, timber was purchased from Biggin Grange. Eighty trees were bought from there in early 1781, and a saw pit made to cut the timber up. In 1786, the mine paid the significant sum of £440 for oak from Castern at the time when both Ecton and the Colliery were demanding more and more timber. In March 1786, 88 trees had been felled at Castern under this agreement. In mid-1786, three saw-pits were built there, with another by November.

The saw-pits enabled planks and boards to be cut on site and a wagon load of these were taken to Whiston at the end of 1787 (R. December 1787).

Many of the larger pieces of timber were oak and ash. Alder was also purchased as part of the smelting process to de-oxidise the smelt. They were also used for ladder poles (i.e., the sides of ladders). Alder wood had other uses too. It was used at Belper for turning into bobbins and spindles for the textile mills. Alder bark was used by dyers in Manchester, fetching £6.16.10d (? per ton). (16)

There is a single reference to the purchase of sycamore (R. August 1780) when it was bought from Mr Beech of the Shaw estate near Cheadle. Significant amounts of cut timber was also bought. It came in units of 120, called dales, or deals, which made up a 'hundred'. It was carried to the mine from suppliers in Bakewell, Stoke-on-Trent and elsewhere, such as Monyash (which may have been a collection point). It was carried by cart, wagon or drug, which was used for tree trunks or other large or long baulks. (e.g. '4 drug load of wood from Castern' at 14s.0d per load – £2.16.8d).

Some particularly large baulks, possibly of the very strong Norway spruce came from Kenwrights of Stoke-on-Trent. They were called 'Dantzick [Danzig] fir balks, (R. November 1787). They generally sent their timber by canal to Froghall where it was collected and taken on to Ecton. Quite often their invoices even state the name of the master of the narrow boat!

Wood ash was purchased regularly by the strike ($3^{1}/_{2}$ lb) at 1s 4d per strike. It was used in the smelting process at Whiston (but not Ecton, where lime ash was used). Other by-products were charcoal and wood kids (presumably branches). The latter were sold at 4s 6d per hundred. Charcoal was made at Castern and as much as 6 tons at a time sent to Whiston for use in the refining process. It was made from cordwood, believed to be another name for wood kids.

The incessant demand for timber in an area (i.e., at Ecton) where it did not grow in quantity saw the mine buying it from a wide area. These are shown on Fig 116. In 1779 timber was being delivered to the mine from Ilam Wood, but this probably means Castern, as it is a single entry (R. March 1787 [sic]).

The timber for the slagmill waterwheel came from Sheffield. As mentioned in Chapter 9, this was unusual and it may be because elm was required – a timber not mentioned in the accounts.

The Visit by the 5th Duke

The 5th Duke appears to have visited the mine in the early autumn of 1783. Where he went to underground is not known. His father descended to at least the 34 fathoms level, if not lower, in 1763. Much more was available to be seen twenty years on.

Reference is made elsewhere (chapter 13 Gratuities) to the contribution made by Flint to the purse left by the Duke, which Mr Heaton reimbursed.

The precise nature of the accounting indicates that five candles at $5^{3}/_{4}$d each were used during his visit.

Malt and hops were purchased in September 1783 and more in November. The first lot could have been to make beer for the Duke's visit for consumption by the workers. Whether he had

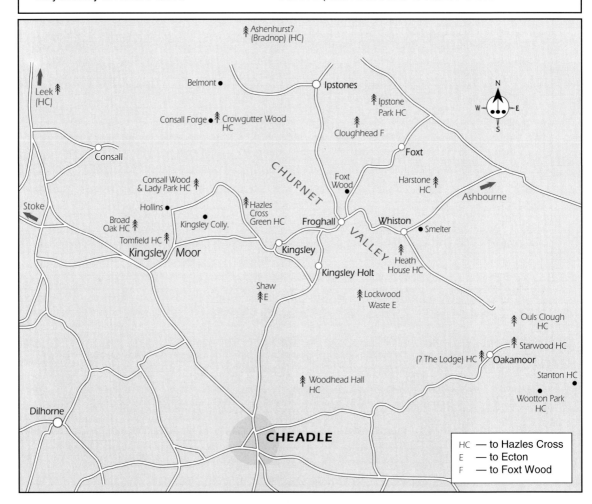

Received 21st Nov. 1787 of His Grace the Duke of Devonshire by payment by Mr Coen. Hunt One Hundred & forty six Pounds 13/4 being a payment on account of Castern wood, recd for the use of Francis Hurt Esqr &

For Messr Wilkinson

James Croft

£146.13.4

Part-payment invoice of one-third of £440 for timber from the Hurt Estate at Castern Wood

Known sources of Timber for Ecton & the Collieries

Plus Castern to Ecton/Hazles Cross

Barleyford (R, Dane) to Ecton

Swythamley to Hazles Cross

Stoke on Trent to Ecton

Bakewell to Ecton

Stanton (near Ashbourne to Hazles Cross

Ashenhurst? (Bradnop) (HC)

Leek (HC)

Belmont

Ipstones

Ipstone Park HC

Consall Forge • Crowgutter Wood HC

Cloughhead F

Consall

Foxt

CHURNET

Foxt Wood

Harstone HC

Ashbourne

Stoke

Consall Wood & Lady Park HC

Hollins

Broad Oak HC

Kingsley Colly.

Hazles Cross Green HC

Froghall

Whiston

• Smelter

Tomfield HC

Kingsley Moor

Kingsley

VALLEY

Heath House HC

Kingsley Holt

Shaw E

Lockwood Waste E

Ouls Clough HC

Starwood HC

(? The Lodge) HC Oakamoor

Stanton HC

Woodhead Hall HC

Wootton Park HC

Dilhorne

CHEADLE

HC — to Hazles Cross
E — to Ecton
F — to Foxt Wood

a soft spot for bread and butter pudding has succumbed to the passage of time, but the ingredients seem to have been purchased from Robert Low prior to his visit. Amongst the ingredients were nutmeg (2d) and 1oz Ginger (1d)! Low also supplied Green tea and 1oz of Bohea Tea plus 1lb of lump sugar (on September 23rd). Low operated from Warslow and he supplied virtually all the 'domestic items' to the mine for years.

Perhaps the point needs making that all the extra expense of the visit was paid for by the Duke, but one suspects that he was used to that. Robert Low seemed to be doing well from his business. He occupied several parcels of land around Warslow. He had 2 acres at the Dale, a small amount in two open fields called the Littion and Copside and another parcel of 3 acres called Miery Acre in 1773. (14)

A Robert Lowe was Joint Treasurer of the Alstonefield, Wetton and Hartington Association for the prosecuting of felons and other offenders. (15)

The Duke's wife, Georgiana, collected minerals and was encouraged by White Watson, the Bakewell geologist. Her collection survives at Chatsworth and it includes several specimens of copper and spar from Ecton. See also chapter 2. The Grotto in the garden (not open to the public) is lined with spar and copper ore from Ecton, but whether this was removed to Chatsworth at about this time is not known.

Miscellaneous Domestic items purchased in August 1780 per Robert Lowe

2 pint ink	4d
1 stone tarr	3/6 p stone
40 Wiskatts at	4d
5 stone of pitch	3/6 per stone
42 qts Train Oil at	8d p qt
3 yds Cloth at	13d
1 yds Cloth at	11d
44lb sope at	7d a lb
Pack thread at	3d do at 2d, do at 1d, do at 2d
various locks	
For the Mine House (presumably):	
4 yds window hangings at	15d
9 yds lace 1½ doz rings	6d Incle 1d and cost of making up
Looking Glass	5/- Carriage 3d
6 yds Flannel at	10d
3 yds Flannel at	8d
Capling leather	8d
½ Resin	
45 yds Bagging at	9½d and twine 3d
2 yds Flannel at	12d
17½ yds bagging at	9d, twine 6d, Cording 7d
5 Sackbands	
4 yds Diapor for Tablecloths at	2/3
Thread & making	6d
1 yd Cloth at	9d & incle 1d

It is thought that the tar and pitch was used to seal paving stones in the buildings to stop ingress of damp. The stones being laid on the pitch and the gap between stones being filled with the tar.

Tradesmen with a known address

Armstrong, John; candlemaker, Ashbourne

Barnes, W.; candle supplier, Ashbourne

Bassett, Thomas & Sons, Iron Forge, Hanging Bridge, Mayfield

Bate, Sam & George; filemakers, Sheffield

Bingham, John; sieves, Hathersage (Abney)

Bradley, Joseph; candle and powder supplier, Ashbourne

Buxton, Richard; tanner, Ashbourne

Cresswell, George; candle supplier, Ashford-in-the-Water

Ellam, John; ropemaker, Ashbourne

Flint, Henry; spade supplier, Bonsall

Fogg & Sterndale; powder suppliers, Manchester

Goodwin, Samuel; rope maker, Leek

Gosling, Francis; iron supplier, Pethills Forge, Winkhill, Staffs

Harrison, Abraham; nailmaker etc, Belper

Hawley, William; spades, Middleton Cross

Hilliard, F; stationer, Leek

Hodgkinson, James; riddles/sieves, Hathersage

Johnson, William; timber merchant, Longnor

Knowles, George & Henry; fluorspar supplier, Masson Mine, Matlock Bath

Langford, Thomas; clay supplier, Milkhillgate Green, Cauldon

Linley, Jn; supplied bellows; Allercliffe (? Attercliffe)

Longden, Robert; iron supplier, Ashbourne

Low, Robert; 'grocer', Warslow

Needham J.; printer and stationer, Leek

Newton, Ann; candlemaker, Ashbourne

Phillips, Sam; sand maker, Warslow Common

Poyser, Wm and George; brickmakers, Newhaven and Whiston

Ratcliffe, Joseph; clay supplier to Whiston, Cauldon Lowe

Ride, Joseph; warehouse man and carrier, Compton, Ashbourne

Roberts, Richard; candlemaker, Winster

Rowbottom, J.; chain supplier, Foolow

Rowland, William; brickmaker, supplier to Ecton, Newhaven

Sellors, Daniel; supplier of barrels, Bonsall

Shaw, John; nail supplier, ? of Belper

Smith, George; charcoal maker, Castern Wood, Wetton

Smith, Thomas; lock supplier, Ashbourne (R. Dec. 1786)

Storrs, Joseph; iron supplier, Chesterfield

Tonge, Robert & William; ? shippers or wholesalers; Stockwith, Lincs

Topliss, R; candle supplier, Wirksworth, (R. Nov. 1786)

Wain, John; candlemaker, Longnor

Wardle Joseph; supplier of furnace bottoms, sand and paving stones to Whiston

Webster, John; nail maker, Belper (R. Dec. 1786)

Willcock, Caleb; rope maker, Winster

Wood, Gervase; thatch, ? Pikehall

References

1   Cox, A., *Brick Making, A History & Gazetteer*, published by Bedfordshire County Council, 1979, p. 31

2   Dodd, A.E., & E.M., 'Blythe Marsh to Thorpe Turnpike', *North Staffs., Journal of Field Studies*, 1965, Vol 5, p 13, quoting The Geological Survey, 1917, *Special Report on Mineral Resources of Gt. Britain:VI, Refactory Materials: Ganister & Silica Rock etc.*

3   Dodd, E.M., 1965, North Staffs., Journal of Field Studies, Vol 5, pp 13-14

4   *Memories of Mayfield*, p 51 and Glover, *Directory of Derbyshire*, 1829, p 4, when it was occupied by Bassett & Shaw

5   Chester, H., *Churnet Valley Iron: The Mills and the Mines*, 2003, p 46

6   *Staffs Advertiser*, 18/5/1833, p. 1. col. 6

7   Glover, *History of Derby*, p 80

8   Victoria County History, Vol 7, *Leek and the Moorlands*, p 214

9   pers.comm., Faith Cleverdon, Leek

10 Cocroft, W.D., *Dangerous Energy*, 2000

11 Cocroft, op cit., p 27; 12 George III. c.61

12 Cocroft, op cit., p 27

13 Willies, L., 'John Taylor in Derbyshire', 1839-1851, *Bull. PDMHS*, Vol.6, No.5, p 228

14 Derby Mercury, 10 December 1773 p 4, col 4

15 Derby Mercury, 24 December, 1789

16 Victoria County History: *Derbyshire*, Vol 1, p 422, quoting Farey J., *General View of the Agriculture of Derbyshire*, 1815. Vol 2, pp 244-315

Ore Smelting

The Process at Whiston

After running the mine for three years, the decision was taken to reduce transport costs of ore. This was achieved by reducing the ore by calcining or roasting it and then later smelting it to coarse metal. The calcining furnace was described as looking like a potter's bottle kiln and this can be clearly identified on the 1809 plan, by Potter. (1) It was built with an extension towards what is now the road, although in 1764 at the time of its construction, it was east of the road, as may be seen on the plan. In 1765 may be seen the payment for the construction of the smelting furnace, which received its clock a year later. This building was erected immediately to the south side of the calciner. Both were adjacent to the dressing floor. The bottle kiln would have been built of brick and many still litter the site of the calciner.

A further 'Smilt House' was built in 1768, probably the South Smelthouse. This linked with the decision to smelt all of the ore within the business. The number of smelters was to grow

The Whiston Works in the 1880s. The house on the top right-hand corner is the Stable House

further, with a lead smelt mill in 1782 and a slagmill for lead in 1784. In December 1764, Henry Sleigh was paid £1.5s.0d 'for a pare of bellows', which may have been to get the fires lit rather than for production.

A hint of the construction of the calcining furnace is given in a bill from Thomas Bassett & Sons, of Mayfield (Invoice 19, R. February 1786). Bassetts sent '3 plates and 3 sides for a Calsineing Furnace' (Weight 1 ton 7 cwt, 29q 4lbs) plus 3 frames (4 cwt) and 3 tunnels (2½ cwt), sent to the mine on 30th November, 1785. A similar consignment was sent to Whiston 7 weeks later viz: 3 plates, 3 sides and 3 tunnels, plus eight 60lb weights. All of this was made of iron.

A Swedish visitor, Eric Geisler, described the furnaces to Swedish readers stating that the calciner or roasting furnace was 9 feet long and 6 feet wide on the inside, whilst the smelting furnace was 6 feet long and 1½ feet wide. (2) Both of the cupolas were 1½ feet high and a little lower nearer to the external opening. The furnace bridge appears to have been just nine inches high and 15 inches long (i.e. the opening to the ore hearth from the coal hearth – the ore or regulas being heated by heat reverberating from the roof of the cupola). Geisler recorded that both furnaces – the calciner and the smelting – were under the same roof, which is confusing.

Fortunately, he described the process at Ecton. The cycle of calcining and smelting occurred three times. In cycle one, the ore was calcined for 12 hours with 15 cwt of ore and 5 cwt of coal. It was then smelted for 4 hours to a much higher temperature using 4 cwt of roasted ore and 16 cwt of coal to produce the regulas, after the slag had been drawn off into 6in x 6in x 3in deep moulds. The second cycle involved putting 12 cwt of the regulas back into the furnace with 4 cwt of coal for another 12 hours. After drawing off and cooling, it went into the smelting furnace for 36 hours using 18 cwt of regulas and 36 cwt of coal. The regulas was then tapped into long rounded forms or moulds made of cast iron. For the 3rd cycle, 15 cwt of the regulas went back into the calciner for another 12 hours with 12 cwt of coal. The slag was tapped off every 4-6 hours and the copper then tapped into squared moulds. Finally, these copper squares went back into the smelter for a last 12 hours, 15 cwt of metal with 15 or 16 cwt of coal. This was tapped off as coarse copper metal into round moulds. Where the metal went then is unclear. It was possibly sold or sent to Whiston for refining to pure copper metal. The process took 88 hours and used 88 cwt of coal.

In March 1785 the accounts show a rare glimpse of what happened to at least some of the Ecton copper metal with details of the carriage of coarse copper to Whiston. Most records either refer to 'ore' or 'copper' deliveries.

After the construction of the Whiston smelter, it has previously been held that the Duke smelted all copper ore there. This is not correct however. Substantial volumes of ore were sold to Pattens of Warrington and also to Roe & Co and Messrs Rotton. Also both 'fine' and 'coarse' copper metal (at £100 and £92 per ton respectively) was sold to Rotton & Co. It is unclear whether the ore sales resulted in the disposal of ores surplus to the needs of Whiston or not. The audited accounts reveal that ore sales between 1770 and the end of 1774 amounted to 2,575 tons. This fetched £32,498, while metal sales of 303 tons realised £28,900. So clearly the majority of the revenue continued to be made from ore sales. The account book of sales from July 1775 – 1780 indicates that only 41 tons of ore was sold in the second half of the decade.

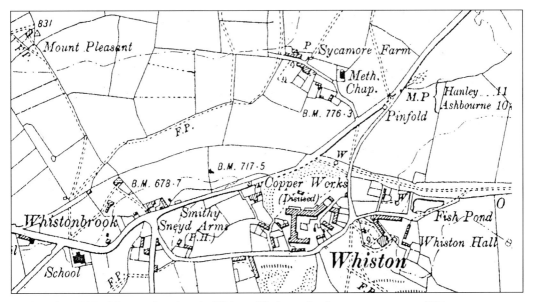

Fig 9.1 The 1880s OS map showing the Whiston Works and enlargement on page 127

Ore Sales 1770-1774

1770	Botham Ore	Mr Patten & Co	300 tons
		Mr Roe & Co	100 tons
1771		Mr Patten & Co	457 tons
		Mr Rotton	10 tons
		Messrs Roe	94 tons
1772		Messrs Patten & Co	410 tons
1773		Mr Patten	788 tons
1774		Mr Patten	406 tons
		Mr Rotton	10 tons

Metal Sales 1770-1774

1770	Mr Rotton	14 tons 17 cwt at £100 p.ton
1771	Mr Rotton	43 tons 7 cwt
1772	Mr Rotton	87 tons 19 cwt
1773	Mr Rotton	74 tons 7 cwt
1774	Mr Rotton	82 tons 11 cwt

The construction of the 1768 smelter at Ecton corresponded with coarse copper metal prices reaching a 'high' of £100-£101 per ton. The price obtained for metal in 1769 dropped to £96 which may reflect poorer quality metal being manufactured from poorer ores ahead of the opening of the Whiston smelter a year later. Thereafter it levelled off at £100 per ton until 1772 when some sales dropped to £92 per ton and this price held through 1773 and 1774.

After the opening of the Whiston works, all slime ores – the small particles of copper ore recovered in the dressing process – were smelted within the Company, presumably at Whiston. No slime ore sales are recorded in the audited accounts for 1770-1774. Prior to that from 1763, when the first slime sales were made, to 1769, the price obtained was between £9 and £13.10s per ton.

Layout of the Whiston Works

It is far from clear how the furnace layout existed at Whiston, but it is possible to appreciate certain aspects.

The early Bristol smelting industry was replaced by furnaces arranged in long halls. At Bristol, furnaces were arranged in small clusters of smelting houses containing no more than four furnaces, not that dissimilar to Ecton. In 1717, a smelting hall 80ft x 40ft together with a smaller one 36ft x 40ft was built at Llangyfelach, Swansea. This was to set a precedent for long halls – often 40ft wide like the prototype – but significantly longer. (3) The Middle Bank Copper Works at Swansea started in 1755 with one single, long range, but by 1771 had five such structures extending to 1,038 feet long. (4)

They tended to be two stories in height, to help ventilate the noxious fumes they generated to the atmosphere. The furnaces were reverbatory furnaces or cupolas. They consisted of two parts, an ore hearth and the fire hearth, where the coal was burnt. There was a low roof which reflected the intense heat across the ore and regulas (coarse metal). A tall chimney beyond the ore or metal hearth helped to create the necessary draught which increased the temperature in the furnace.

The roasting or calcining furnaces were larger than the smelting and refining furnaces. The regulas ('matte' in S.Wales) had to be broken down – hence the stone crushing wheel at Whiston – but a water bath was developed in South Wales. The liquid from the first melting was turned into these baths, where it granulated rather than solidified into lumps. This method of smelting copper became known as the Welsh Process. (5)

This system was probably introduced at Whiston in 1780, although some calcining and

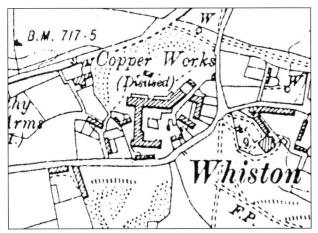

Fig 9.2

roasting was done at Ecton as we have seen. The 1772 report on the Whiston process does not mention the water bath, but Garner does in 1844 and it is likely that this was introduced in 1780. (6) Working from the 1880s O S map, the main furnace building would appear to have been about 160 feet long by 40 feet wide. A further long building protruded at right angles to the furnace building and was probably the battery mill. This was to produce the copper bowls made initially and was where John Orme had the cakes dressed which seem to have been the main form of metal production. Presumably the coal was kept either in the yard or in this building. The stables were by the roadside, although the horses were few in number in the 1780s. The O S map shows a tramway to carry away the slag waste. It is traditionally held that the slag heap glowed red hot through the nights. The noxious fumes damaged neighbouring land and the smelter paid £15 p.a. to the Manor of Whiston in compensation, plus extra to other neighbours.

The rear of the Stable House showing slag blocks from the Whiston Smelter

The work of 'one' of the women, Mary Dean & Co., (indicating she had assistance) is given in March, 1782. She was paid for knocking 14 'old Finery Bottoms' and 12 'Smilting Bottoms'. Presumably this was removing slag from abandoned stones comprising the base of the furnaces. Ann Burgin (again '& Co') was paid for washing old furnace bottoms. Presumably these operations were also done in the building running south of the smelting hall. Ann Burgin was paid 5s.0d per ton and had washed 10 tons in the Reckoning period of six weeks. Mary Dean was paid 5s.0d per ton for the Finery Bottoms and 3s.0d for the 'Smilting' Bottoms.

The provision of clothes for mine workers (grove clothes) is not unknown in the Derbyshire orefield (7) but seldom hinted at Ecton. Unusually, Mary Dean received:

'A pair of stais [stays or corsets]	8s. 0d
A Gound [gown]	1s. 4d
2 Peticoats	0s. 8d
Shifts Aprons Hankerchiefs	1s. 0d'

The amount was the sum paid to Wm. Collier, who made them. Why this exception was made is not known. A year later, a pair of shoes were made for her. She must have been held in high regard for her funeral costs of £1. 4s. 5d was paid for by the mine (R. December 1788). Prior to that, having retired, she received a pension of 4s.0d per week.

Smelter Clocks

Both the smelters at Ecton (The Clock House Smelter) and Whiston were provided with clocks and although they received regular maintenance, the manufacturer was unfortunately not stated. Andrew Holmes was paid 10s.6d for cleaning the Whiston clock in August 1784 and he provided a new stop 'to the Strikeing' in the following September and a new wire to the hammer at the same time (R. December 1784). There are many references of this nature. The smelter also had a bell.

The Smelting Process

The system of smelting is described below. The process used reverberatory furnaces or cupolas which were elongated ovens with an arched, stone built roof. Early in the 18th century they were about six feet long in the Bristol area (8) and at the end of that century were about 12 feet in length in South Wales, the main area for copper smelting in the world at that time. (9) The length of the Whiston furnaces is not known. The ore was initially reduced in a calcining furnace to remove sulphur and oxidise the iron content. The process of smelting involved the use of other materials and the accounts include many details of the movements of these items.

At Bristol, the ore was laid on a bed of sand, whilst other surfaces of the furnace were lined with fireclay, the furnace being heated for one or two days. The calcined ore was then loaded into a second furnace along with copper slag (to extract copper from it, of course) along with lime (³/₄ bushel of lime to 300lb of ore) and more sand.

In this process, the furnace was recharged every four hours and the slag tapped every 12

Production of fine Copper at Whiston in 1772

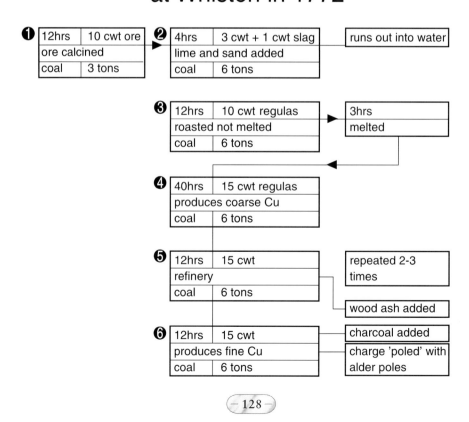

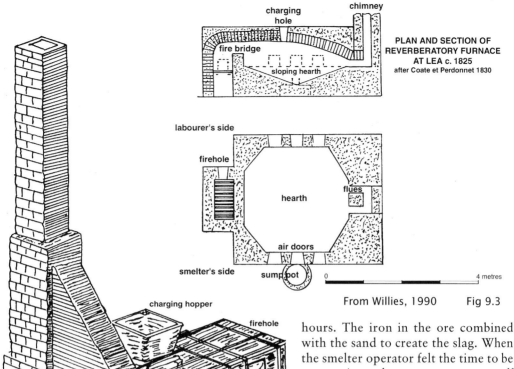

charging hole

chimney

PLAN AND SECTION OF
REVERBERATORY FURNACE
AT LEA c. 1825
after Coate et Perdonnet 1830

fire bridge

sloping hearth

labourer's side

firehole

hearth

flues

air doors

smelter's side

sump pot

0   4 metres

From Willies, 1990   Fig 9.3

charging hopper

firehole

iron strapping

sump-pot

smelters side

0   4 metres

REVERBERATORY OR CUPOLA FURNACE
in the mid-eighteenth century

hours. The iron in the ore combined with the sand to create the slag. When the smelter operator felt the time to be appropriate, the copper was run off into oblong moulds hollowed out of sand. Once hardened, the material was known as regulas, or matte. The regulas was remelted several times – perhaps as much as 20 times – to gradually remove the iron content. High quality copper ores produced slag with higher values of copper. As Ecton ores were usually in that bracket, remelting the slag to extract the copper was important.

The final stage was refining. An analysis of the labourers at Ecton in 1779 shows that there were about 24 men involved in calcining and smelting copper ore. At Bristol, this process took place in a narrower furnace. The regulas was piled on a layer of bone ash. This does not appear to have been purchased at Ecton or Whiston, but lots of wood ash was. In lead smelting (see below) lime was added to help separate the slag from the molten lead. Perhaps the use of wood or lime ash in the copper smelting process was in a similar manner.

In fact it would appear that wood ash was used at Whiston and lime ash (from the Apes Tor Limekiln in all probability) at Ecton. The wood ash was supplied by John Orme (the head refiner) at the rate of 4 to 5 strikes per Reckoning, sometimes as much as 8 strikes, a minimum of around 2lb per week. Orme was paid for the dressing of the cakes of copper, removing surface irregularities. In the absence of metal production figures, the amount of cake copper dressed by him gives a control figure for the metal output per Reckoning. The cakes were heavy: the average weight being a little over 100lb each.

At Bristol, the regulas was refined twice, initially for 12 to 14 hours, using coal as fuel to produce blister copper. It was then reheated a second time with charcoal but only for two hours or so to produce 'fine copper'. At Whiston, the copper metal was produced into 'cakes, tiles and bowls'. The metal was taken by Joseph Ride's to his warehouse in Compton, Ashbourne at 8s.0d per ton. His firm then took it to Derby for shipment. In 1772 copper samples went to London by 'Basses waggon'. From 1775, the bulk of the copper metal went down the River Trent to the Humber and on to London – see Sea Transportation, Chapter 10.

The production process at Bristol is given because it is more detailed than the record of metal production at Whiston, especially with regard to the materials used in the process. The only contemporary description of ore smelting at Whiston is dated 28 October, 1772 and was sent to John White, a coppersmith living in Houndsditch, London. It was written by Robert Shore.

There were eight furnaces, of which six were used for calcining and smelting and two for refining. (Thomas Dutton billed (R.February 1780) for building eight chimney stacks at a cost of £13.10s.0d). Five of the six 'ore' furnaces were regularly at work, which implies that the sixth was being rebuilt. Of these five, two were used for calcining and three for smelting. The calcining furnaces worked 11 charges per week, each charge lasting for 12 hours, i.e. they were in use for 132 hours per week. The smelting furnaces worked 30 charges per week, each charge lasting for 4 hours. They therefore worked for 120 hours per week. Maximum capacity of the works was dependent on the capacity of the two calciners and, with a six-day week, the calciners were working to capacity.

The process involved was as follows:
Ore was calcined for 12 hours with 10 cwt to a charge.
Three hundred weight of the above was then put into a smelting furnace with 1 cwt of slag for four hours and run off as 'black regulas'.
Then 10cwt of the latter was calcined (i.e. roasted but not melted) for 12 hours, then melted for three hours and run off.
When cooled, 15cwt was put into another furnace for 40 hours and run off as coarse copper.
The coarse copper was then taken to the refinery and 15cwt to a charge was calcined for 12 hours and laded off into square iron pots. This operation was repeated two or three times until fit for the refining furnace.
Finally, 14-15cwt was put into the refining furnace and calcined again for a further 12 hours and toughened in the process before being run into moulds prior to sale as fine copper metal.

The total processing time recorded above adds up to 107 or 119 hours, depending on the repeat heatings at stage 5. The employees totalled 23: 12 smelters, 4 labourers and 7 carriers.

The two calcining furnaces for stage 1 used three tons of coal each and the three smelters used six tons of coal each. Presumably the two refinery furnaces used six tons also, making 1,872 tons per annum. This figure grew substantially after the rebuilding of the works in 1780. At Ecton, there were two furnaces in 1772, one calcining and the other smelting, taking the process to the end of stage 4. This coarse metal was then sold – (from 1770-1774 inclusive) – and it was bought by Rotton & Co.

The same letter gives the number of employees at Ecton:

Dressing ore	90
Workmen & labourers underground	154
Coal carriers	12
Smelters [men, not furnaces]	4
(there were 12 Engine horses)	260

The quality of ore is also given:

Botham ore (i.e. ore from the main deposit)	20%
Waste ore	$7\frac{1}{2}$%
Best regulas (i.e. partly smelted ore, probably at the end of stage 4)	66%

In 1844, Garner tells us of the production process at Whiston: (10)

'The small ore is first calcined in a furnace, being frequently stirred to prevent fusion: this rids it of a portion of its sulpher, arsenic &c, and it is then melted in a second furnace, where part of the slag, iron, &c, is got rid of: the melted ore is then run out into water, when it puts on the form of coarse shot, of a dark colour: the ore may now contain one third metal. It is again several times recalcinated, and remelted, being each time granulated, or else formed into large pigs. It is next roasted, previous to the processes of refining and toughening.

In the operation of toughening, the brittle, crystalline, purplish-red metal is covered, in the melted state, with charcoal; and then a pole of wood (birch or larch) is inserted into the melted metal, which is attended with an ebullition, owing to the escape of carbonic acid gas, and the copper, on cooling, obtains the desired properties of malleability, &c.

This process of poling requires care, and if overdone, produces effects different from those desired; in which case an opposite course must be pursued, the air being freely admitted. After poling, the metal at Whiston is formed into large cakes, small ingots, or shot; the last being obtained by letting the melted copper fall into a well of water'.

In the 1770s and 1780s poling was done using alder poles. The mine paid the same price for alder poles as it did for hardwoods such as ash poles – 1s.3d per foot (R. 18 December 1784). Other materials used have been mentioned above, or at least alluded to from the process in Bristol. Sand was obtained locally from sandstone, which was then reduced to sand. Supplies were worked on Warslow Common (Revidge). An example of this is an invoice for Dale Toll Bar (R. August 1780) 'for the passage of carriages carrying Sand etc for the use of his Grace, 20 carts 9s.9d.' The bill is endorsed 'Dukes Cart Carr. of Sand etc for the use of Furnaces.' From the same source came stone for furnace bottoms for the Ecton furnaces.

An invoice of May 1780 for twenty furnace bottoms delivered to Whiston indicates that three stones comprised a furnace bottom. The supplier, Josh. Wardle, also delivered sand, 8 tons of it at 10d a ton, similar to the deliveries of stone and sand to Ecton from Warslow. The rebuilding of a furnace bottom involved the breaking down of the previous hearth, cutting of new stones and their rebuilding at Whiston at 10s.0d a hearth. The stone came from Whiston Common. Another invoice (R. August 1787) reveals that a further two stones were used to roof the hearth.

When a new furnace was built, the hearth was sealed with molten slag to protect it. A reference to 'running the bottom' (R. December 1787) must relate to this. This invoice also charged for 'Custom Ale' when building the lead furnace 6s. 6d. – probably for 39 pints. The loss of this custom will no doubt be regretted in some quarters.

Fireclay for the Whiston furnaces came from Cauldon Lowe, where Joseph Ratcliff supplied it in loads of 60+ tons at a time. At Ecton, clay seems to have been supplied from Newhaven. Both mine and smelter seem to have been prodigious users of bricks. It was coal however which was used in huge quantities. Some 4 tons of coal was needed to smelt 1 ton of ore. Consequently, to produce 1 ton of metal using ores which averaged 10% quality, it took 10 tons of ore and up to 40 tons of coal. In 1780, a cursory examination of coal tonnage purchased and ore smelted would seem to suggest that more than 4 tons of coal for each ton of ore was being purchased, but the accounts are insufficiently complete to be sure. However a figure nearer to 5 tons is suggested, at least at that time. Clearly it would vary according to ore quality.

By the 1780s, despite the high volumes of coal needed to produce one ton of metal, it would appear that the trend was downwards, an average of $3^1/_2$ to 4 tons perhaps being nearer the truth for the period 1780-85. This may be because less coarse ore was being smelted as the backlog was worked through. Purer ores would need less processing to get rid of the impurities such as iron. However, an average taken over the years 1781-1788 indicates an ore raised to coal ratio of 3:1, but how much ore was actually smelted is unknown.

At that time, 1780, coal was being brought from Shaw Colliery (Mr Beech) north of Cheadle, Hazels Cross (the Duke's own pit) and Ross Colliery, close to the smelter.

Ore Yields

The ore at Ecton has always been traditionally held to have been very rich. However modern opencast mines working copper ores in Third World countries can operate on very poor levels of quality relative to Ecton principally because of the huge size of the deposits. Even if there is some measure of exaggeration in the 20% quality given above for the main deposit, even 15% was very rich. The percentage relates to the amount of copper metal from the ore after reduction in smelting.

It is known that the poorer ores – perhaps those with a higher iron content – known to the miners as waste ores, coarse ores, or Hillock ore (the ores dumped on one side on the mine hillock because their extraction from host rock was more cumbersome) were often smelted with the richer ores. This aided the reduction of the poorer ores at a lower cost and acted as a flux for the richer ores (per R. Shore). It would bring down the yield from the richer ores, however.

It is possible to ascertain the % yield from activities at the mine and smelter. It is stressed that these calculations should be regarded as giving an indication of yield rather then being finite. In the five years 1770-1774, the ore raised (figures from the Reckoning accounts) was 3,689 tons.

Ore production 1770-74	3,689	
Ore on the bank in 1770 (per R. Shore) see p33	2,797	
	6,486 tons	
allow for ore raised in 1770 (it is in both sets of figures) say 600 tons		
& ore still 'on the bank' at		
Whiston, Ecton, Pen etc say 200 tons	(800)	5,686 tons
Ore Sales (from audited accounts)	2,575	
metal sales = 305 tons		
If taken at 10%, 305 tons metal = ore tonnage of	3,050	5,625 tons

It would therefore seem that the average ore yield of the metal smelted by the Duke was in the order of 10% in the period 1770-1774. This is less than one might have expected. In view of the ore sales of 2,575 tons during this period, it may be that the better ores were sold on, more money being made from smelting the poorer ores at Whiston with only as much better quality ore as was needed to run the works at full production with two calcining furnaces.

When the poorer, coarse ores were in short supply, it is suggested that more of the better quality ores were used, producing more copper metal. This situation existed until 1780 when the works was extended. (11)

In 1781-1789 the average yield of ore raised to refined metal gives a figure of 17%. As the 1781 figure of 34% (see below) seems high, the figure for 1782-89 still gives 16%. It was this high yield which made the mine so profitable.

This is supported by a Chatsworth document headed 'an estimate of making Fine copper from Ecton coarse ores which holds and yields two Tuns in Twenty' (1770s Voucher Box). This document probably dates from 1769.

This was referred to by John Robey (12) who goes on to state that this may have been a deliberate attempt to sway metal production to Whiston rather than Denby as the tonnage of coal required to smelt 10 tons of ore is shown as 4 tons rather than 40 tons. He goes on to say that once corrected, Whiston is marginally ahead of Denby, where there was the prospect of buying the works of Cooper & Rotton following the death of Mr Cooper. In fact Rotton was to continue on his own, as we have seen above.

My view is that the document is no more than an aide memoire for Godfrey Heathcote, or someone else above Shore in the Chatsworth management structure. Shore had only recently escaped imprisonment for fraud and kept his lucrative job in the process. It seems unlikely that he would 'pull a stroke' so soon afterwards. Details of the document are given below. It shows transport costs to Denby, Kingsley & Ecton. Correcting 4 tons to 40 shows Kingsley performing better that Denby by 24%. However this slip would have been corrected on the document which carried the actual calculation of not only the transport costs but the purchase costs of the coal too.

Ten tons referred to in the document supports the 10% value of the ore in terms of metal production referred to above as the average for 1770-1774.

Shore's Calculations
Fine Cu from Coarse Ores (i.e. not Botham ore)
@ 10% quality (which confirms its not Botham ore)

to Denby
10 tons ore – Denby 18s p.t	£9. 0s. 0d
+ 4 ton Coal at 3/4d per ton	£0. 13s. 4d
	£9. 13s. 4d

to Kingsley
10 tons ore – to Kingsley 12s p.t	£6 0s. 0d
+ 4 ton coal at 3/4d per ton	£0. 13s. 4d
	£6. 13s. 4d

Smelting at Ecton
10 ton – no cost	
6 ton of coal at 12s per ton	£3. 1s. 0d
Mettle to Denby/Derby 18s	£0. 18s. 0d
	£4. 10s. 0d

Ditto
10 ton – no cost	
4 ton of Denby coal @ 20s per ton	£4. 0s. 0d
Carriage to Derby/Denby 18s	£0. 18s. 0d
	£4. 18s. 0d

The figures on all four examples show the amount of coal to smelt one ton of ore. They seem to show that more Cheadle coal would be needed at Ecton than at Kingsley and this does seem odd. However it is noted above that coal purchases in 1780 would seem to show a consumption rate in excess of 4 tons of coal per ton of ore. The transport rates show movements at 1s 0d per mile for ore and coal, although Shore was probably guessing the distance to Denby and at 18 miles, may be a little light with his guesswork. The 12 miles to Ecton is the distance from the Hazles Cross area to Whiston and then to Ecton via the Highmoor Pen.

However something more intriguing may be buried in this document and that is the reference to Kingsley. It will be noted that under that calculation, the coal is being brought from just over 3 miles away (at 1s 0d per mile). (It was still 1s 0d a mile in 1808, see chapter 13, p170). Therefore construction at Hazles Cross Colliery was not envisaged. It is about 3 miles from Hazles Cross to Whiston, but then the ore would be moved 9 miles (at 8s 6d) and not 12 miles. However these calculations are accurate if the property concerned was Patten's newly erected copper smelter on the roadside between Cheadle and Kingsley Holt, at a site now on the outskirts of Cheadle. It is just over 3 miles to Patten's smelter if a more direct route via Whiston Bridge over the River Churnet was envisaged. Both Shaw Colliery and Hazels Cross Collieries are about 3 miles from Patten's smelter too. Morton in his history of Thomas Boltons (13) makes no reference to this so it may not have been formally discussed with or by the Cheadle Company partners. It would have given the Duke a ready made smelter for metal production. In the event, the Duke had to build on a green field site and he chose land at Whiston, which was purchased for £250. Annual payments of £3 each were made to keep local farmers happy for 'trespass of smoke'. No doubt there was a lot of it.

Why Whiston? It would have been cheaper to have taken the ore across the Churnet Valley to the coal, rather than the other way around. The answer must be the fact that it allowed pack mules to be packed at Pen or Ecton (maybe the decision to build the Pen stockyard has not yet been taken), unpacked at Whiston and reloaded with coal for the return journey. Perhaps the extra six miles across the Churnet and back would have taken too long for one day.

So this one small document tells us that the ore was expected to give a return of 10% (10 tons of ore to one ton of metal); transport rates were 1s.0d. per mile with no differential for carts and packhorses; Whiston was probably not the first choice; and the probable intention of the smelter was to smelt the coarser ores, not the high quality ones for which a ready market existed.

An analysis of dressed metal figures per annum in the 1780s shows unrealistic yields relative to the ore raised. The figures drop from a yield of over 34% in 1780 down to over 17% in 1783. Thereafter the figures continue to drop from 16.68% in 1784 down to 13.65% in 1786. In the years 1780-1783, 1,956 tons of metal were manufactured (plus 31 tons of furnace bottoms ignored in these calculations). If the yield of metal from the ore was 15%, some 13,000 tons of ore would have been required, but only 7,990 tons was raised; a shortfall of 5,000 tons.

To obtain 1,956 tons of metal from 8,000 tons of ore requires a yield of 25%, suggesting that the eighth deposit at the bottom of the mine was particularly rich. The use of poorer ores to reduce the volume about the mine would reduce the yield below 25%, so either it was not being used, the ore yield was even higher, than supposed or there was an enormous backload of unsmelted ore. It would be nice to know the answer. It might be that the Ecton smelter continued smelting surplus poorer ores to metal so that coarse metal of a 'reasonable' quality was fed into the smelting process at Whiston.

Cooper and Rotton, Denby, near Derby

Towards the end of the 1760s this business was sold. A document survives which appears to be in the hand of Godfrey Heathcote and which contains information about the works. It is undated, but indicates that it was on the market and that it 'requires capital of £3,000'. We have seen above that Mr Rotton continued in business on his own, as he purchased ore and metal into the 1770s.

The document giving details of the works informing us that carriage of ore to Derby from Ecton cost 19s.0d. Conversion of ore to metal used 3 tons of coal per ton of ore, thereby requiring 30 tons of coal with 10% quality ore to produce a ton of metal. Apparently Derbyshire coal was superior to coal from the Cheadle Coalfield and 2 tons of Denby coal was enough to do the work obtained using 2½ tons of Cheadle coal. Denby coal cost 3s.8d 'laid down' (delivered).

There were 10 furnaces in all: 3 for calcining, 5 for smelting and 2 for refining, but 2 were usually out of use being re-built. Two men worked at each furnace at 1s.4d per man per day for the smelter and 1s.2d for the calciners. Carriage costs were 6d per ton to Derby, 8s.0d to Gainsborough (for sea shipment, see p 182) and 10s.0d to London. The furnaces cost £70 and £50 respectively for smelting and calcining. There is a comment, not totally readable, which would seem to suggest that the works was available to rent at 4% (£120 p.a.) on a full repairing lease, but as indicated above, a substantial sum was needed for repairs (and presumably the purchase of the equipment). There was a battery mill 'like an iron furnace' and the copper was sold to the 'E.I.C.' (East India Company).

Recasting Shore's carriage costs using this information and correcting the coal volume required we find:

To Denby
10 tons ore to Denby at 19s.0d p.ton   £9.10s. 0d
40 tons coal at 3s.8d per ton   £7. 6s. 8d
                                        £16.16s. 8d

To Kingsley
10 tons ore at 12s   £6. 0s. 0d
40 tons coal at 3s.4d (carriage only)   £6.13s. 4d
                                        £12.13s. 4d

On the basis of the transport costs, smelting at Kingsley was clearly much cheaper. With the benefit of hindsight it is now known that Whiston needed about 4 tons of coal per ton of ore as at Denby.

Whiston after 1770

After the opening of the Whiston smelter, the amount of ore raised in the 5 years 1770-1774 averaged about 738 tons p.a. This was comparable to the average figure for 1767-68. (1769 saw a significant reduction in ore raised. This could have been because of a contraction of the ore-mass being worked but is more likely to have been deliberate back-peddling). Ore tonnages for 1762-64 had been higher, averaging nearly 1,100 tons p.a.

Despite a steady extraction rate, one might have expected the dressed ore tonnages to have increased after the smelter opened, yielding more ore for smelting. Yet this did not happen. The dressed ore production rate for the five years 1764-68 was virtually the same as that for 1770-74. Prior to 1770, the Ecton smelter seems to have been used exclusively for the reduction of

The 18th century Limekiln at Froghall. Lime from here was used
in the extension of the Whiston Works in 1780

coarse ores owned by the Trustees of the 4th Duke's younger sons. Hence the double accounting after 1764 – one set of accounts for the above and another set for fresh ores extracted after the 5th Duke succeeded. As noted elsewhere, the volume of these undressed coarse ores in 1770 amounted to 2,000 tons. Following the opening of the new smelter, the 5th Duke appears to have agreed to a request from Robert Shore that he purchase this quantity.

One would have expected to see a reduction in this tonnage, but clearly the rate of dressing remained unchanged and indeed, it is known that the volume had increased (according to Shore) to 3,500 tons by 1772 (although this must have been a 'best guess'). There is a problem here for total output in 1771-72 was 1,500 tons. Shore's figures indicate that no ore was therefore dressed, (i.e., 2,000 + 1,500 = 3,500 tons) which is not the case, as 1,409 tons was dressed. The accounts for 1775-76 are missing, but in 1777, dressed ore tonnage was 946, with 875 tons in 1778. It was therefore being accelerated, possibly from increased demand for copper cake/fine metal, as the decade progressed. Following the extension of the works, the dressed ore output for 1780 rose to 2,700 tons. This must have resulted from a similar extension of dressing capacity at Ecton.

Raised ore tonnages did not increase however until 1778, when it went above 1,000 tons (to 1,042) for the first time since 1764. The acceleration continued: 1,200 tons (approx) in 1779; 1,530 tons in 1780; 2,200 tons in 1781 and 2,060 tons in 1782 (these figures include notional amounts for the occasional missing 6-7 week Reckoning). As no ore was being sold, the increase in ore smelted at Whiston could have come mostly from 'Botham' ores; one would be unwise to speculate on how much of the coarse ore was being used up. However as it was a useful flux for the smelting of the richer 'Botham' ores, presumably more of the latter called for more of the poorer, 'coarse' ores, as they were known.

There had been other changes at Ecton too. The increased coal tonnages reflect more smelting at the mine and this fits in with an increased demand for the poorer ores – which would be smelted to a type of poor quality metal (called regulas) which was then transported to Whiston. There is a suspicion which raises its head at this point – the Ecton/Whiston carriage accounts related to movements of ore and coal – never cake copper, regulas or anything else. Did the mine ship high and low quality ores to Whiston and sell off the Ecton cake copper or did the term 'ore' include the partly smelted ore (regulas)?

A draft agreement, dated 7 July 1775, survives between the Duke and a John Dawes of Cannonbury House, Middlesex for the latter to be a factor or agent of all copper to be produced from Ecton Mine and refined at Ecton or Whiston. Dawes was to be responsible for bad debts, carriage to purchasers, ware-housing, expenses of sale etc at a $2^1/2$% commission on sales. The agreement was for 7 years.

Dawes agreed to 'pay and Manage' the freight and insurance from Derby of ore/metal sent for sale on the London market to Somers Hey (sic, Key is meant) upon the River Thames in the Port of London. All sales through this warehouse were to attract a 2% commission. (14)

A restriction was placed upon the sale of more than 10 tons to anyone in Derby or the county of Derbyshire without the approval of the Duke. The reason for this is unclear. In the period when invoices become more complete (from 1779) there is no reference to Dawes, however, in the Reckoning for June 1788 is the following ' To an ac't with Mr Heaton that he settled with the late Mr Daws for a loss in the weight of copper betwixt the works and the Market as p.note £129.4s.0d'. This was a lot of money at the time and indicates that the arrangement for selling on the London market existed.

An account book of sales from July 1775 also indicates that this agreement was signed. (15) It indicates that between July 1775 and August 1780, 58,087 cakes (and some bowls) of copper metal weighing 1,202 tons were carted to Derby and then on to London via Gainsborough. This clearly suggests that they were taken down the River Trent by boat and then loaded into ships at Gainsborough for the sea voyage to the River Thames and London. (16)

The accounts indicate who was buying Ecton's metal (see across) and the chief purchaser was the East India Company. In 1777-80, they purchased metal to the value of £38,532 (497 tons).

Sales of Copper Metal 1775-1780

	1775		1776		1777		1778		1779		1780		Remarks
	Value £	Tons	Value £	Tons	Value £	Tons	Value £	Tons	Value £	Tons	Value £	Tons	
Thomas Gibson & Co	83	1											
George Forbes	22	0.25	80	1	380	5	626	8	347	5	918	13	
E Evans	5571	72											
Adventure to Lisbon	835	10	852	10	796	10							
Sir H Mackworth & Co			745	10									
French & Co			1581	20									
Somers Key Porters													1 cake lost £2.5s
East India Co					15330	199	9024	110	7701	105	6477	83	
Thoyts & Co					565	7	2110	29	5491	78	1055	15	
Anthony Villion					79	1	392	5					
Mr Chabot							12	0.15					
Messrs Kines									724	10			
Ship 'Neptune'											600	13	
Cazalet & Co									5439	81	2830	40	
Mr Monkland											216	3	
Lilley & Roberts											91	1	
	6511	83.25	3258	41	17150	222	12164	152.15	19702	279	12187	168	
Total Value	£70972												
Total Tonnage	945												

Total sales between July 1775 and August 1780 amounted to £71,000 (945 tons of metal, plus 41 tons of ore sold to Sir H Mackworth & Co for £550). Despite the strange agreement with Dawes requiring the Duke's approval for sales of copper metal within Derbyshire, E Evans (presumably the Derby company) purchased 72 tons in 1775 but perhaps significantly none afterwards, although they rolled copper for Whiston into sheets. This was presumably for the East India Company. Sir Herbert Mackworth was a principal shareholder in the Gnoll Copper Company, smelters of Swansea. He took a lease of land west of Ecton at Hill House Mine in 1781/82, no doubt with the intention of hoping to locate another Ecton-sized ore deposit (17). This makes one wonder whether Mackworth was raising poor quality ores near Ecton which the mine smelted, adding better quality ore to produce reasonable quality metal. It would explain the occasional ore sales at a time when the mine was not selling ore. It would also be done to maintain good terms with a customer. The ore sales were in 1776-77 and 1781.

An intriguing purchaser was 'The Adventure to Lisbon' while two major copper manufacturers, Messrs Thoyts, and Messrs Cazalet and Cooke were significant purchasers of Whiston's output. Lilley & Roberts took a ton in 1780, presumably an introductory sample to see what it was like. The good ship *Neptune* purchased 13 tons in 1780, presumably delivered in sheets for sheathing the vessel. The purchase price of £600 would be recovered in the increased value of the ship and the extension of its working life. It will be noted that sales to Patten & Roe & Co. ended by 1775. Why this happened is not clear.

Confirmation of the connection with Somers Key is provided by the reference to the 'Somers Key Porters' who 'lost' a cake of copper, valued at £2.5s.0d: perhaps five weeks wages for the man who stole it.

In 1775, unsold stock would appear to have been 257 tons. It was described in the accounts as 'resting'! The table on p.4 indicates sales of 83 tons, but this is for the second half of the year only. Sales for 1776 at 41 tons is misleading, as it must include part of the East India Contract which is all included in their invoice of March 1777.

John Dawes was also a banker. He leant money to Thomas Williams and the Earl of Uxbridge for the Parys & Mona Mine Organisations. In 1786 he took a 1/6th share in the Parys Mine Company. He died in 1788 and was succeeded in his business by his son John. Somers Key was one of the Legal Keys of the City of London. Its site is now covered by the previous Billingsgate Fish Market with a frontage to the River Thames. Once the ship carrying Ecton copper reached London, the warehouse was close to hand. (18)

Costs of shipment forward to sale was more than the 2% commission indicated above in the Dawes agreement. In 1778 for instance, the cash received was £18,780. The sum of £9,000 was remitted to the Duke. Most of the rest went to the mine for payment of expenses, except freight, insurance and other charges at and from Gainsborough to London which amounted to £677. On top of this were commission and charges for guarantee of all debts (and other expenses) attending the sales amounting to $4\frac{1}{2}$% of sales (£12,200). It is fascinating to observe that debt insurance is nothing new.

In 1779-80, the works was redeveloped. It involved the delivery of some 126,500 bricks from Mr William Toplis. Over 50,500 tiles were purchased from H Henshall & R Williamson of Froghall Wharf. The bricks included 12,000 unburnt ones. During this period, over 13,000 bricks went to Ecton, together with almost 40,000 tiles, the latter from Henshall & Williamson. Additional to this was ashlar stone to Whiston. Ecton had its own 'stone pit' for bedded limestone for building purposes. Four bricklayers were employed at the work at Whiston and three stone masons at Ecton. Although the Whiston works has been demolished, some of the stone was used in the construction of Whiston church.

The unburnt bricks would appear to be commons, but at the end of 1780 there is a bill for making and burning 22,850 bricks which perhaps signifies the making of furnace bricks at Whiston had commenced. Another purchase in 1780 was 378 beesoms. They cost 2s.0d per dozen (2d each).

Activities at Whiston after 1780

The development of the works at Whiston in 1780 was followed by the construction of a further building in 1781 and in September 1783, five tons of smelting machinery ('sundry millworks') was purchased from Warrington – presumably Pattens – and sent to Whiston via the Caldon Canal. It seems probable that brick production at Whiston was underway by late 1783 (whatever the provenance of the 22,850 bricks in 1780). The November 1783 Reckoning records the payment of £1. 4s 0d for trespass 'for the Brickilfields' – the brickhill fields – a brickhill being a local term for a brickworks. A year earlier, Samuel Bostock was paid for

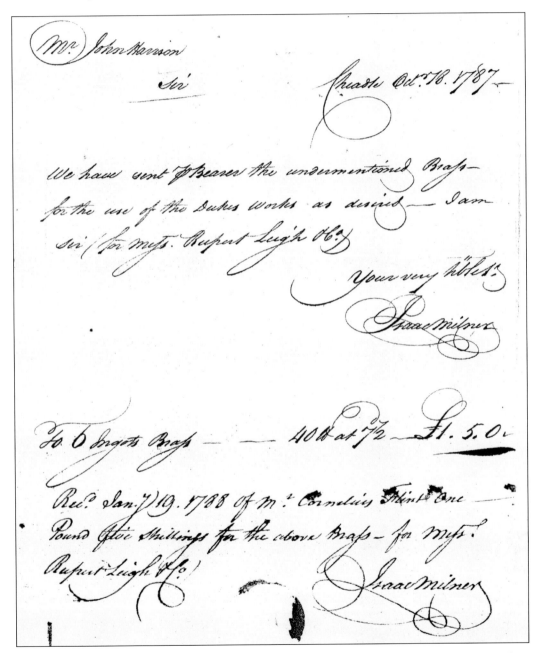

A letter from 'Pattens' at Cheadle. Note the company name at this time was 'Rupert Leigh & Co'

carriage of 7,800 bricks 'betwixt Wiston and Ectton'. They weighed 22³/₄ tons and he charged 6s.8d per ton. Very little is known of the developments at Whiston in 1780, although perhaps the works was redeveloped on the 'Welsh principle' with all the furnaces in one long hall, rather than in separate buildings as at Ecton and perhaps also at Whiston in the 1770-80 period. It is possible that the old works was not demolished, for in R. November 1787 there is a reference to picking the slags at the 'ould works' and the same at the new works. The flow chart (page 128) shows that one ton was calcined per day in a Whiston calciner. There were two calciners at Whiston and one at Ecton. In order to achieve greater production larger furnaces were needed and this must have been the reason for the expansion in 1780. The number of employees remained consistent, with just over 60 people, plus the occasional group working a specific contract (quantity of workers not known), and five carriers of coal. It is suggested that there were seven workers per furnace (of which there were seven) equalling 49 men or thereabouts. Additionally, there were up to eight women and a few boys employed. The bulk of the men were paid 9s.0d or 8s.0d per week; the head smelter and the refiner were each paid 12s.0d; the six women 2s.6d per week and the boys 1s.6d per week.

In the Autumn of 1779, there appear to have been two head men – Thomas Byatt (Smelter & blacksmith) and John Orme (Refiner), both on 12s.0d per week. William Bassett, the blacksmith earned 12s.0d per week too and the mason, Thomas Cartwright, a little less at 10s.0d. As the furnaces were relit at Whiston in late-1780, the head smelter (Thomas Brindley) at Ecton was paid for 'extra attendance at Furnaces 7 weeks at 1s.6d per day (in a 7 week Reckoning) and the same in the December Reckoning.

The reasons for this are not clear, but it probably relates to increased output. Certainly raised and dressed ore volumes started to increase at the mine at this time. There is some evidence to suggest that perhaps the mine was working double shifts at the smelters to lift production and the head smelter's attendance was required as this started. The uncertainty is because the number of men shown under each category of employment had ceased in the labourers' account. There would seem to have been perhaps at least another six men (i.e. a total of 30 employed by March 1782 at 8s.0d to 9s.0d per week). This level was maintained for several years.

In the seven weeks ending 11 November 1780 there were 63 employees at Whiston works. John Orme was paid the most, 12s.0d per week. There were 29 men on 9s.0d per week. The works employed 11 children, including six girls on 2s.6d down to 1s.6d per week. Thomas Byatt, the blacksmith, still earned 12s.0d per week, the same as John Orme. Both the smith and the carpenters commanded a good wage on account of their skills.

The annual wage bill therefore remained fairly static from this point of view, although increased coal deliveries saw it rising through to £400 per Reckoning for most of 1780-81. The high consumption of coal post-1780 indicates a high metal production rate, so it follows that the furnaces were either being worked longer or were enlarged to take a higher charge for smelting. The coal consumption rose to over 50% more than the pre-1780 rate. The number of men per furnace might indicate shiftwork. One might have expected that there would be interaction of workers between Ecton & Whiston but it seems that it might have been 1786 before this happened to any extent. George Poyser was regularly supervising the production of bricks at Newhaven as well as at Whiston as his invoice shows (R. June 1786): 15,000 bricks at Newhaven and 23,000 at Whiston, plus 'two times comeing over from Whiston to Newhaven for the use of Bricking at 2/6d p.Day'. He also found labourers to grind clay for brick production (23 days) at Whiston. In the same Reckoning, William Dutton worked for 27 days at Whiston at 2s.0d p.day and built a Brick oven at 'Haven' for 16s.0d.

Also, James Ashton the mason billed (R. August 1786) for setting 2,020 cubic feet of stone in three pillars at Whiston and in the same bill for three days spent measuring stone at Sheen quarry for 'furnaces and chimney' – presumably for the lead slag mill.

The Cutting Engine

It has been shown that the regulas was re-smelted several times during the manufacture of fine copper and it was broken down by an edge-runner crusher worked by a horse. This would also include the smelted ore from Ecton. A more efficient system became necessary in 1786, for Wm. Bassett the blacksmith and his brother Ralph were paid for making an 'Ingeon to cut coper with at Wistone'. In September, their invoice covered iron and steel, wood, 'coles' and files for the 'Cutting Engine'. The reference to coal suggests steam and wood suggests a tilt hammer but if it was steam powered, there is no indication of the purchase of a steam cylinder or casting one. Although a small reservoir existed east of the works, there was insufficient water for a waterwheel. In December 1779, there is a reference to water being brought by horse, presumably with a water cart carrying a barrel. Perhaps it was a horse operated crusher.

During 1786 (August Reckoning) 23 tons of copper metal, were sent to Froghall, instigating a different method of despatch. Thirty tons were consigned by the canal in each of the September, November and December Reckonings. Some copper metal was sent via Froghall to the end of the decade. An interesting invoice of this period was when William Hodkinson & Co were paid for nicking 30 tons of copper. They were not stealing it, but were chipping at the ingots on each side and prising a slight gap between the ingot and the piece being prised away. This ensured that when a rope was passed around the ingot, it snagged on the metal that had been prised from the side of the ingot, enabling the latter to be lifted by the rope. This suggests larger ingots and maybe the need to lift them onto a ship or even onto the narrowboat at Froghall.

Copper Metal Sales from 1780

Following the expansion of the Whiston Smelter, the sales for 1780 showed a modest start. Cake copper, sent from Whiston to Jos. Ride's warehouse in Compton, Ashbourne was stockpiled there awaiting sale. Some cake copper is known to have been processed to fine copper at Evans' refinery in Derby in 1780 when some 30 tons was produced.

Sales of cake copper, bearing one of the following initials E.C.T.O.N or H A R D W I C K, were made viz:

	tons	£
Thoyts and Co	12 tons 4 cwt	928
Cazalet & Cooke	12 tons	962
Lilley & Roberts	15 tons	10, 800
		12, 690

This would appear to be after the sales mentioned above.

The following year (1781), Thoyts took 68 tons at £5,386; Cazalet & Cooke 234 tons at £19,375 and the East India Company took 221 tons of 'cake copper, bowls and sheets'. They paid £19,305 for this consignment, including sheet copper at £101 per ton for sheathing ships bound for the tropics. The copper sheets protected the ship's timbers from worm attack, prolonging the life (and value) of the vessel. For convenience these 1781 details are also shown tabulated:

	tons	£
Thoyts & Co	68 tons	5, 386
Gazalet & Cooke	234 tons	19, 375
East India Co	221 tons	19, 305
		44, 066

Cakes produced in the February Reckoning bore the mark 'H', March 'A' and so on, spelling the word HARDWICK over the eight Reckonings.

An account survives for 'Dressing the Mettle Lead and copper at Ecton Mine'. The account was paid entirely to Job White on behalf of 53 people. Of these 16 were males (one person's sex is undetermined). Twelve people were earning less than 6d per day, which probably indicates that they were children. Only three did not sign for their money with a X.

In addition to rolling copper at Evans' works in Derby, in mid-1780, over 18 tons of copper was weighed at 'Heath & Soresby's Warehouse in Derby'.

Thomas Evans' Rolling Mill, Derby

The rolling mills in Derby were established in 1734 in the Morledge on the River Derwent. The works were for rolling and slitting iron and for smelting, rolling and preparing copper for sheathing the navy. (19) Angerstein (20) stated that bars of copper were obtained from nine miles away, which must be Cooper & Rotton of Denby. Three lengths of copper sheet could be produced – 14, 18, 30 inches long. However the works was inactive when he visited it in 1754. A shortage of the Russian iron used for rolling – hoop iron – was to blame. The works used some 150 tons per annum of Russian iron. In 1754, the works belonged to Mr Evans & Mr Storrer, so it would appear a change of proprietors might have taken place. Evans certainly rolled Whiston cake copper, but the volume is unclear. All the cake copper delivered to Derby went via Joseph Ride's Ashbourne warehouse. Sometimes he clearly referred to deliveries to Evans' works. However most payments relate to charges for carriage between Ashbourne and Derby and one cannot tell if this was to a carrier for onward shipment or to Evans's works.

Other rolling was done at Oakamoor, by George Kendal and then by Smith & Knifton (see below).

Deliveries to the Smelters

In 1783, just under $\frac{1}{2}$ ton of charcoal was delivered to Whiston (Deliveries were to grow substantially, see below) and the delivery of 378 loads (probably of 2 cwt each) of lime would seem to indicate further building work, (with 2,000 tiles despatched from Ipstones to Whiston paid in May 1784) following on from 1,000 sent in the previous Autumn by the Caldon Canal Company at Froghall. (The lime was probably from the Caldon Canal Co's lime kiln at Froghall Wharf). The construction work was for a new mill for the breaking down of metal by the 'Cutting Engine'. This would be to reduce the size of regulas prior to it being resmelted.

Some of the fine copper cakes were rolled into sheets, presumably for East India Company or Admiralty contracts. Some appears to have been rolled in Derby (see above under Thomas Evans) and more at Smith & Knifton's rolling mill at Oakamoor. The latter was packed in 'boxes' and a further 114 boxes of them were sent by Thomas Smith from Ashbourne in mid 1784. See note on Smith & Knifton below.

Both Ecton and Whiston appear to have started grinding clay, at least by 1784, together with clay and Barrow lime (quick setting lime from Leicestershire) at Newhaven. In May 1784 at Whiston, there are payments for grinding clay and regulas and these became regular items. In 1784, there was a 'large stone' delivered from Froghall to Whiston, before being taken on to Newhaven, presumably for grinding purposes. This is complicated by a further stone being delivered by Joseph Wardle of Warslow Common for 'grinding at Clay Mill, 10s.0d.' Unfortunately Thomas Bassett of the foundry at Hanging Bridge, Mayfield near Ashbourne could have been more helpful if he had indicated where he sent '4 Quarter Sircles for the Grinding Stone', weighing nearly $1\frac{1}{2}$ tons. Perhaps one stone was for clay and the other for the sand, or to replace the broken one at Ecton (see page 35).

The clay would have been used in the manufacture of bricks, but especially fire bricks used as furnace linings. It is noted elsewhere (see p. 35) that there would appear to have been an edge grinder at Ecton in 1760 and there were clearly others in use, probably one each at Ecton,

Newhaven & Whiston in 1784 with another shown at the Stone Pit on the 1809 plan (see p 11). Rieuwerts (21) states that the earliest documented edge grinder in the area is in 1817 at Cross Grove, Moss Rake, Bakewell. Clearly this can be predated by 57 years at Ecton. Moreover, the 1760 edge grinder, in all probability, still survives on the hillside, or at least half of it!

An indication of the demand for bricks at Whiston survives from the November 1783 Reckoning, just prior to their apparent manufacture at the smelter. John Gilbert & Co. sent 19,584 bricks from Whiston Common 'betwixt 3rd March and 10 July 1783' and a further 10,600 (presumably a different kind) between 8 April – 7 July 1783, totalling 30,184. This one invoice gives a further insight into the business interests of John Gilbert of Cotton. He also owned Ross Pit with his brother, Thomas; the Cauldon Lowe quarry; Clayton Mine at Ecton along with other metaliferous mines in the area and their lead smelter at Dimmingsdale near Alton. (22)

In 1784 at Ecton, a new smelt house (the lead slagmill) was completed as indicated above. The sale and delivery of 5,420 tiles plus 100 Ridge tiles from the Caldon Canal Company at Froghall in August-October 1783 may have been for this building. A further 3,000 tiles were delivered to Ecton in early 1784 and 2,000 more to Whiston. Clearly there was a phase of continuing development at both places at this period. There is however, a need for a short note of caution. In 1785, tiles were collected from the Pen and delivered to Wetton Mill, where a new kiln was being built. (23) This was in the daily course of operations of the mine, so far as delivery to the Pen was concerned, although the cost of delivery from The Pen to Wetton Mill was set against the Wetton Receipts account. The purchase of the tiles also seems to have been set against the mine.

The Ecton furnaces were continually being repaired. Bottom stones or harks, sand and building stone were supplied by Samuel Phillips from Revidge on Warslow Common. The quarry was at the side of the road to Leek, but the site has been subsequently reclaimed (in the 1970s). In August 1780, 50 furnace bottoms were delivered to the mine from Revidge near Warslow indicating some changes there. At the same time, six waggon loads 'of lesser stone' were also delivered by the same carrier, Thomas Shenton (R. August 1780).

J. Wardle had a similar occupation at Whiston. In 1782, Wardle delivered in excess of 80 harks, with three being used to a hearth. This means that some 27-28 hearths were rebuilt during the year – more if any of the stones were reuseable, by turning over etc., which seems likely. This would seem to imply three hearths being changed monthly.

During the same year (1782), he also supplied some 350 tons of sand, crushed from the sandstone in his quarry. He supplied building and paving stones by the yard, so the tonnage is unknown for these, unfortunately. Nonetheless, he must have moved some 400 tons of stone and sand during the year on his one ton cart.

Farey (24) states that 'at Buxton, large edge or rolling stones are used for crushing gritstone to make sand'. Clearly, the same process was in use at Warslow and Whiston thirty years earlier. In the Reckoning of February 1787, William Goodwin was charged for carrying just over 2 tons of sand from 'Oakeover' to Whiston, at 6s.8d per ton. He was a coal carrier from Hazles Cross to Whiston. Perhaps this was a mistake for Oakamoor.

In the ore smelting process outlined above, mention is made of covering the regulas with charcoal in the later part of the process. It is not possible to determine the tonnage involved as it was supplied in sticks, viz: in the same Reckoning of December, 1787, George Smith delivered 1,768 stricks (strikes) of charcoal at 7d per strick (£51.11s.4d). A strike (3½ lbs) x 1,750 equals 2 tons 15¼ cwt exactly). In August 1789 there was a charcoal burner working for the mine at Castern Wood. He had been there at least two years for in December 1786 George Smith submitted his bill for delivering to Whiston 1,768 strikes of charcoal (2¾ tons). The following June 2,243 strikes were delivered (3½ tons). Charcoal was made from cordwood (it was the underwood or tops of larger trees). (25)

In the Reckoning of March 1787 is a bill from John Wharton which clearly indicates that one of the Ecton furnaces was being replaced. In addition to 10 days' work at 3s.0d per day, he was also paid 1s.0d 'when the old furnace was pulled down' and 'custom ale for the new furnace building 6s. 6d'. This may explain the purchase of 5 tons of 'melting pig iron' from the Apedale Furnace, northwest of Newcastle-under-Lyme, Staffs., operated by George Parker & Co. It was sent via Froghall. (26)

This new furnace would appear to be working by around March 1787 for Sampson Hambleton and Co. were moving copper from the 'Round House Pen to the new Smelt House Pen'. Storehouses were known as 'pens' at the mine. A reference to the movement of lead ore from this pen to the 'Lower Cupola' would seem to indicate that the lead mill housed a second cupola. (R. December 1787, Labourers & Smelters Account) There would appear to have been an 'upper pen', presumably near to the Smithy Shaft where the dressed coarse ore was kept prior to smelting.

It was not the slag mill, for at the end of the year, stone was being obtained from Over Holm (between Sheen and Hulme End) for the slag hearth which was not of cupola design. Slate was bought from Cheddleton Wharf on the Caldon Canal and this may have been for the same building. Between January and March 1788, the water channel was completed and ale was bought to celebrate. How the slag mill bellows operated prior to this is not clear.

Copper Metal Production

After 1770, when the Whiston works was built, production in 1770-1775 was a total of 305 tons of metal. Figures for the latter half of the decade are missing except for an audited figure for 1776 of 182 tons, so production was clearly rising.

Using the tonnage of metal dressed from payments to John Orme per Reckoning, it is possible to determine the output, for his figures coincide with the tonnages despatched to Joseph Ride's warehouse in Compton, Ashbourne.

With an absence of sales figures, as indicated above, the dressed cake copper figures of John Orme give a fairly accurate indicator of production. The cake copper metal, once removed from their moulds were trimmed of imperfections – bits of sand, slag or jagged edges presumably. Whatever it was, the tonnages handled each Reckoning period may be added up to give what would appear to be a reasonable figure of smelter output. Incomplete figures are available with gaps each year because documents are sometimes, and frustratingly, missing. However, a reasoned estimate may be made to cover the omissions and a fairly accurate annual figure obtained.

In the 1770s, 1,080 tons of copper were sold. The ore tonnage raised was 8,166 tons which indicates a yield of 13.2% if poorer ores were not being added. If any of the ore raised included lead ore, this would have increased the yield of course. None the less, despite all the 'ifs & buts', the figure indicates a relatively high level of yield most mines could only dream about.

Output in Aug-Dec 1779 was 80 tons, but this may reflect start of work on the extensions. Output in 1780 was about 530 tons, rising to about 600 tons for 1781. In the period to August 1782, 344 tons were made, but then production fell dramatically to a total of 108 tons for the last three Reckonings (giving a figure of 454 tons for the year). This level continued in the February 1783 Reckoning (36 tons) rising to 47 tons in March. It was at this level in December of that year.

Production seems to have risen in 1784, but not by much, although woodash purchases were also rising ($3^1/_2$-4 tons of copper metal were produced to 1lb of woodash).

It may be that there was a difficulty in finding a market. Despite the fact that Ecton copper was supposedly sought after because of its ductile characteristics and the supposed impact on national copper metal supply by Thomas Williams (see Chapter 14) the mine had unsold metal at the end of 1780. A document survives in the Devonshire Collection which shows that at the end of 1780, the smelter had 327 tons of metal unsold. At the end of 1781, this had risen to 397 tons, perhaps worth some £4,000. It may indicate a desire on behalf of the Duke not to enter a price war with Williams. It was a battle he could not have won and cash flow was not a concept particularly understood, one suspects, by the Duke on account of his wealth. Stockpiling of metal for another day was a policy he could afford.

In the period 1780-1785, 13,890 tons of ore were raised and metal output was 2,900 tons. If the yield of ore was 10%, one would expect the metal quantity to be 1,389 tons. This would seem to indicate that the rich ores were not being 'diluted' by the poorer ores, for at 20% richness (the figures quoted by Robert Shore in 1772), the ore tonnage would have 2,778 tons of metal, a figure not too far removed from the suggested output of 2,900 tons.

During 1781, 21,270 'pieces' of copper metal (cakes) were made, weighing approximately half a hundredweight each. The use of the word 'piece' in the document is confusing. With lead ingots, a 'piece' was a term of measurement, there being 16 to a fother. With the copper, it would appear to be the expression of the book-keeper. Total output for 1781 was 567 tons. It will be recalled from above that the cakes originally weighed about 1 cwt.

In the eight Reckonings, the highest output per Reckoning was 92 tons in May, the lowest being 60 tons in August. An analysis of the first half of 1781 (the accounts for the latter half of the year are missing) shows an output of 290 tons of metal. In the same period 320 tons of copper was dressed by John Orme (or at least to his account, he was the head smelter; and about 3,500 tons of coal were delivered).

Lead Smelting

In 1782 a lead smelter was built at Ecton and in the September 1782 Reckoning there are recorded payments to two men employed there – Ralph and Thomas Salt, who were paid 8s.0d per week. There were 21 smelting copper – 16 paid 10s.6d per week and five paid 8s.0d, so the lead smelters were not highly paid by the standard of most of their contemporaries at Ecton.

It was a cupola or reverberatory furnace, in a building with a slate roof (R. February, 1788), built a little distance away from Clayton Adit entrance, beyond the Burgoyne dressing floor. The draught, to maintain high temperatures, was provided by a tall chimney. There was no need to provide a blast to effect the required heat. This was not the case with the lead slag and water power was usually needed to power waterwheel driven bellows. For some reason, the provision of water did not commence until a year later. It came from the Fish Pond at East Ecton. This took some time, for the water had to be brought around the hill via Apes Tor. It was 1784 before the slag mill with its blast furnace was ready. There may have been a waterwheel at the mine already for in October 1781, three 'bends' for a wheel were purchased (R. May, 1782), containing 77 feet 'solid' timber.

The lead smelter had a flue which is thought to have been laid straight up the hill towards Hamnook Mine, your author has not investigated this. However an initial length of flue was given a stone covering extending to 19 $\frac{1}{2}$ yards. It cost 1s.0d a yard (R. September 1782). The oldest flue in a Peak District cupola was built in 1778 at the Upper Cupola in Middleton Dale.

It was usual for cupolas to have a horizontal length of flue in which to reduce the toxicity of the fumes and smoke. With a condensing chamber often built into them, lead residues were often precipitated, which were then put back into the furnace.

Lead ore tonnages were not great however. There are no records for 1781-2. In 1783 output seems to have been at least 365 tons. The figures for 1784 are far from complete as the records are largely missing. It is unknown if the Duke's lead ore from the Wetton area was used here. Farey records that the lead ore from the Warslow mines was particularly difficult to smelt because 'of the extraneous matters which the shale seems to communicate to it'. (27) Ecton lead ore would not be in this category, being obtained from limestone beds. (29)

The Ecton mine purchased unburnt bricks and either fired them in the furnaces or used them unburnt (they would be fired during smelting). If the former, this could have been transferred to the lead smelter following increased output from the copper furnaces.

The possible need for supplementary ores, mentioned above, focuses one's thoughts on the adjacent Clayton Mine. The mine was rich in copper, but with a significant amount of lead ore. The Chadwick Lead Mine, at Back Ecton, was essentially a large 'stringer' to the Clayton ore-body in fact and in the 1880s, the manager complained that the vein in Clayton was yielding a mix of copper and lead ores, which increased costs of ore dressing. The mine was possibly a interface between the copper deposits and the lead ores prevalent to the south. The Duke of Devonshire was also a 1/12th shareholder in Clayton. It has been noted in Chapter 2 that the lead ore is likely to have come from pipe veins above their contact with a saddle bed zone. Did the lead smelter use Clayton lead ore?

In order to reduce the temperature of ores which were more difficult to smelt, it was usual to add a flux. This tended to be calcite or fluorspar. The latter must have been the better of the two, for calcite rather than fluorspar predominated at Ecton. It would have been found in large quantities in the mineralised areas of the saddle beds underneath the copper ore particularly, according to Watson (see Chapter 2).

The fluorspar was bought from Henry Knowles of Masson Mine, Matlock. Farey confirms that it was used at Ecton as a flux (30) and also wrote that 'there is a consumption of the yellow and interior kinds of this spar [fluor] at Ecton copper works from Knowles' Mine.' (31). It was initially supplied at the rate of 30-40 tons per Reckoning (say 250-300 tons per annum), delivered via Brightgate, west of Matlock, where it was picked up. Early in 1785, deliveries drop to very low amounts. Much of Henry Knowles' fluorspar mine has now disappeared as a result of late 20th century opencast working for fluor (32). In August 1785, Joseph Bower was paid for 2 days and a horse 'fetching to the mine different spars', but no more is known.

It is probable that different 'spar' to that of Henry Knowles was used in the lead smelter, for in January 1789 there is an invoice 'To the Executors of the late Mr John Twigg for spar for the use of the lead smelting from 7/2/1788 to the 7/2/1789'; 98 tons had been bought at 1s.0d per ton. The previous year it had been 89 tons (R. March 1788).

The lead mill would have had a tall chimney to create the necessary draught, but presumably much of this was hidden in the mill building. See Fig 9.3 for a drawing of a typical lead or copper ore cupola smelter. (33) This same article describes the mills and reducing processes of both the lead smelter and the slag mill. It also covers the earlier ore hearth, but this is not relevant as Ecton's mill was the ore hearth's replacement – the cupola or reverberatory furnace.

An invoice exists from a George Noble for the period (1 June-28 August 1783) for the supply of bricks which may have been for the lead cupola furnace, despite the date suggesting the slagmill (see below). If it is the former, a rebuild so soon after its completion is unusual and it therefore may suggest a second cupola. (R. November.1783). The invoice was for 3,054 Circular bricks; 646 Narrow square; 412 Large square; 509 Arch bricks; 1,563 Furnace roofs; 213 Large flues and 639 Large keys. The slagmill illustration indicates that it did not have an arched roof (see p.149) and may therefore be discounted.

In February 1784, Joseph Bowler and seven other smelters were 'assisting to repair lead furnaces 117 days'. This was over 2 weeks work for the eight men, who were paid 16d each per day – double the usual daily pay. What the problem was is not revealed in the accounts.

A description of the smelting process and both the cupola and slagmill is given by Dr Lynn Willies in a good article on lead smelting. (33) The quote starts with a description of the cupola (but not specifically the Ecton cupola). However the design had 'settled down' and there is unlikely to have been much that was different. Ecton was probably the only lead cupola in Staffordshire and the only one on a mine in the Peak. All the rest were in or north of Middleton Dale near Stoney Middleton or largely east of a line drawn roughly from Chesterfield to Wirksworth via Matlock. A notable exception was the Alport smelter east of Youlgreave and that did not open until 1847. There were less than 20 in the Peak when Ecton's lead cupola was built.

Willies quotes Bishop Watson of c.1780 viz:

'The furnace is so contrived, that the ore is melted, not by coming into contact with the fuel, but by the reverberation of the flame upon it. The bottom of the furnace, on which the lead ore is placed, is somewhat concave, shelving from the sides towards the middle; its roof is low and arched, resembling the roof of a baker's oven; the fire is placed at one end of the furnace, upon an iron grate, to the bottom of which the air has access; at the other end, opposite the fire place, is a high perpendicular chimney; the direction of the flame when all the apertures in the side of the furnace are closed up, is necessarily determined by the stream of air which enters at the grate, towards the chimney, and intending hither it strikes upon the roof of the furnace, and being reverberated from thence upon the ore it soon melts it.

They generally put into the cupola-furnace a ton of ore, previously beat small, and properly dressed, at one time; this quantity they call a charge; if the ore is very poor in lead, they put in somewhat more, and they work off three charges of ore in every twenty four hours. In about six hours from the time of charging, the ore becomes as fluid as milk. Before the ore becomes fluid, and even whilst it continues in a state of fusion, a considerable portion of its weight is carried off through the chimney; what remains in the furnace consists of two different substances – of the lead... and of the slag or scoria... the lead being heavier than the slag, sinks through it as it is formed, and settles into the concavity in the bottom of the furnace.... . In order to obtain the lead free from the slag... the smelters usually throw in a bushel of lime... to dry up the slag ... (which) is raked towards the side of the furnace. There is a hole in one of the sides of the furnace, which is properly stopped during the smelting of the ore; when the slag is raked off this hole is opened, the lead gushes through it into an iron pot placed contiguous to the side of the furnace.'

This process was then repeated for the lime/slag mixture which yielded a further small quantity of lead, after which a further charge of lead ore was let into the hearth. Watson remarked also that recently a second and higher tap hole had been introduced by which the liquid slag was let off without the use of lime. The furnace was then known as a macaroni, from the form of the slag as it cooled upon the floor. (34)

The usual furnace was constructed of ashlar gritstone, lined with firebrick bound with clay and lime, and strapped together with iron bars to withstand stresses. The bottom of the hearth was constructed over a vault to protect from moisture, and was made in the form of a tiled saucer, with the one or two tap holes plugged with lime on the lower side. The bricks were preserved and the shape of the bottom maintained by a layer of slag 15 to 30cm deep, which was repaired daily between charges, and sometimes more fully 'run' at weekends.

The top of the furnace was also arched – the Derbyshire furnace was often referred to as 'low arched' – the form of the arch designed to focus and distribute the heat as effectively as possible. A hole in the top of the arch, the crown hole, was surmounted by a wooden hopper in which the next charge was kept ready. The hearth into which the ore was placed was kept separate from the coal fire by means of the firebridge, a low wall. Flames and hot gases from the coal fire were drawn over the hearth by the draught from the tall chimney, the heating effect coming from the reverberation. Early furnaces were usually contiguous to the chimney, but later it became normal for smaller or longer lengths of horizontal flue to be interposed. The front of the furnace was known as the smelter's or working side with three small doors into the hearth, the sump pot, and also an ashpit. Lead, and in later years, the tapped slag, was drawn off at this side, the former into the iron pot of about 110 litres (25 gallons) capacity which was kept hot by its own small fire. Tapped slag was allowed to run on to the floor where it solidified, to be broken up and removed when cool. On the opposite, or labourer's side, was the firehole, and three more air doors, from which drawn slag, i.e. not molton, was raked out.

Regulation of the furnace was by means of the doors, both the fire doors, and also the three air doors on each side. By closing all the doors the fire was drawn more effectively, and the furnace raised to a high temperature, whilst the restriction of air led to reducing conditions. Opening of the doors led to gentler heat and oxidising conditions. The actual operation was something of an acquired art, some five or six (35) sorts of ore requiring to be mixed for the best results. The first operation after a short heat was a gentle heating with the doors open to roast the ore, during which it was turned over by rabbles. This was followed by a quick heat with a mixture of lime and coal (36) in reducing conditions, to secure the release of the metal which was then tapped off, with sometimes also the liquid portion of the slag. This was followed by one or more even stronger heats to release much more of the metal as possible, at the end of which the metal and slags were tapped or drawn off and the furnaces recharged.

Early furnaces, and those in other areas, seem generally to have been charged with rather more ore than later. About 0.8 or 0.9 tons (16 or 18 cwt) appears to have been more normal in the early nineteenth century. (37) The average yield was about 66%, but good ore could produce somewhat more, though it had been less in the early years. The time taken to smelt was also reduced, due probably in part to design improvements to the furnace, as an unspecified improvement to the fire at Stonedge (38), which allowed the temperature and speed of reaction to be raised, allowing also for the slag to be tapped and probably the omission of one of the reheats, the slag being further treated in the slagmill. Thus it took about twelve hours in the 1760s (39), of which half was used for the first operation though this was much reduced by the end of the century. By Farey's time (40) the whole operation was complete in about eight hours. Fuel consumption also tended to decline: at Olda in the 1740s the ration of ore to coal was about 1:1 or even higher. By the early 19th century the consumption was only half this.

Apart from the possible late use of iron plates about the furnace, design changes were mainly minor adjustments to dimensions, and perhaps surprisingly no consensus seems to have emerged. Possibly the fairly frequent rebuildings which were necessary, every seven or ten years or so, encouraged experiment. The main changes were in the hearth dimensions and form, with the triple intention of saving time, fuel, and lead loss in slag or fume. Illustrations of every furnace show the hearth had an elliptical form, which by the time of Jar's visit (41) was about 9 by 7 feet.

Other minor improvements or changes included the size of fire grate, particularly the height of the firebridge, and the gap between it and the roof – generally this was about 17 or 18 inches. In early furnaces the chimney is usually depicted as coming vertically from the furnace (42), but later versions as Stonedge had the horizontal flue to a free-standing chimney'. (43) Ecton seems to have had its chimney within the smelter building.

Slags

Lead was lost in both ore hearth and cupola processes to the slags either by chemical bonding or interstitially. In the latter case, crushing and washing as for lead ores affected a primary separation, and in the eighteenth century this was the normal treatment, the heavier fraction only being resmelted.

The amount of lead in slag could be reduced by increasing the temperature of the furnace, since tapped slag had much less lead remaining than had drawn, but this often could be attained only by increased loss of lead in the fume: Watson remarked (44) that he had seen much lead lost in this way which might have been saved by a gentler fire. Presence of fluxes, notably fluorspar, but also apparently calcite contributed to the slaggy proportion being melted at a lower temperature, and with difficult ores where it was not already present, fluorspar was added, as at Ecton. (45) The mixing of several varieties of ore probably had a similar purpose. It is possible iron oxide or other iron compounds were added to improve fluxing and lower the temperatures necessary for separation, (but not, it seems, at Ecton).

In March 1788, limestone might have been used – or perhaps calcite, from Wetton Hill. See 'Easing Stone' under Terms (Chapter 15).

The Slag Hearth or Mill

The basic slag hearth was of simple construction with an open topped rectangular shaft about three feet high, with a tuuyere entering about half way up the rear. The tapping opening was at the front base. Fuel was coke, or cinder from the cupola fire. Molten material was run into a hollow in front of the furnace, the slag either floating on the lead, or separated from it by riddled cinder, through which the lead could run to the bottom, but which the lighter and thicker slag could not penetrate. In later hearths the slag was run into water, which caused it to granulate for rewashing, or sometimes was allowed to run over the floor, to be broken with a sledge hammer.

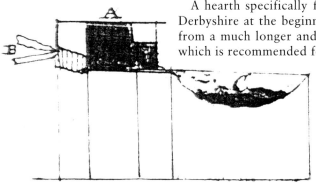

A hearth specifically for slag smelting was certainly in use in Derbyshire at the beginning of the 18th century. This extract is from a much longer and well researched article by Lynn Willies which is recommended for further information.

R.R. Angerstein, a 18th Century industrial spy, visited Derbyshire in 1754. (46) He described a lead reverbatory furnace 'two miles from Crich on the way to Matlock Bath'. He described it as having 'a chimney to take away the fumes from the slag that falls down from the grate. The furnace is charged with one ton of galena, previously mixed in the ore store with pitcoal and limestone. Smelting takes nine hours. The wages for the workers at the furnace are 8 shillings per week' [the same as at Ecton in 1784, thirty years later].

Fig 9.4 The Ecton Slag Mill, drawn by Watson. A: is the ore furnace; B: the bellows; C: the receptacle into which the molten metal ran.

He then described the slagmill: 'A little farther down there was another furnace in operation, blown by bellows approximately two feet square and long, provided with a crucible at the front to receive the molten lead and slag. The type of coal used here is known as coke or coked pitcoal. Slag from the reverbatory furnaces was being smelted'. The text is accompanied by drawings of the reverbatory furnace (or cupola) and the slagmill. The arrangement at Ecton must have been similar to this, although the cupola at Ecton probably had a flue along the ground to the chimney. (47)

A notebook compiled by White Watson includes a drawing of the Ecton copper smelter and the lead slag mill. (48) The drawings, see Figs. 9.4 and 9.5, are crude and give no dimensions, but nonetheless, they are invaluable. The drawing of the copper furnace is clearly a standard cupola and was within a building. The purpose of the slagmill is given as being to retrieve lead from copper slags. This is different from the purpose given by Dr Hatchet, see below. It is comparable however. The slag mill could be used for the recovery of both lead and copper. The notes with the diagrams (which are not in the handwriting of White Watson) confirmed that the heat was produced at the slag mill by two bellows, worked by a waterwheel. They confirm that the slag was mixed with 'coak', which had been made at Hazles Cross since the late 1780s. The buildings containing the slag fur-

Fig 9.5 The Ecton Cupola-type Copper Furnace. A: where they put in the ore; B: where they tap; C: fire

nace had a slate roof rather that a tiled one (R.February 1788).

Dr Hatchet, writing in 1796 (49) stated 'At this Mine they roast the copper ore but do not smelt it. The galena is not now smelted here but it is carried to near Cheadle, but the lead slag is here worked over again in what is called a Slag Hearth worked with bellows. The second slag contains copper and is again smelted for it'. He must have been incorrect in writing that the galena was carried to near Cheadle: presumably he meant copper. The bellows appear to have been 30-inch Broad Bellows, costing four guineas (£4.4s.0d) and purchased from John Linley of Sheffield in May 1786. They seem to have been supplied through an agent, Samual Marshall, who also paid for files and handsaws bought off S.A.Bates and a new smith's anvil weighing 2 cwt and costing £3.12s.0d, bought of S.Hill. The firms were probably in the Sheffield area. The anvil seems to have been delivered to Monyash, from where it was collected.

By May 1788, production of lead from slag was well established. The smelting of the slags to retrieve more metal was contracted to Green & Co. – James Green (paid 15s.0d per week), Theodorus Howard (paid 10s.0d) and Chris Green who helped out for just one week at 15s.0d in the Reckoning ending 3 May.

The Ecton Lead Mill

The Ecton lead cupola and slagmill is shown on Potter's map of 1809. It is an L-shaped building with the waterwheel furthest away from the road at the rear of the building, fed by the waterchannel from the Fish Pond. The channel also fed a long building stretching almost to the Clayton Adit entrance and which must be the Burgoyne dressing floor. It appears that the slagmill was built with its tailrace water being used by the Burgoyne dressers.

If this assumption is correct, the wheel would have been overshot, with buckets rather than paddles. The wheel provided power for bellows to create the blast required to smelt the slag. Prior to the erection of the slagmill, it is likely that the slag was retained for smelting once conditions were available. In all probability both the cupola and slagmill were together. The slagmill furnace mentioned by Angerstein (50) was 2 feet square and long and did not have a chimney. Its situation was more accommodating for a flue and if avoidance of the smoke was of any consideration, the site beyond the Clayton dressing floor looks preferable. Potter's plan of 1809 seems to indicate a chimney on the corner of the building nearest the mine (north-east corner); see page 11.

The erection of the lead slag mill also involved the construction of a watercourse from the Fishpond. The period of construction saw the collection of bars of cast steel 'melted from the Best Bar Iron'. The same delivery also included (from Messrs Marshall of Sheffied) '3 faggotts Newcastle spun steel 120 lbs each'. In November 1787, Joseph Gregory charged for two pairs of bellow pipes and Thomas Gregory carried them from Sheffield to Monyash. The same invoice included payment for a man sent 'seeking planks' and a team sent to Sheffield to collect the same. This is confused by the next entry on the bill for 'Two teames taking the planks to Curbar....' These planks were for the buckets of the overshot waterwheel which powered the lead slag mill. The need to go to Sheffield is curious. Of all the timber sent to the mine, none of the invoices mentions elm and one wonders if the planks were elm and this accounted for the need to fetch planks from Sheffield. There was no local shortage of oak, ash, beech etc., but none of these would be best suited for a waterwheel.

The planks were delivered to Curbar by two teams and a team sent 'to Sheffield' to collect planks was probably heading to Curbar to bring them onto the mine. The former charged 13s.8d and the latter 6s.0d, so the delivery cost was just short of £1. The steel mentioned above was delivered to 'SM' – probably Stoney Middleton – and fetched from there.

Four bulls' hides were purchased from Richard Buxton (R.December, 1787) in Ashbourne, to provide the leather for the bellows and a Mathew Fearn provided the arms, axle and shafting for the waterwheel. The wheel diameter would appear to have been 32ft. The wood appears to have come from Bakewell – or at least the 'mill armes' or spokes which were 15ft long. The timber purchased for the wheel included two millshafts 11½ feet each, one 21 inches square and the other 22 inches square, plus two 'cants in the round' both 6 feet long, one 18 inches square and the other 19 inches. The largest one is likely to have been the mill axle or wheel-shaft. The other mill shaft could have been to convey the power away from the wheel-pit to the bellows site, either in the same direction as the wheel shaft or at a right angle to it in plan.

The necessity of a second shaft was presumably because of the distance or direction, to allow a pair of gears to be inserted between the two drives to enable a stage of gearing up or down to be achieved. The 'Cants in the Round' could then be the final drives to the two sets of bellows, with cams mortised in to operate the bellows. Why the drives and the Cants have slightly different cross-sectional dimensions is not clear. (51) Additionally, slate for the roof was from Froghall, Cheddleton and Leek canal wharves and two wagon loads of stone from the Roaches, north of Leek was also delivered, but the exact purpose of this is unclear. At the end of 1787, the watercourse was still under construction. The stone, with its channel cut in the top to a depth of about six inches and a foot in width continued to be delivered from Sheen, with a limestone cover delivered from Wetton Hill Quarry. Why this job was taking so long is not known. A calculation of the wheel diameter is important, as will be explained below. The mill arms were 15 feet each side of the axle. Adding the latter gives approximately 31ft 6ins (a little less assuming the arms were mortised). Add the buckets and a width of about 32ft may be assumed.

When the work wound down with the failure of the ore deposit, the smelters eventually became redundant. In 1823, the water engine(s) used for pumping was replaced by a waterwheel. Its size is known – 32ft by 6ft. (52) Clearly the slagmill waterwheel found a new lease of life pumping the mine water and was re-erected adjacent to the Water Engine Shaft. Here it survived until the aqueduct at Apes Tor, which brought the water to turn it, collapsed. This happened possibly c.1856 although the mine had been allowed to fill with water from 1850. (53) It is traditionally held that the mine took seven years to fill with water.

An examination of the site of the slagmill reveals no sign of the leat on the bank of the river. This is because another leat begins a few feet above where it would have reached the river. It also affected the siting of the dam to the second leat, which from 1818 took water to the Stamps Yard waterwheel at Swainsley. Here ore was crushed mechanically until the mid-1860s. The slagmill leat must run into the second leat which runs behind the river bank wall adjacent to the river.

Lead Ingots

The lead was cast in pigs which were marked by the letters H.A.R.D.W.I.C.K. and E.M.P.L.O.Y.S. Metallic lead from the main smelting process was cast in moulds with a round end. Lead extracted from the slag had a square end. Whether EMPLOYS marked the latter is not known, but possible as none of these letters occurs in the more valuable HARDWICK. Each letter consisted of 100 'pieces'. A 'piece' weighed as close to 168¾lbs as possible (approximately 1½ cwt). The 100 'pieces' therefore weighed about 7¾ tons, or a little less. Each lot of 100 pieces weighed differently, as the exact weight depended upon when the furnace man stopped pouring the molton lead. There were 16 'pieces' to a 'fother'.

The movement of such heavy loads did not come cheap. It was taken from the mine and warehoused at Newhaven. Much of this activity was undertaken by a couple of carriers, including William Mellor of West Side Mill, Ecton. Often it went as part of a double load – lead to Newhaven; clay and brick from there to the mine. This cost 3s.0d per ton. If there was no back carriage it was 4s.0d per ton.

From Newhaven, it was collected and delivered by John Bown to Derby at 13s.0d per ton, the cost increased by toll charges on the roads. The principal market for lead was Hull, so unless the mine had a customer, presumably the ingots went down the River Trent to Stockwith, where it would have been loaded onto ships for the rest of the journey down the River Humber. No Ecton ingots are known to have survived.

Angerstein (54) reported in 1754 that the River Trent was navigable up to both Burton-on-Trent and Derby (sic) i.e. the River Derwent was navigable to Derby from the River Trent.

The River Derwent downstream from Derby remained navigable until 1794 when the Derby Canal was completed. The River Trent to Burton Bridge from Shardlow was discontinued in 1805 in favour of the Trent and Mersey Canal. (55) In January 1789, ingots of slag lead were being taken to Froghall, but the name of the customer and the destination are unknown.

Froghall and The Caldon Tramway

In 1776-78, a railway was built between Froghall Wharf and the limestone quarry at Cauldon Lowe. It was the first railway using iron rails to be built with an authority derived from a legislative enactment. (56) The railway was realigned in 1785, but there are no records of it being used to bring materials to the Whiston works. A sketch of Froghall Wharf dated 1795 shows a brick kiln at the western end of the battery of limekilns. References to the supply of bricks and tile from Froghall must relate to this kiln rather than to products coming down the canal. (57) Until 1785, the canal wharf was at the western end of the tunnel. The latter, dating from 1785, was part of an extension of the canal to the current wharf which is of the same date. Thereafter the tramway commenced from the new wharf and the brick kiln must date from this time too. Was there a brick kiln near the initial wharf? It seems reasonable to suggest that this may have been the case. The cost of rebuilding the kiln would not be expensive.

At the side of the road to Ipstones, virtually over the tunnel existed The Navigation Inn. This would appear to have, in all probability, been built prior to 1785 and did not relocate to the new site. No new inn was built at the new wharf. Carriers heading for Ecton up the turnpike road to Ipstones would no doubt know of this inn. (58)

Smith & Knifton, Oakamoor

The works of Smith & Knifton at Froghall commenced operations as a slitting mill in the 17th century. This was a process where sheet metal was cut into strips for drawing into wire. By 1761, the buildings were in use as a tin plating works. In July of that year John Ludvig Robsahm, a Swedish industrialist, recorded his visit to the works:

> 'The rolls were only 15 inches long. The iron that was rolled was English, but made of American pig iron. The mill furnace was long and narrow and was not provided with a fireplace by the side which could produce a flame because the coal was placed inside the furnace itself. The fire was practically burnt down before the furnace was charged with bars or sheets when 8 of them were put in, three on each side and two in the middle. The iron in the furnace was carefully watched, so that as soon as a piece became a little hotter than worm-red it was taken out for rolling and another charged into the furnace to replace it. Each bar or pack of sheets was given five to six passes through the rolls in the same heat until it no longer showed any red when another bar or pack was taken out from the furnace and rolled in the same way. When the sheet had become so long that it could be folded it was dubbled, heated again and rolled until it could be folded again to a pack of four. This pack was reheated and rolled to a length that permitted a third folding resulting in a pack of eight. Yet another reheating followed after which the sheets were rolled to the desired final length and thickness. During this operation the temperature had to be watched particularly carefully as an overheating would cause the sheets to stick together.
>
> The folded edges of the pack were sheared off and the sheets separated and placed in a mixture of fat, salt and some kind of acid so that it would be easier to remove the scale during the scouring which was carried out with sand. I was not able to find out the exact composition of the mixture, but it did smell worse than anything else nasty that I could think of.

After the scouring the sheets were rolled again by another mill driven by the same waterwheel as the first one, but located in a separate workshop. The rolling was done cold without heating the sheets and made them flat and smoothed before they were tinned. The tinning took place in pots three feet in length and about six inches wide and the tin was kept molten by a fire beneath them. The tin was covered by a half inch thick layer of fat to prevent oxidisation of the metal by excluding the air. After the first dip the sheets were turned upside-down and dipped again. Excess tin was removed by a brush or wad of 'cotton waste'. (59)

This account is of interest for it must have been a similar type of roller which turned Whiston fine copper from cakes into sheets for the East India Company and other purchasers. The 'boxes' used for transporting the tinned sheets were also used by Whiston and there are references to the supply and repair of boxes for the copper sheets by the Oakamoor Works.

At this time, the works was being run by George Kendall, who had business interests in other parts of the country. He entered into a partnership in 1771 with Johnathan and Henry Kendall (presumably relatives) and John & Thomas Hopkins. This partnership had a capital of £10,000. The latter two were operating ironworks in Shropshire, Staffordshire and Cheshire. (60) The works became part of a much larger organisation covering those counties. However this arrangement did not last long. The last reference to George Kendall in the Ecton accounts was in July 1779, for rolling iron. The earliest record of Smith & Knifton, Kendall's successors is in May 1780. (61)

The tin plated sheets were polished and despatched in boxes, containing 225 sheets or plates, each about $13\frac{3}{4}$ in by 10 in in size and weighing about 1 cwt per box. (62) Smith & Knifton supplied copper sheets rolled from cakes sent from Whiston. It is unclear why the latter did not invest in a rolling mill for this purpose. Larger quantities of cake copper was rolled at Thomas Evan's works in Derby and although the nature of the contract for copper sheets (for the Navy's warm water fleets) was fickle, it seems strange that the investment was not made. Presumably the lack of water power was the problem.

The actual Ecton invoice for Smith & Knifton of May 1780 does not survive, but one does for the next Reckoning in June 1780. This was for the supply of just over 1 cwt of 'Black Plate' (tinned iron sheets). The order consisted of 24 plates in total, with an average weight of 6lb 6oz. This is significantly more than the 8oz iron-tinned sheets mentioned above (= 225 per 1cwt or thereabouts). The reference to Smith & Knifton in May 1780 predates Herbert

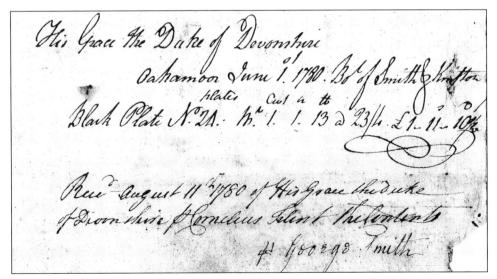

An invoice for Smith & Knifton for 'black plate' (tinned iron), paid on 11 August, 1780

Chester's thinking, as their lease of the works was not agreed until 1784 (from the lessor, Robert Foley). Either they took an assignment from Kendall or the lawyers seemed dilatory in the extreme.

The purpose behind the purchase of these plates is not known and it could not have been for the tank on the end of the Water Engine Beam, which was made three years later. How nice it would have been to have speculated differently!

Smith & Knifton found regular work rolling copper sheets for Whiston but in 1790, the works was purchased by the Cheadle Copper & Brass Company and used as

This building was built by R. Leigh & Co in 1792 on the Smith & Knifton site, as the plaque indicates. Leigh & Co was a Cheadle Copper & Brass Company subsidiary. The building is now demolished.

a copper rolling mill, the tin plating work seemingly run down and it was soon abandoned. (63)

The tin plate works was the only one built in Staffordshire in the 18th century of which the location is known. (58) However as has been seen above, the VCH is incorrect in stating that the date it was built was 1777. There are occasional references to the purchase by the mine of tin-plate. In August, 1782, the mine purchased 51 yards of tin pipes from Smith & Knifton. In R. December 1787, there is an invoice for 25 sheets of tin at 7d each.

References

1   Chatsworth; Dev.Coll. Plan Press

2   Althin T., Eric Geisler & his Journey Abroad 1772-1773, *Med hammare och Fackla*, Vol XXVI, pp 53-127

3   Hughes, S., *Copperopolis*, 2000, p 26

4   Hughes, S., op.cit. p 27

5   Hughes, S., op.cit. p 25

6   Garner, R., *History of Staffordshire*, 1844, p 513

7   Rieuwerts, J., *Dictionary of Derbyshire Lead Mining Terms*, 1998, p 82

8   Day, J., *Bristol Brass*, 1973, pp 54-55

9   Richardson, JB., *Metal Mining*, 1974, pp 104-05

10 Garner, R., op. cit.,1844

11 Confirmation that the works was extended rather than just rebuilt is provided by Farey. J., 1811, op.cit.p 353

12 Porter, L., & Robey, J.A., op. cit p. 239

13 Morton, J., *Thomas Bolton & Sons Ltd, 1783-1983*, 1983, privately printed

14 Dev.Coll. AS/800

15 Dev.Coll. AS/623 Account of Sales of Copper at Derby, Gainsborough & London 1775 - 1780

16 pers. comm. the late Edward Paget-Tomlinson

17 Porter, L., & Robey, *The Copper & Lead Mines around the Manifold Valley* 2000, pp 135-37

18 Somers Key (sometimes spelt Somar's) was on the south side of Thames Street, fronting the river, next to Billingsgate west. Horben's *A Dictionary of London*, p 538

19 Glover, S., *The History & Directory of the Borough of Derby*, 1843, p 80

20 op. cit., p 202

21 Rieuwerts, J.H., *Glossary of Derbyshire Lead Mining Terms*, 1998, p 54

22 Porter. L., & Robey, J.A., *Copper & Lead Mines Around the Manifold Valley*, 2000, pp 67-68, 204-05

23 Dev. Coll., AS/1471

24 Farey J., General view of the agriculture & minerals of Derbyshire, 1811, Vol. I, p 463

25 VCH Derbyshire p 422 quoting Farey, 1815, Vol 2, ch 9

26 Apedale Furnace was established c.1768 as a coke furnace by the Parker family. The invoice included a note from Abraham Parker soliciting more business

27 Farey, op.cit., p 390. The 'Warslow mines' would appear to be a reference to the Hayesbrook mine near Warslow Hall. In the two years 1805-06, 830 and 873 tons of lead ore were raised out of the shale beds above the limestone at Hayesbrook. Once the limestone was reached, the vein pinched out to an insignificant scrin. The best quality lead ore was termed 'bull bouse', the only known reference to this term. (28) The lead (galena) was sold to Sykes, Milnes & Co by the mine owners – the Dale Mine Co., – it was not smelted with the Ecton lead ore.
    There is a traditional story that once the Hayesbrook Mine reached the limestone, it was drowned out by water held beneath the shale covering. The miners are understood to have had to run for their lives and six or seven men failed to get out and were sealed in the mine. The account by Watson does not mention this. Indeed his description of the vein (see above) indicated that it was worked in the limestone, at least to some extent, hoping that the scrin opened out. The best of the ore was reached at a depth of 12 or 14 fathoms. It is known that a Newcomen Engine existed at the mine, early in the nineteenth century, so pumping of water, even from a relatively shallow depth is inferred. Perhaps the lead ore had a higher sulphur content or something similar, resulting in it being harder to smelt.

28 W. Watson's Scrapbook, Derby Local Studies Library

29 Thanks to Jim Rieuwerts and Roger Flindall for providing this information – Jim for retrieving it and Roger for locating it in the first place

30 Farey, op.cit., p 392

31 op.cit., p 461

32 Ford, T.D., Geology of the Matlock Mines, a review, 2001, *Bull. PDMHS.*, Vol.14, No. 6. pp1-34

33 From Willies L., Derbyshire lead Smelting in the Eighteenth and Nineteenth Centuries, *Bull. PDMHS.*, 1990, Vol II, No 1. pp 6 & 8. A special thanks to Lynn

34 Watson, W., *Chemical Essays*, 1793, pp274-92

35 Farey op.cit., p 388

36 Jars, G., *Voyages Metallurgiques*, Tomell, p 551

37 Farey op.cit., p 386

38 White Watson, *The Strata of Derbyshire*, 1811 p 57

39 Jars op.cit., pp 550-51

40 Farey, J. op.cit., p 390

41 Jars., op.cit., p 227

42 e.g. Jars., 1780 plate 27

43 Farey op.cit., p 387

44 Watson, W., op.cit., p 288

45 Farey op.cit., p 392

46 Borg, T. & P., (translators), R R Angerstein's *Illustrated Travel Diary, 1753-1755*, 2001

47 op.cit., p 206

48 Derbys. Record Office, Microfilm M878 – originals with Mr Bradbury of Winster, thanks to Dr Jim Rieuwerts for finding this and forwarding it on

49 Hatchet, Dr., *A tour through the counties of England and Scotland in 1796 visiting mines and manufactories*, edited by A Raistrick,1967, p 66

50 Borg, T., op.cit., p 206

51 Thanks to Alan Stoyel for providing this information

52 Anon, *Ashbourne and the Valley of the Dove, 1839*, p 154

53 Porter L., and Robey J.A., op.cit., pp 82-83

54 Borg, T., op.cit., p 194

55 Farey, J., op.cit., Vol 1, p 470

56 Lead P., *Agents of Revolution: John & Thomas Gilbert – Entrepreneurs*, 1989, p 85

57 Jeuda B., *The Limestone Quarries of Caldon Low*, Pt 1, Archive Magazine, 19/9/1998, p 19

58 A photograph of this building exists in Porter, L. & Walton, C., *The Staffordshire Moorlands and Churnet Valley*, 2000, p 39

59 Quoted by Chester, H., *Churnet Valley Iron*, 2003, pp 69-70

60 Victoria County History (VCH): *Staffordshire*, Vol 2 p 173. The minute book of Cheadle Brassworks records on 12/02/1763 that Mr Robert Hurst bought 3 cwt 2 st 12 lbs of black plates from Kendall & Co at 24s. 0d per cwt for £4.6.7d and also 13 furnace bars weighing 6 cwt at 10s. 0d per cwt

61 A Kendall iron furnace building and waterwheel of 1755 survives at Furnace just out of Machynlleth on the road to Aberystwyth in Wales. It is cared for by Cadw – the Welsh equivalent of English Heritage. It also had two bellows driven by a (more recent replacement) waterwheel, the same as the Ecton Slagmill. The bellows were worked by cams (little iron pieces) which stood proud of the waterwheel-driven shafting rotated by the wheel axle. These cams pressed down on the top half of the bellows as the shaft rotated. Once the cam reached the underside of the shaft, it disconnected allowing the bellows top to lift back up and refill with air. While this was happening, another cam had engaged with the other pair of bellows, allowing two blasts for every rotation of the shafting

62 VCH: op.cit., p 173

63 Chester, op.cit., pp 73-74. The minutes of the Cheadle Company of 3/8/1790 states that 'the Oakamoor Mill be emptied at present in the tin trade and not altered for making wire and that the debt due to the Rev. Thos. Hurst (£2,572.3.8d) from the Old Wire Co. be paid into this concern as soon as possible to furnish capital for purchasing the mill and carrying on the trade'. At the meeting of 8/10/1790 it was agreed that 'Oakamoor Mill be altered to Roll & Slit Brass & Cu and to draw thick wire and Guinea Rods and that the tin trade be carried on as usual.' The Company did leave the tin trade, however, for the Company agreed to re-enter the trade again at Oakamoor in November 1807.

64 VCH, op.cit., Vol 2, p 173

Roads and Transportation

The efficient running of the mine depended upon the road system reaching out from it. Whether it was the mundane and myriad footpaths which linked the mine with neighbouring villages where its workforce lived or the new and supposedly well maintained turnpike roads, they all had their part to play in enabling the exploitation and development of the mine to continue apace.

Although it has been possible to piece together some of the history of these roads, it has highlighted that much more remains unearthed. To some extent this was a blessing in disguise, as it would have been easy to stray into the realm of transport history rather than mining history. There definitely lies much fertile ground for an aspiring research historian on the former highways and byways of the area. Like much of this history, so much that was taken for granted two centuries ago now seems so obscure.

Local Roads & Transportation in the early Ecton Accounts

From the first year of the Duke's expense accounts there are a few references to the repairs of local roads. The earliest, in 1761, relate to 'leveling the road in lower Lee'. Some 36 roods were levelled at 1s.0d or 1s.3d a rood by John Hall and Anthony Abill (? Abel). Lower Lee is no doubt the current Ecton Lee.

Several references in 1764 to making a road frustratingly do not tell us where. In November of the same year, Wm Lomas was 'making a Bridge', but we do not know where, or even if it is above ground. It was probably the footbridge to the meadow opposite the mine, however.

In 1765, 1766 and 1769, men were repairing Rakes Lane. The origin of this name is the uphill way out of a given village or place. In the case of Ecton, this could only have been the road to Warslow, now known as the Dale. It is the only uphill roadway near to the mine – the Swainsley road to Butterton did not exist in those days.

An intriguing entry in February 1767 is the payment of £0.18s.7d to Wm Beeby 'for estimates of Bridges'. It may have been the preliminary activity ahead of the Butterton Moor End turnpike road (see below). Almost certainly two other references relate to a proposed road to bypass the turnpike, viz August 1768: 'John Nuttal bill for a Plan of Cheadle road' and May 1769 'Mr Marsdens bill for Estimating Cheadle road'. However the Duke was not going to need a road to Cheadle: he built his smelter at Whiston, but perhaps the use of the word 'Cheadle' may have encompassed Whiston in the abstract nature of mine accounts. More interestingly, it could indicate a desire to take over the new Cheadle copper works – see pp 133-34.

The Development of the Turnpike Roads

During the 1760s extensive road improvements were made to the road system of Staffordshire and almost all parts of the county had been provided with some measure of turnpike communication. (1) In the Staffordshire Moorlands, Leek and Cheadle became focal points of turnpike systems which reached out to the Potteries and to the Derbyshire border (at Axe Edge, Crowdecote, Hanging Bridge (near Ashbourne) and Rocester. (2) At the beginning of the following decade came the development of turnpike roads which improved communication for the mine and its associated businesses.

Authorised in 1769 was the Cheadle to Butterton Moor End turnpike (near Onecote) road and the Darley Moor (south of Ashbourne) to Winkhill road. The latter went via Ellastone and Ramshorn to Winkhill on the Leek-Ashbourne road. Here a lane went up to Winkhill Cross to join the Duke's Lane between The Pen and Whiston. It also crossed the Whiston-Cauldon Lowe road for Whiston traffic and of course, Duke's Lane a few yards beyond it. A year later came the Butterton Moor End-Brierlow road, with its extensions to Newhaven and Ecton. This was followed a year later (1771) with the Shelton (Stoke-on-Trent) to Cauldon road which passed through Whiston.

To the east of the mine, the Ashbourne to Buxton road had been turnpiked in 1738 with the Newhaven to Cromford (and on to Alfreton and Nottingham) road being authorised in 1759. There were other roads of course, but these are the main ones of interest, either, in Staffordshire or Derbyshire, to the mine.

The Butterton Moor End to Brierlow Bar
& Hartington Turnpike Road

The Duke's plans for a smelter of his own coincided with the plans to turnpike the Onecote-Longnor road and the road that went from this through Warslow to Hartington. This effectively boxed the mine in on two sides: to the west and north. The Duke would appear to have put as many allies on the list of trustees as he could. They included the Lords John, George and Frederick Cavendish (the Duke's uncles) and some other trustees were no doubt looking after his interests, including Thomas Gilbert and possibly Sir Henry Harpur and Lord Chetwynd.

No doubt of considerable annoyance was the turnpiking of the road from Warslow down to Dale Bridge at Ecton. It meant that access to the mine by cart from Warslow involved paying tolls. The road to Butterton via Swainsley did not exist and the way to Warslow via Hulme End was barred (quite literally) at Hulme End Bridge. The Act is dated 1770 and it no doubt took a while to build tollhouses etc., but the effect of the Act clearly exercised the minds of the Duke's advisers prior to its enactment. So much so, that it included a clause stating that the Act would not hinder or prevent the owner or occupier of Ecton Copper Mine from opening or making any road or way leading from the mine to Wetton Mill, or making use of the road with any horses, cattle or carriages whatsoever.

In anticipation of the turnpike, work on the construction of a 'horse road' to Wetton Mill

Hulme End Bridge

commenced in February, 1770. It is the road on the east side of the river between Swainsley and Wetton Mill. The Mill was owned by the Devonshire Estate and had probably been included in the purchase of the Manifold Valley estate in 1575, (the Duke purchased 5,560 acres from Richard Flyre, a mercier from Uttoxeter, together with a water-mill. In 1717, the estate had the mill rebuilt by John Smith of Youlgreave. There was a bridge across the River Manifold and a road to Grindon Moor via Hillsdale. Brian Rich advises that there was a further bridge – Lees Bridge – across the River Manifold, which possibly served a road between (or past) Lees Farm at Back Ecton, due west to the Manifold perhaps leading to, or north of, Butterton. However the date for this is 1617 and it had probably gone by 1770. (3)

A further feature of the Act was that carts travelling up the turnpike and returning along it the same day, returned free of toll. Thus it was possible for delivery men using the road from Whiston, Froghall, or the Duke's coal mines at Kingsley Moor and Foxt Wood to take copper ore/metal from Ecton to Whiston as back carriage without incurring tolls. It was a concession which the mine no doubt made good use of when it could.

However there was an impediment to this: the hill from the mine to Warslow and the hill from the Warslow Brook to Butterton Moor (Butterton Clewes) meant that the carriage of a ton of ore was virtually impracticable. A single horse could not pull a cart load of stone/ore (weighing up to 1 ton) up the hill out of the valley. Either more horse power had to be used, using two or three horses, (which coast more) or the amount brought up the hill in two trips. This must be why the lower pen was built at Onecote in c. 1805 (4) and, it is suggested, served as a depot for carts rather than pack mules/horses.

From Onecote, the turnpike road extended from 'Butterton Moor End to Brierlow Bar (the Three Milestone in the Turnpike Road leading from Buxton to Ashborne (sic) and from Blacton Moor (to the west of Warslow) to near Newhaven and from Warslow to Ecton Mine.'

The original Act enabled the 'repairing, widening, turning and altering' existing roads and had been passed in 1770. A further Act had been obtained in 1791 'for continuing the term and altering and enlarging the powers' of the 1770 enactment. A further Act of 1812, gave further powers and more were sought in 1833.

This was because, having 'made great progress in repairing, widening' etc the roads, the capital borrowed and the interest thereon was not being redeemed by the income from tolls. The trustees sought to repeal the previous enactments in favour of 'more effectual powers'.

The 1833 Act (it received Royal assent on 18 June), involved various diversions of the roads and established various other powers.

The diversions were:

1 From near Warslow Mill (formerly situated adjacent to Brownlow Bridge over the Warslow Brook and on its north-east side) at Grid Ref 074577 to Warslow Church, meeting the existing turnpike at GR 087587.

2 The turnpike then was headed towards Ecton, turning towards Hulme End at the top of the Dale (GR 091588) and dropping down to Cowlow Farm. This was replaced by the current road to Hulme End from just south of Warslow Hall. The current road towards Reapsmoor had replaced the earlier route to Reapsmoor which had gone from Revidge (Blacton Moor) along the east side of the ridge heading to the Butchers Arms on Reapsmoor.

3 A further diversion was westwards from Hartington Mill, the current roadway being created then. It had previously carried straight on from the bridge up the hill to Crossland Sides rather than taking the bend as it does now. The old road probably reached the lane to Sheen and then turned down to the current Hulme End-Hartington road at GR 113596.

4 Finally, there was a short alteration near to the A515. It formerly met the latter where the green road to Middleton crosses the A515. The unsealed section of this green road west of the A515 still shows the original turnpike and its construction.

The toll charges were:

'For every horse, mare, gelding, mule or other beast drawing any carriage – 3d; For every horse, mare, gelding etc laden or unladen and not drawing – the sum of 1d; For every drove of oxen, cows or neat cattle – the sum of 10d per score and so in proportion for any greater or less number; for every drove of calves, hogs, sheep or lambs – 5d per score and so on in proportion'.

Having paid a toll at a particular gate or chain, one could pass through that gate or chain that day without further payment unless the horse was drawing a different carriage or wagon.

His Grace the Duke of Devonshire Debtor
at Hulm-End Toll=gate for John Allcocks passage
forwith Materials for the Mine.

			£	s	d
1784 Oct 9. A Two Horse Cart with Brick			0	"	9
An 3d 1785 Ditto with Brick			0	"	9
June 29. a Three Hors Cart with Tile			1	"	1½
Nov. 9 Do Wood to Sheen			1	"	6½
Nov. 11 Ditto Clay from the Haven			1	"	1½
Dec. 7 Do with Iron			1	"	1½
1786. March 1st Sand from Haven			1	"	1½
March 2d Brick from Do			1	"	1½
6 Days Leading Stone from Sheen to the Mine					
Half Toll or three full Tolls			3	"	4½

At Dale Bar | | | 11 | " | 7½ |

			£	s	d
3 Days with Stone full Toll			3	"	4½
1785 Sep 26 2 Carts 3 horses			1	"	4½
Nov. 27 a three Horse Cart with Stone			1	"	1½
March 14 Do with Stone			1	"	1½
			18	"	7½

Received July 27th 1786 of His Grace the Duke of
Devonshire by the payment of Cornelius Flint
the Contents By me Wm Poyser

An invoice for both 'Hulm-End Tollgate' & 'Dale Bar' for 1784-1786

Stagecoaches of course had to pay for each time they passed along the road. Each cart, drawn by one horse or two oxen, was limited to $1^1/_2$ tons (in summer) and $1^1/_4$ tons in winter, including the weight of the cart. The Act provided for the erection of a weighing machine to weigh the carts. The overweight element was to be charged as if carried by two or more horses.

Nails were a problem: from 1 January 1835, nails protruding from the wheel resulted in a toll of the same price as if the wheels were of 3 inches or less. Such wheels were likely to cause the most damage to the surface of the roadway.

The tolls collected were to be used in this order of preference: payment of the costs of obtaining the new Act; interest due to mortgagees of the tolls and any duties payable on the roads; expenses of road maintenance, improvements etc; and finally in repaying the initial capital borrowed (an unlikely event). However, no more money was to be expended on the repair of roads than was collected on them. The Act was to last until the end of 31 years thereafter and then at the end of the then next session of Parliament.

The date of construction of the diversions are not known. The first O S map of 1840 shows the way into Warslow coming by way of Blacton Moor, but some time lapse presumably occurred between the survey and printing. If the date of construction is unclear, the method is not. The stone for the Warslow-Brownlow Bridge section was brought from the Dale Mine waste tips by John Grindon. His son confirmed this in a deposition relating to the law suit between Richard Roscoe and the Dale Mine in 1872. This presumably accounts for the loss of tips at Hayesbrook Gate and Cow Close Mines to the north – the stone being used on the diversion to Hulme End and perhaps the earlier diversion of the road to Reapsmoor.

The siting of the toll gates would have been crucial to users of the road. In 1781 they were as follows: Brownlow Bar (just north of the bridge at Grid Ref 075578); Dale Bar, at the top of the lane to the Dale and Ecton (GR 089588); Glutton Bar (GR 084666); Holme End (now Hulme End, the toll house surviving at the east end of the bridge across the River Manifold; and Hartington Mill, just to the west of the bridge over the River Dove). (5)

The Effect upon the Ecton Mine

During the 1760s, the Ecton Mine had developed into a major business, yielding substantial profits for the 4th and 5th Dukes of Devonshire. The movement of coal to the mine plus tons of other material, e.g. wood, powder, iron tools etc. and the shipment of ore (both copper and lead) and copper metal was substantial. In 1770, the year the road was turnpiked, some 2,500 tons of ore was stockpiled at the mine – its iridescent yellow colour must have been quite striking. The turnpiking of the road to Warslow must have grated on suppliers to both Ecton and the Dale Mines from the west. It also resulted in the Duke developing a new route to his smelter at Whiston, which opened in Autumn, 1770. It avoided the toll road by heading to Wetton Mill, Grindon Moor, Waterfall Cross, Ipstones Edge and then down to Whiston.

Traffic from the mine bound for Sheen and Longnor would have turned north at Harecops Farm, although cart ways out of Longnor were controlled by gates in the middle of the village by the crossroads and at others at Crowdecote and Glutton.

In the early years of the 19th century (about 1809) the Duke of Devonshire built a cart road from Swainsley to Butterton and from there to Grindon Moor to his ore pen (now Pen Farm). It included a substantial bridge over the River Manifold at Swainsley. Situated by the former Stamps Yard of the Ecton Mine (built in 1818), it later is known as Stamps Bridge.

Despite the fact that the road over Butterton Moor was not turnpiked until 1770, there is an intriguing reference in the Ecton accounts of 9 February 1765: 'charge of Butterton Road for coal £0.17s.0d', which cannot be explained. If the mine generally avoided the costs of using toll roads, there were times when it must have been expedient to do so. There was no turnpike road at that time and therefore why was there a charge?

No tollgate could be erected between Butterton Moor End and a gate leading into Butterton Cloughs, which presumably led to Butterton village. This was, presumably, to ensure people from Butterton did not have to pay tolls twice in order to reach Onecote, but this would not be much use to the mine. To construct the road or to maintain it – the trustees could enter land to take quarry waste free of charge. There is no mention of mine waste, but presumably it was also taken from the mines. The virtual lack of tips at the Dale and Hayesbrook mines (the latter was north of Warslow Hall and beside the road, like the Dale Mine) together with the complete absence of mine waste at Cow Close Mine (which is on the Dale Mine adit level but was worked also for lead ore) shows the probability that the waste forms the base of the current roads which were formerly turnpiked.

The Froghall-Onecote Road

In 1769, an Act was passed for repairing and widening the road from Cheadle to Bottom House and thence to Butterton Moor End (9 Geo III c.80). It ran from Greenhill, between Wetley Rocks and Tean, via Froghall, Ipstones, Bottom House and Onecote. It met the Butterton Moor End turnpike referred to above just outside Onecote.

Some of its trustees are familiar, being recorded in the Act of the Butterton Moor End turnpike, viz: Lords George, Frederick and John Cavendish, no doubt looking after the family interests. Sir Joseph Banks and several local industrialists may be recognised in the list of trustees – Thomas & John Gilbert, Robert Hurst, Joseph Ingleby, Francis Leigh, George Kendall, John Beech and Edward Coyney for instance. Also familiar are the rates of the tolls, they are the same! However, there was no exemption for the Duke of Devonshire. The only relaxation was a half toll at any gate erected at or near to Froghall for, or in respect of, any horse, mare, mule etc drawing any carriage or for any single horse etc going for or returning from being laden with slack for the burning of lime or with lime to be used for the improvement of land only. The trustees also had the right to rebuild Froghall Bridge.

Thus the owners of Cauldon Lowe Quarry (the unusual spelling of Cauldon Lowe is not new. Lowe was being used in 1785 on invoices in the Ecton Accounts for the delivery of clay by Joseph Ratcliff) had the concession on the gates across the Ipstones road and the embankment to Froghall Bridge. There was nothing for the coal carriers heading for Whiston – the Duke's mines were not purchased until 1780. Tollhouses were erected at Cheadle, Froghall Bridge, Ipstones and Butterton Moor End. There does not appear to have been a toll house at Bottom House. The Ipstones tollhouse still survives although much extended.

The Duke clearly intended avoiding the payment of tolls to Whiston and his road from the mine to his smelter is discussed in more detail below. It must have saved a considerable sum of money in toll fees. The Duke seems to have had an unrestricted route to Froghall from Kingsley and the 1804 tramway line to Cauldon Lowe Quarry had a spur into the smelter. Clearly the intention here was to avoid charges but the extent that the tramway was used is not clear.

Charges on the canal to Froghall from Etruria were cheaper than the turnpike and records from the 1780s show that timber was moved from within Stoke to Etruria and then brought by narrow boat to Froghall. Assuming that it was too long to transport by horse or mule, presumably the timber was moved by carriage to the mine along the turnpike. A requirement of the latter was that timber was only moved along the road on a wheeled carriage.

Avoiding Tolls

At that time, there were bridges over the River Manifold at Wetton Mill; Dale Bridge (to Warslow via Dale Toll Bar); Archford Bridge at Hulme End and another there on the turnpike road; Shawmergate (north of Hulme End); Brund Mill (where there was a small packhorse bridge); Ludburn; Waterhouse (GR 634898); and at Longnor (on the turnpike road).

For traffic heading north or to the northwest, Shawmergate Bridge offered the best route of avoiding tolls. Brian Rich has recently uncovered evidence of this bridge in the Constable's

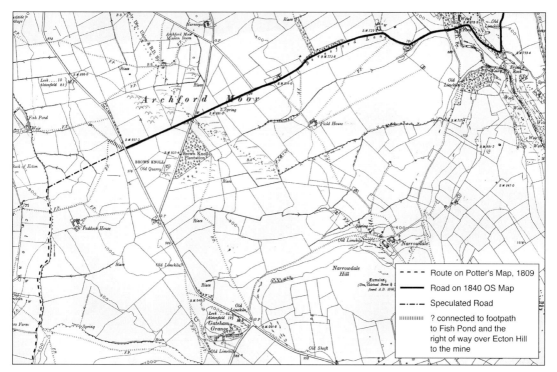

Fig 10. 1 & 2 The route across Archford Moor to Beresford Ford (above) and from Beresford Ford to Hartington, Pikehall and Biggin (below). Based on 1922 O S map.

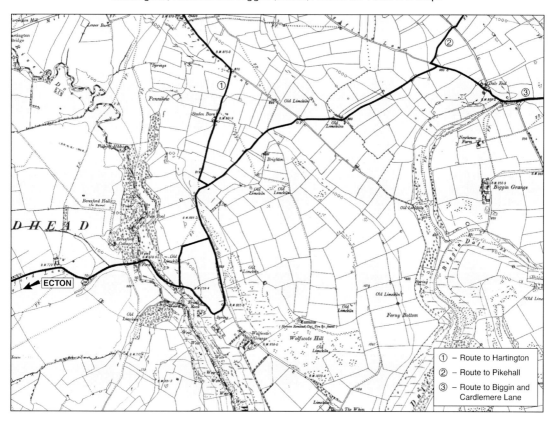

Accounts for Alstonfield (pers.comm.). It existed at GR 102600 on the route between Hayes Gate and Town End, Sheen. The bridge must have had some significance for the mine for in 1824, the Constable's Accounts reveal that 'a great expense was incurred for Shawmergate Bridge between Alstonfield and Sheen... it is agreed by Mr Gouldsworthy, the Duke of Devonshire's agent at Ecton, that it should be kept in good repair in future at the Duke's expense.' (6)

The way to it would either be from Westside, Endon House, Scaldersitch Farm to Town End, or off the Hartington road from the mine at Archford Moor, heading past Harecops to join the above route near Endon House. Once over the River Manifold a variety of packhorse routes were available, but Hayesgate Lane could be used to pick up the Drovers Road across the Warslow Moors to the Mermaid Inn on Morridge or by a choice of routes towards Three Shires Head and Panniers Pool Bridge across the River Dane.

Today Shawmergate Bridge is a modern footbridge across the River Manifold behind Hayesgate Farm. It has a delightful setting unknown to the majority of visitors to the valley a little down river.

Roads Around the Mine

The Hulme End Area

Initially, the road from Warslow descended from the top of the Dale to Cowlow Farm. It is now a quiet country lane. The current bridge in Hulme End was built by the turnpike trustees and its predecessor, Archford Bridge, was further downstream. The lane between Cowlow and Warslow is quite steep and the current road (B5054) created a more gradual gradient. Archford Bridge existed at a point where an extension of the Hayesgate Lane reached the river. Today there is little field evidence of the roadway above the bridge on the Alstonfield side of the river. There is a slight depression which may mark the site of the road as it descended to the bridge. The field north of West Side Farm would have had a crossroads where the

Hulme End Toll house

Ecton, Hartington and Alstonfield roads met the southern end of Hayesgate Lane.

The Hartington road must have curled around the rear of the current hotel to meet the road to Sheen at GR 108594. Looking north at the field south of this point, there is a depression heading for the stream at the point where it is crossed by the current footpath, which could mark the site of the road. It would also explain the alignment of the road to Sheen north of its junction with the B5054: it meets it on a curve.

The toll bar was Holme Tollbar (or Toolbar, as it was spelt on the invoices from the lady keeper, Frances Bassett). The house on the Sheen Road – Hole End – should correctly be called Holme End, which gave its name to the current community. From the Holme Crossroads, south of Archford Bridge, the Ecton road headed for West Side Farm and the Alstonfield road probably went to the east of the current road. After the current bridge was built the layout of several adjacent roads was altered. The current line of the B5354 to Warslow and Hartington Mill was adopted and the road to Alstonfield also realigned. The old crossroads was abandoned

Roads around the Mine
Fig 10.3

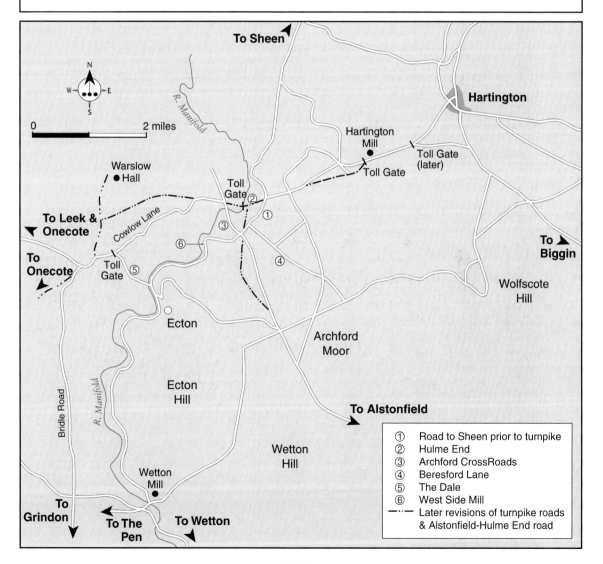

at some point, probably when the old Archford bridge disappeared.

There are bills indicating that carts from the mine went through the tollgate, through lack of choice in reaching the road to Longnor, although detours to Shawmergate Bridge (see above) or even going via Sheen were available. The mine did manage to bypass the tollgate to reach

William Mellor's bill of 13 September 1788 showing tonnages of goods moved since 4 August

Hartington as mentioned below.

In 1779, payment was made to William Mellor (West Side) for 'six years priviledge and damages of land by a road leading from the mine to Hartington, 5s per year. Sir Henry Harpurs ten't' (tenant). Mellor lived at West Side Mill. This agreement had existed then since 1775 at least, but where was the road? It was six years later before the bill was paid again (for the six years at 5s 0d per year: R. August 1785). The bill was for 'Tresspass and priveledge of a Road. In Sir Henry Harpurs Estate adjoining to West Side Mill'. It is suggested that the roadway is the lane from the mill to West Side Farm (i.e. the current road from the mill to the current Hulme End – Alstonfield road. It may have continued eastwards to join what is now Beresford Lane, giving access to Hartington via Beresford Dale ford across the River Dove and Wolfscote Hill (see below).

Although the invoice states 'adjoining West Side Mill', the footbridge at West Side Mill over the River Manifold may be discounted. Brian Rich has found, from an analysis of the Alstonfield Constable's accounts, that this footbridge was built in 1818 (pers.comm). It was initially maintained by the Parish, but in 1823, it was ordered that 'no more allowance should be made for the said bridge by the Parish, as there are now five bridges over the said river within the span of half a mile'. (7) These would be Dale (at Ecton), West Side Mill, Archford, Hulme End Bridges and Shawmergate. As late as 1816, the Constable's Accounts show Archford Bridge being repaired. The late John Bonsall of Apes Tor (whose information has always proved to be factual) advised that a road went up the hillside from the end of the Fish Pond to the Alstonfield road. The barn at the top end was a beer house. A wall curls south by this barn which would have met Beresford Lane which once extended to the Alstonfield road and is shown on the 1st Edition of the OS map. See Fig. 10.1

This cuts the Archford Moor to Harecops Road and would give yet another alternative route. Beresford Lane joins the road which runs along Wolfscote Hill, having crossed the River Dove by a ford. This latter road is shown on the map of Hartington of 1614 in the Devonshire Collection. It curls around to the east and was available to suppliers coming in from Heathcote or Biggin. It's also a cart road and would be a useful bypass for carters wishing to avoid the Hulme End tollgate. A further tollgate existed near Hartington in Mill Lane at GR 125600, it was built following the road realignment at Hartington Mill in the 1830s. Suppliers may have made use of this road, but the mine did not use it. No invoices have been seen and there are no entries in the expense summary sheets for it. Beresford Lane must have been used instead unless the construction of this tollgate came much later. Unfortunately, the date of its erection is not known.

Beresford Lane seems to have connected with the lane which goes from Pepper Inn (The Manor House) down the valley to Redhurst and Wetton Mill in the Manifold Valley. Potter's 1809 map of Ecton Mill (8) shows the lane continuing along the valley bottom from Pepper Inn towards the Fish Pond. Right on the edge of the map, it turns right precisely where it could run straight up the hillside to reach Beresford Lane (from the 2nd field south of Back of Ecton Farm). Joining the lane at Beresford Ford, which we know (see above) existed in 1614, this road would seem to have been one of some antiquity, heading for Leek via Butterton.

Also of interest is the road from Hulme End (just south of the hotel) to Beresford Lane. There

Main Photograph and inset: The engine chamber from opposite directions. The metal scaffolding surrounds the Water Engine Shaft

is a kink in this road which maybe as it was originally aligned. A line from the abandoned crossroads, south of Archford Bridge GR103593, drawn direct to the curve in this road meets it precisely on the line of the current road east of the curve, suggesting a subsequent realignment, however. The above, together with the existence of two bridges which have now disappeared – Lees Bridge at GR091572 and Shawmergate Bridge at GR102601 indicated that there is a fascinating history to the road pattern around the mine in its own right.

All this concerns the road pattern east of the River Manifold and the last comment is equally true west of the river. The Dale tollbar was probably on the junction of the lanes to Cowlow and that to Ecton. When the current B5053/B5054 layout was constructed, the tollbar was moved to the junction of the B5053 and the turning right to Ecton (GR089587). Prior to this the Longnor road from Onecote was west of Warslow village and crossed the east flank of Revidge. It's very boggy ground in places and a more direct route through Warslow would have avoided this as well as been more convenient for Warslow. There is another packhorse route which runs direct from Warslow to Grindon and is today a quiet and scenic footpath. At its northern end, a path from Villa Farm curves to the right heading for Dale Bridge. Prior to the construction of Stamps Bridge at Swainsley, this was probably the route taken by workers from the Butterton area.

The bringing of materials to Ecton and the taking away of copper ore established a need for carrying which grew significantly as the mine expanded. Farey tells us that pack mules were used to carry the ore to Whiston (see below), but it is also clear that two wheeled carts were used to bring materials. The method of transportation is rarely referred to in the accounts, but it is sometimes possible to infer whether wheeled transport or packhorse was being used.

An example was provided by William Hurd of Ashbourne on 19th July 1786 (invoice 1 R. August 1786). He was responding to an order for stayed Butts, other Butts (barrels), a cask for oil and two quarts of oil. He wrote – 'the stayed Butts which cant go on horseback so shall send them by Mr Banks waggon the first opportunity'. Ann Newton supplied candles from Ashbourne in September 1788. She sent 20 dozen 'with 2 panyars', indicating the use of a packhorse.

The poor state of the roads prior to the turnpiking of some neighbouring highways would tend to restrict wheeled transportation. Small loads would most likely be carried by horse in any event as it would be quicker and cheaper. The mine bought $\frac{1}{2}$lb of pack thread in November 1779 (and regularly bought more thereafter) but it is likely that the horses (or mules) would be owned by carriers rather than the mine and some may well have been farm horses used by a part-time carrier, as occasion demanded. Perhaps the mine did have some transport of its own for in 1783, Samuel Bonsall was paid for 'Making, repairing and drying packsheets'. Presumably pack sheets were used to protect the ore from rain. A year later '1 piece of ore bagging', delivered in January 1784 must have been somewhat substantial for it cost 33s.0d and three months later more bagging was bought.

Joseph Wain put in his bill for making '100 Copper Baggs' (9s.0d) at the same time. Further invoices followed for copper bags and one in February 1786 included for '6 bagg bands', for closing the top of the bag or fastening it to the packhorse's harness.

The use of carts may be inferred in the delivery of over 27 tons of iron plates and bars by Francis Furness, including grate bars for the mine smelter. These were carried in 1779 from Barnes & Co at the Chesterfield foundry to Longstone in 1 ton lots (Reckoning Dec 1779). The traditional load of a two wheeled cart was about 1 ton, depending upon the hills and the number of horses used. Furness charged 11s.8d per ton and this was also the price paid for clay from Newhaven (R. Aug. 1779) from another carrier; it was possibly a standard charge.

Richard Cleulow charged for the use of a cart and horses (R. Dec 1779) at Whiston viz: 1 cart and 3 horses – 6s per day; 1 cart and 2 horses – 5s per day; 2 carts and 4 horses – 8s per day. Thus cart hire was probably 3s per day for a single cart with horses 1s each per day but not for 2 carts and 4 horses! Coal from the Cheadle Coalfield was carried to Whiston by cart and it was charged for at 4s per ton (1s 0d per mile). The steepness of the roads into and out of Froghall did not preclude carts, but more horses had to be used. The use of a wagon (i.e. a vehicle with four wheels) is first recorded in 1779 (R. December 1779): 'for carreing one waggon load of Dale Planks from Stoke to Whiston £1.3s.0d'. The journey took two days and was immediately followed by another, similar trip. The carrier, Thomas Allcock, then transported 27,500 bricks from near Kingsley to Whiston at 7s per thousand, presumably also by waggon. He also moved timber from Lockwood Waste to Whiston probably via Ross Road, which runs directly towards this wood, south west of Whiston. He then moved 235½ feet of timber to Ecton at 5d per foot from Lockwood Waste and Eaves Woods. Presumably he used the turnpike road: there was probably no another road which would allow him to reach Ecton. His route would be from Froghall to Ipstones, Onecote and Warslow. He would have gone through tollgates at Ipstones, Butterton Moor End, Brownlow Bar and Dale Bar before descending to Dale Bridge adjacent to the mine, incurring 1s in toll charges per horse used. There is a further invoice for Thomas Allcock delivering 23,150 building bricks to Ecton between August and 29 October 1779 at 10s per thousand plus 1,600 bricks to Whiston in four lots of 400 bricks at £1 per thousand. His wagon was clearly kept busy.

There is some evidence to suggest that the steep descent to Dale Bridge was avoided. Robert Alsope went to Leek with a cart to collect Barrow Lime (quick drying lime) and paid a toll of 3d at Hulme End Tollgate on the return journey. This raises some questions: why was there no toll at Dale Tollgate? Somehow he avoided it, perhaps by travelling via Reapsmoor and Hayesgate Lane. Why did he not avoid the Hulme End Tollgate by using the adjacent Archford Bridge? Had it been blocked off to carts? (R. August 1787)

'Dale Planks' refer to Deals, 120 of which made a 'hundred'. An example of this also occurs in the December 1779 Reckoning when '120 x 20 feet 3 inch deals', weighing 9 tons was conveyed by the Caldon Canal Company from Etruria to Froghall at 2s.1d (25d) per ton. It's a pity we cannot make a direct comparison with Thomas Allcock's charges from Stoke, but we do not know how much his wagon load weighed. However, it is unlikely that it was 9 tons and the canal would seem to be cheaper, although there would be extra costs from Froghall to Whiston. The canal had opened in 1777. An invoice dated 29th August 1786 for timber from William Kenwright & Co of Stoke (R. September, 1786) indicates that the weight was 1 ton and the carriage cost to Froghall (it was usually loaded at Etruria) was 4s.0d., quite a significant rise. The bargee was Richard Heath.

The Route to Macclesfield

Details of this are unsure but one would expect the packhorses to take a route without steep climbs. One such route may be suggested (except for inbound horses leaving Flash Bottom). Leaving the mine for Archford Bridge, Hayesgate, Hulme

The route descending to Flash Bottom

The road from Allgreave to Flash Bottom

House and Rewlatch, the route then starts to skirt around the north side of Reapsmoor via The Low, School Clough, and on via Fawfieldhead and Shining Ford to Merril Grove Farm. The old road was north of the present road to Royal Cottage, so the packhorses would have headed to Pyeclough Head & Morridge Top Farm. Having reached this high point, the route descended to Adder's Green and then on to Flash Bottom (or via Bradley Howel) to reach Quarnford.

Thereafter, the route would have gone on to Allgreave, Greenway Bridge and Sutton to reach Macclesfield and the works of Charles Roe & Co. A similar route might have been taken for deliveries to Warrington to Patten & Co. (9).

The Ecton to Whiston Road

The study by Gerhold (10) states that 'packhorses disappeared from almost all local carrying by the end of the eighteenth century'. This was supported by Farey (11) who stated:

> 'The Carriage of Ore, in common with that of every other article, was on Pack-Horses formerly, a drove of such horses being called a Jag, and the persons who carried ore for hire, were called Ore-Jaggers, a name still often applied, though carts and waggons are now universally used in those parts, except a few Pack-Horses that may yet be seen about Buxton, Hathersage, and the very mountainous parts, the mules used in bringing coals and ore to Whiston Copper Works in Staffordshire, and the horses and asses used to supply some of the poor with coals from the pits in different parts. The average price of carrying ore in 1808, appeared to be 1s per ton per mile'.

Why did the pack mules of Ecton survive so long? The costs of transport of ore and coal by mule or cart were the same – perhaps a policy dictated by the mine as packhorse charges were traditionally higher than by cart (12). The terrain made carriage by wagon or cart difficult except on the turnpike and this was compounded by the bad state of many roads. This reduced the efficiency of wheeled transport. Indeed, packhorses were faster, more readily adapting to

Fig 10.3 'Pack mules carrying bags of Copper Ore'. Unless this represents mules overseas, it must show the Ecton mules. From "The Mine" by Rev Isaac Taylor. The first edition was early in the 19th century, when Ecton was probably the only British mine moving copper ore by mules. The building in the background is a fanciful re-creation with a beam at each end and no chimney!

the terrain.

At first, it would appear that the loading and unloading of ore and then the loading of coal as a back-carriage would reduce efficiency when pack mules only carried 2 cwt. However this clearly was not the case.

The establishment of a depot at The Pen on Grindon Moor must originally have been planned because of a shortage of space at Ecton. It was six miles from there to Whiston. The system worked well – ore was moved principally from the mine to the Pen where it was stockpiled for transportation on to Whiston. Coal was brought back to The Pen for separate movement on to the Mine. The coal was brought from Hazles Cross and Foxt Wood Pits to Whiston to await the trans-shipment to Ecton. Roberts, writing in 1900, stated that a Mr L Fallows, presumably a Wetton resident, had seven bells formerly worn by his grandfather's mules at the mines of the parish. This presumably includes Ecton. (13)

Construction of the Whiston road was at the Duke's expense, as the detailed mine accounts show. A horse road was less expensive to construct than a cart road and was no doubt influenced by comparative cost advantages of pack mules over carts in 1769. These advantages must have included speed, quicker turnaround, no practical problems of carts trying to pass each other, or needing extra horses hitched to the cart on the hills especially from Wetton Mill to Grindon Moor. No turnpike costs were incurred either.

After the late-1780s as production dropped, at a time when the use of wagons could have made carriage conveyance more efficient, packmules would have maintained their edge. The need to upgrade the ore road to wagon standards would have introduced capital expense presumably considered to be too high. Even though the packmules would have been increasingly seen as outmoded, their use avoided the capital expense of a new road at the time of diminishing revenue. However at some point it seems that this road did use carts.

Despite the demise of the packhorse in the late 18th Century, Glover (14) records Packhorse Inns in 1829 at Alderwasley, Ashbourne, Calver, Chapel-en-le-Frith, Hayfield, Kings Newton & Peak Forest. Those at Little Longstone and Crowdecote he presumably missed.

Dukes Lane looking north to Winkhill Cross

The horizontal stone (? guide stone) marked No 6 below

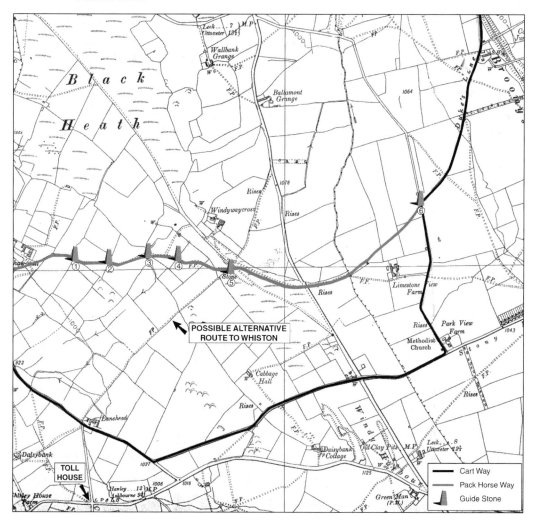

Fig 10.4 The area around Windyway Cross (Guide Stone No.5). Based on the 1923 OS map

The view to Windyway Cross (shown ringed) from Dukes Lane at Guidestone 6 (see fig 10.4)

The route from Ecton to Whiston was along the newly created road from Ecton to Wetton Mill which ran on the east side of the River Manifold. At Wetton Mill, the road crossed the bridge and proceeded up an existing trackway in the valley of the Hoo Brook. It left this to head up Hillsdale Hall and onto Grindon Moor and the depot at the Pen (GR074552).

A map in the Chatsworth plan press by P Potter and dated 1809 shows the road at Wetton Mill which crossed the bridge there to reach the mill and road to Ecton. A further lane forded the Hoo Brook heading for Wetton. This road, like the road to Ecton is still there, but the bridge at Darfur Crags is not shown. The crags are marked as Darford Tor and a ford existing on the site of the bridge.

The Duke maintained the Wetton Mill Bridge. Eight days unspecified work was done there by John Wheeldon at 2s.0d. per day in late 1786 (Reckoning, December 1786).

Much of this route is clear and in parts is still known as 'Duke's Lane'. Regrettably, a map charting the route and referred to by Dr & Mrs Dodd and supposedly in the Chatsworth Archive is now missing. (15) It is dated 1769. The route was to Wetton Mill and then to the Highmoor Pen on Grindon Moor (now Pen Farm) via Hillsdale Hall. This route was originally used exclusively by packmules (i.e. between Wetton Mill and The Pen).

In May 1780, Sampson Phillips was paid for 'Assisting in making a road through Grin Liberty'. "Liberty" is another word for township and therefore excludes the area of Grin Quarry at Ladmanlow. Grin, however, is an abbreviation for Grindon. Many local people refer to Grindon Moor as Grin Moor to this day. This could refer to the stretch of road south of Grindon Moor Gate. It is not shown on Yates' map of 1775 (although the road across the moor to the Onecote-Longnor road isn't shown either).

The route then went south via Felthouse to Waterfall Cross and then due south down Benty Grange Lane to cross the A523 and then the River Hamps, presumably fording the water. The Dodds suggest that the route then made for Ballamont Grange and Windyway Cross – as indicated by the old map. However if this route was actually constructed, one wonders how long it remained in use. The volume of traffic was significant and yet there is no evidence of a road aligned with the cross. The current stone must be a replacement: it is dated 1892.

An easier route is the lane to Park View Farm, which is still called Duke's Lane. Perhaps of significance is that where the surfaced road changes direction at SK065493, there is a very substantial stone built into the wall. Now horizontal and some 6 feet in length, it is persuasive to think of this as a former guide stone for the jaggermen. It is of sandstone and now cracked in half. The accounts record work on the road in the early 1770s which may be on this alternative route. From Park View Farm, the road turned up the lane to cross the main road at GR 062486. A footpath south of Cabbage Hall cuts over to the A52 and this is likely to be a route to Whiston (but involved going through Lanehead tollgate).

This leaves two questions unresolved. Was the route negotiable by cart? It looks as though it might have been, for coal deliveries as far as The Pen. However the price per ton was the same and the horses would have been quicker for the drivers. Secondly, a tollgate was built at some date across what is now the A52 at 053482, south of Lanehead. Did the Duke have a dispensation, or did the copper and coal bypass it? It could only have done the latter by some agreement. The date of construction of this tollgate is unknown, but it is on the first O.S. Map of 1836. It may have come too late for the bulk of the traffic. A little to the east, the Ruehill gate opened in 1792 and Stanton Dale gate in 1790. These were, however, on the Blythe Marsh-Thorpe Turnpike. The Dodd's map (see above) shows an alternative route – via Onecote, Ipstones and Froghall, but the Cheadle-Butterton Moor End Turnpike was enacted in 1769, unknown to the original cartographer. It was soon to have tollgates at Froghall, Ipstones (on the corner of the road to Foxt, where it still survives) and Butterton Moor End. This, and the turnpike trust to the north of Butterton Moor End, precluded the regular use of this route.

Yates' map of Staffordshire, dated 1775, clearly shows the current A52 between Froghall and Ruehill at Cauldon Lowe, so it's clear that the Duke's road, if it followed the line of the A52, did not last long. Of equal interest is that the road from Grindon Moor to Waterfall Cross is shown along with its extension to Park View Farm, although the latter is not marked.

If the tollgate across the road to the south of Lanehead Farm at Cotton Lane prevented use of the direct route via Park View Farm, an altenative route may have existed and although currently unproved, it seems entirely plauseable. (16) The alignment of a section of field boundary immediately to the west of Limestone View Farm points towards the road junction on Duke's Lane and the horizontal cross. It also links up with a footpath which curls around to meet Windyway Cross. A footpath from here descends Ipstones Edge to Lanehead Farm and then Daisybank Farm where a lane runs along the parish boundary to the A52 (and is marked on the 1836 OS map). This route also misses the tollgate on the junction of the Windy Harbour-New Street road and the lane across Ipstones Edge. The route from here to Whiston continues on p 180.

Windyway Cross (No 5 on Fig 10.4)

The road towards Ipstones Edge is shown too by Yates, but not the descent towards the current A52. However Yates did not show many roads across moors and common land, which is why the road from Hillsdale Hall across Grindon Moor via The Pen is also not shown.

At the Reckoning for 29 September 1770 accounts for the movement of ore to Whiston smelter commence. From the start, the Duke's accounts show that ore was taken to Whiston by different methods. Although some ore was taken direct to Whiston, ore was being taken to Hillsdale, on the north side of Grindon Moor and shipped separately to Whiston from there. A stockyard was built here which became known as the Pen. Coal was brought back by the packhorses (Farey states that they were mules, a cross between a horse and a donkey (17)) and unloaded at Hillsdale. It was then taken on to Ecton. The payments for carriage were: Ecton to Whiston – 8s.4d per ton (i.e. 100d); Hillsdale to Whiston – 5s.0d per ton; Whiston to Hillsdale – 5s.0d per ton; Ecton to Hillsdale (and also the return route) – 4s.2d per ton. There were 16 carriers in all. By 1779, these prices had been reduced. An analysis of the carriage costs for the Reckoning at 29 September 1770 reveals that the carriers brought back more coal than ore taken to Whiston:

		tons	cwt	stones
Joseph Salt, carriage	from Hillsdale to Whiston	6t	18	1
	from Whiston to Hillsdale	7t	14	4
Samuel Bostock	from Hillsdale to Whiston	15t	19	0
	from Whiston to Hillsdale	16t	15	4
Josua (sic) Kent	from Hillsdale to Whiston	2t	15	7
	from Whiston to Hillsdale	2t	17	4

One would have thought that this would have been the other way round. The ore would be dressed and crushed smaller than the coal which also has a lower specific gravity. Were the mules loaded more heavily for the return journey?

Mules have certain advantages over horses: weight for weight they are stronger than horses, live longer and have a longer working life. They rarely become ill or lame or suffer wounds and can withstand extremes of temperature. Of no doubt of great interest to the owner of the team, they can live on frugal rations, have tremendous stamina and resilience and are exceptionally sure footed. It is of no coincidence that the animals are used to transport tourists down the Grand Canyon, for their well known stubbornness is in fact a symptom of an excellent talent for self preservation.

There were other carriers carrying smaller amounts of ore and carriers from the pit to Whiston. The latter related to coal shipments from Kingsley Moor, for which they were paid 5s.6d per ton. It will be noticed that this was more than the price from Whiston to Hillsdale, perhaps because the Kingsley horses returned empty or because the mine was in a stronger position to negotiate a better deal with the returning teams from Whiston. Who knows? By 1780, the price for carriage of coal from Hazelcross Colliery on Kingsley Moor to Whiston had dropped to 3s.4d per ton. It remained at this price until late 1786, where it rose to 3s.10d.

No doubt other suppliers and local people used the Pen–Whiston road for their own purposes. Certainly George Critchlow of Pethills Forge did. In March 1780, he took three dozen spades to Grindon Moor Gate to be picked up for carriage to Ecton via The Pen. A month later he supplied about 2½cwt of iron to Whiston which were taken to Waterfall Cross, where the packmules would have picked the iron up.

It has been shown that the mine avoided the cost of turnpike charges wherever possible. However it could not have bargained for excessive feed charges for the mules which seems to have occurred in 1786: In February 1786, 26 carriers were paid 'for scarcity and dearness of fodder' £159.0s.0d; 'a remainder of the money allowed to the carriers & co for the dearness of the Fother as per acc. £24.3s.0d'. This was a substantial sum of money.

Use of the Whiston Route by Carts

The work of William Wooliscroft, delivering red clay from Ecton to Whiston in 1783 would seem to unlock a puzzle which seemed likely to remain unsolved. The puzzle was this: was the packhorse (or packmule) route from Ecton to Whiston used by carts?

Wooliscroft used a cart – usually it seems, with three horses – and did a lot of short distances carrying for the mine. Several of the Dale Tollbar invoices record payments for his passage through that particular gate (or bar). There are no invoices for any tollgates in the area other than Dale and Holme End, although the charges of persons going to the foundries at Ashbourne and Mayfield (usually delivering orders in all probability) do claim expenses for toll charges on the Ashbourne road and presumably for the Clifton Green Lane tollbar too.

So if he was taking clay – usually 22-27 cwt – to Whiston by cart and was not using the Onecote-Ipstones turnpike road, what route did he take? The main alternative would seem to be the packhorse route. There is another route: from Grindon Moor to Ford, New Street and Windyway Cross but the Duke's Lane would probably be better maintained. However both of these routes go via the Highmoor Pen on Grindon Moor and it is suggested that the cart route from Wetton Mill would be up the current Wetton Mill-Butterton road and then via Butterton ford to the Pen.

The fact that much of the way from the Pen to Whiston follows lanes now tarmaced clearly shows that they were wider than a typical packhorse route, adding credence to the belief that the original intention of making a horse way was adapted to allow use by carts too. This would be allowed for when the enclosures were made later.

Transport by Cart

This would appear to have been notionally one ton per cart although often they carried more than this. On the hills around Ecton and out of Froghall, three horses were required. William Wooliscroft, the mine carter, charged 5s.0d per day for himself and a three horse cart (R Sept.1782). Wooliscroft started moving red clay which had been purchased locally from George Poyser to Whiston. The quantities were only small, but he seems to have managed to get 27cwt on his cart for one trip (R.August1782), returning with a back carriage of 20cwt of coal to Ecton.

In the same Reckoning, 4ton 4cwt of sand was delivered probably from Warslow Common, indicating an average weight of 21cwt per trip. The capacity of four-wheeled wagons has not been determined. They were far less frequent and carried goods (e.g. trees or bricks, where the goods were not sold by weight and the number of deliveries is not recorded).

The November 1783 Reckoning records a curious situation regarding the delivery of lime; The volume was 88 horse loads at 11s.0d per score (£2.8s.4d), the horse load in all probability being 2cwt. However the carriage of this quantity was by 8 cart loads at 6d per load, each cart carrying an average of 1ton 2cwt. Clearly the volume was still being calculated by the packhorse standard weight despite the introduction of the cart. The low carriage cost would indicate that the lime was probably being moved to Ecton from Apes Tor.

Confirmation of the horse load being 2cwt occurs in the following Reckoning (December 1783). Gervas Wood submitted his account for six loads of straw, all delivered on six separate dates. His invoice clearly states that there was 12 Hundred in every load. Clearly, Gerhold's inferred statement that packhorses disappeared in the second half of the 18th century (18) is too sweeping. Not only did the Ecton packmules survive into the 19th century, according to Farey (see above), others serving the mine such as Gervas Wood continued until very late into the 18th century at least. It is likely that other small carriers did the same.

Pilkington referred to the movement of lime in 1789. He wrote 'A large quantity of limestone is burnt in the Peak, they are much employed in carrying this article to distant places thro' roads, some of which are scarcely passable with wheeled carriages'. (19)

A year later, (Dec 1784) Thomas Alcock, well accustomed to moving heavy loads for

Whiston Smelter, was paid for 'one Days Work with 5 Horses and 3 men with a verey Large Stone from Froghall to Whiston 12s.0d'. Nearly two years later (R. September 1786) Hazles Cross Colliery was unable to obtain sufficient 'postwood' – pit props – locally and went to Swythamley for it. This may have been to Barleyford Wood which had already supplied timber to Ecton. Thirteen carriers, including Thomas Alcock, brought a total of 24 tons 1cwt from Swythamley and definitely used the turnpike road system, for they incurred the cost of £1.10s.4d for '91 Horses at tool gates at 4d eich (each).' It seems the whole operation did not take long for there was also a payment for 'Drink for 2 Days 6s.3d.' Some additional postwood was fetched from Consall Wood during the same Reckoning by Josiah Fernihough. The invoice shows the complicated process of the accounts. The main shipment from Swythamley was paid by weight. Fernihough was paid for going to Consall Wood and also to Swythamley by measurement in cords and feet!

Noting that the Swythamley timber needed 13 carriers it was observed by Brian Rich, in checking this chapter, that 91 toll charges divided by 13 is 7 and 24 tons 1 cwt divided by 13 is 37cwt. Consequently each timber drug would appear to be carrying an average of 37cwt. The toll charges at 4d would appear to suggest that the group as a whole wrestled a discount at each gate. However, how seven toll charges each works out is decidedly unclear. If four tolls were charged on the way out, the men would have to set off back for Hazles Cross the same day and get through the first gate (free) on the first day. Only then could there be three; charges on the second day. Unfortunately it is conjectural to assume this, plus how the men spent the night – presumably under the carts as there is no bill for accommodation – and even the number of tollgates at which they were actually charged.

In 1785, Nathaniel and James Chadwick were paid for widening and repairing the road to Wetton Mill, including making embankments. During August of that year, Thomas Allen, the surveyor from Leek, spent three days with an assistant 'Levelling and setting out the intended Road from Wetton Mill to the Pen, at 10s 0d pr day' (plus 5s 0d per day for the assistant) was this for carts?

Finally, in the reckoning for May 1780, Sam Bostock was paid for carrying 186 tons between Ecton and the Pen and 46 tons between Whiston and Ecton. An analysis of this would seem to indicate that he had 12 mules/horses. His daily routine would seem to be one journey from Whiston to Ecton plus two journies from the Pen to Ecton before returning to Whiston. He was covering 30 miles a day, excluding any distance between Whiston works and home. It is rather satisfying to be able to discover the way of life of this carrier from the dry nature of the accounts.

Hazles Cross to Whiston

On the current O.S. Map, there is a route from Hazles Cross direct to Kingsley Church and on to Kingsley Holt. A path from here heads for Whiston Bridge. However, a check on the ground reveals nothing to suggest that this was ever used by carts and there must have been on average something like 60 journies (back as well as out) six days a week, year in, year out. There is a defined cart track descending to Whiston Bridge from Kingsley Holt which may have been available, but it may be that although Whiston Bridge may well have been used, this route was not the preferred option to get there.

It is suggested that the route from Hazles Cross was possibly along Banks Lane, (which runs along the top of the valley towards Froghall) then down the current A52 to Froghall Bridge and then down river to Whiston Bridge, now a modern footbridge but seemingly built on much older ashlar masonry.

There is some physical signs of a cartway between Froghall Station and Whiston Bridge, but insufficient to be convincing, but the O.S. Maps show a track leading off upriver from the road descending the valley from Kingsley Holt to Whiston Bridge, which could have been a cart track 200 years ago.

Ross Road

On the east side of the river, the route is still very clearly visible. It follows the river, gradually rising until it reaches Ross Road. This is the old lane from Whiston up which it is likely that coal from Ross and Shawe pits made its way to the smelter having crossed the River Churnet at Ross Bridge. This route is not much longer than going up the current A52, but the gradient is significantly better for a cart with a ton of coal in it.

With over 10,000 tons of coal being moved to Whiston and Ecton in 1784, the cost of using the turnpike and passing through toll gates would have been significant. At only 3d per journey the cost (of 30,000d) would be £125. The carts seemed to have two or three horses and it was usual to charge 3d per horse. The return journey would have been free, if the cart went back the same day, but the outward charge could be levied at up to three gates.

Assuming the presence of only one tollgate (Froghall) and a charge based on two horses (i.e.6d per delivery), the cost of toll charges would be £125 x 2 (horses) – £250 p.a. However regular users 'compounded' their charges, i.e. took advantage of a discount negotiated with the collector of tolls (the tollhouse keeper). None the less, the Ecton policy was to avoid tolls wherever possible. In the mid-1780s direct deliveries to Ecton started and it is probable that these went via Whiston Bridge and Whiston too.

This Ross Road track, marked as Ross Road in Whiston village and as Ross Lane on the 1923 6 inch O.S. Map, descends to Ross Bridge. A substantial stone bridge carries the lane (a green lane for half its length) over the railway and a wooden footbridge now crosses the river. It is not easy to see where the route to Ross Colliery would have crossed. The area around Ross Bridge is interesting as remains of the former Uttoxeter Canal survive here. The lane also served Ross Cottage, situated south of the railway bridge but it has now been demolished.

Foxt Wood and The Pen

A significant amount of coal from Foxt Wood went direct to the Pen, whereas very little went direct from Hazles Cross (until the mid-1780s) compared with the deliveries to Whiston from that colliery. The reason was that the packhorses could climb Ipstones Edge and descend down the causeway, known as The Casey, to Winkhill and having crossed the River Hamps, climb the road to Waterfall Cross. The route over Ipstones Edge from Foxt village is now surfaced via Town Head. The causeway is unlikely to have been double tracked for carts, unless it had been relaid. It was an ancient way to Froghall (20). Yates shows a bridge in 1775 on his map of Staffordshire at Winkhill on the Leek-Ashbourne Road which the packhorses would have used. The point about all this is that the route avoided tollgates. This was a more difficult option for Hazles Cross Colliery, but a route was found via Whiston Bridge (see above).

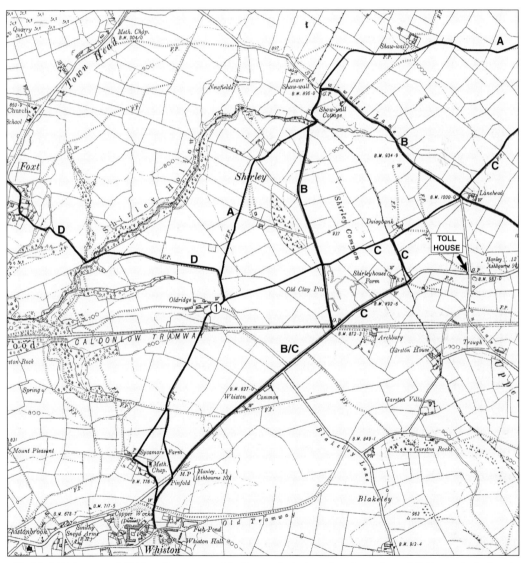

Fig 10.5 Whiston and Shirley Commons. A is the projected packmule route and B the projected cart route. C is perhaps an alternative packmule route to Duke's Lane and D an alternative route to Foxt Wood Colliery. Ref 1 is Oldridge Pinnacle

Some Foxt Wood coal was delivered to Whiston but the tollgate was probably across the junction of the current A52 and the road to Ipstones. It would seem that the coal could be brought to Froghall and up to Whiston without crossing a tollgate. No historians have suggested that one of the benefits of moving the wharf at Froghall from west of the tunnel to its current location was that some deliveries would be relieved of tolls at Froghall, but it would appear to be the case. They avoided the bar or chain across the bottom of the Ipstones road.

Despite the availability of The Casey, examination of on the ground gives what is considered to be the route over Ipstones Edge to Whiston and also the route over the Edge for the Foxt Wood pack horses not using The Casey. From Waterfall Cross, the Duke's road went south and crossed the Leek-Ashbourne road (it is now metalled). It then rose up the end of Ipstones Edge to (GR065493) where it is joined by another route. The lane to this point on OS maps is marked 'Dukes Lane'. At the junction, a very large stone in the wall looks like a guide stone on its side. It is thought that the route went just to the north of Limestone View Farm where it joins a footpath which curls around and heads for Windy Way Cross. From the cross, a footpath heads for Townhead, Foxt.

This must be the path used by pack horses from Foxt Wood Colliery heading for the Pen, (unless as stated they went via The Casey). Much of the way bears no evidence of being used by horses; it must have been ploughed out. However enough evidence does survive to be conclusive. From Windy

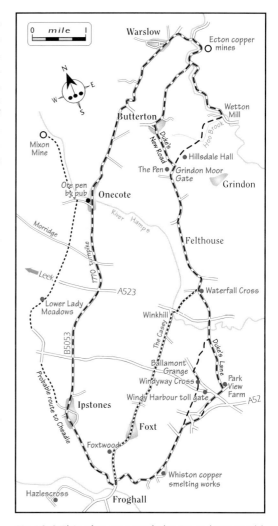

Fig 10.6 This plan was made by Dr and Mrs Dodd from the missing 1769 plan at Chatsworth and also shows other packhorse routes prior to the turnpike era

Way Cross, the footpath has a further two guide stones in direct line with the cross. There are more (see Fig 10.4), but not in a straight line, one showing signs of being moved to become a gate post (Stone 2). As the path descends steeply towards Shaw-Wall Farm there is a distinct hollow way, again with a guide post adjacent, albeit at a jaunty angle now (Stone 1).

From the farm, it is suggested that the Whiston route crossed the field heading for the current T-junction at GR046489. The lane south of here has been embanked to cross a stream and this substantial expenditure could well have been incurred by the Duke. From this point, the lane currently runs to the A52 and the pack mules may have followed this before turning down the A52 to the smelter.

However, this land was formerly Shirley Common and the mules may have headed straight for the smelter. The Whiston Inclosure incurred in 1815 or thereabouts as the Staffordshire Advertiser, of 19th August 1815, mentions the Inclosure and that Thomas Rowley was its Commissioner. It is considered that the carts would have proceeded up the A52 to the above mentioned junction and crossed the embankment to reach the T-junction. Here they could turn

Oldridge Pinnacle, Whiston

right and use a road running just north of the A52 to reach Park View Farm. At this point they could turn north up Duke's Lane to the Pen. (21)

Another potential route due south from Windy Way Cross needs to be noted. Now a footpath, the adjacent wall to Lanehead Farm has several long stones in it which may have originally been guide stones. It may be, of course, that several routes were used across the Common and the absence of guide stones may be explained by a huge pillar of natural stone situated at GR040480. About 30 feet high, it would be very easy to see, although today it is masked by trees. From this pillar of rock, known as the Oldridge Pinnacle according to the adjacent householder, it is probable that the furnace chimnies would be visible. From just south of the rock, Windy Way Cross may also be seen.

Trans-shipment Depots

Reference has been made above to the delivery of over 27 tons of iron plates and bars from Barnes & Co of the Chesterfield Foundry to Longstone in 1779 presumably to rebuild the calcining and smelting furnaces. It is known that a depot existed here which acted as a trans-shipment point for goods in transit. These may have been more common than we now realise. Reference has also been made to the use of inns for collection of goods and clearly these are in the same category. The possible existence of one at Brightgate, north of Bonsall, arises from an invoice of September 1783 (R. November 1783) for the collection of $2\frac{1}{2}$ tons of iron at 9s.0d per ton. It was picked up by Wm Mellor of Westside Mill, Ecton. He may have gone past Brightgate to collect fluorspar from Masson Mine, just to the south of Brightgate Farm. He fetched 33 tons at 10s per ton according to the same invoice. Further invoices indicate that this collection was not a 'one off'.

Similarly, the 36cwt of chains made to drop the horses down to the 34 fathoms level were made in Foolow and delivered to 'Middleton' – presumably Stoney Middleton. The invoice is addressed as from Foolow, but the forge could have been elsewhere. Sieves (from John

Bingham of Abney (R. March 1785) were left at The Cock Inn, Longnor and iron goods from Ambergate Works for Ecton were left at Ashbourne and Breech Gate (another name for Brightgate per Burdett's map of Derbyshire).

It would be interesting to speculate which way William Mellor went from Brightgate to Ecton and whether a route avoiding tollgates was possible. Unfortunately our knowledge of when and where they were erected needs attention from an aspiring researcher to enable us to do so. A potential route may have been via Bonsall Moor (along Bonsall Lane), aiming for Cardlemere Lane and then Biggin and Beresford Ford.

In the account for December 1785, William Salt went to Longnor to collect steel and to Monyash to pick up an anvil. Joseph Storrs of Chesterfield sent bars and bundles of iron plus hoop iron (for barrels) to Richard Roberts of Winster to await collection. Roberts supplied the mine with candles, so the mine would have seemed to have directed supplies to wherever they were known to the recipient.

Shipment by Sea and Canal

Reference was made about the transportation of ore from Derby to Gainsborough at 8s.0d. per ton and 10s.0d to London therefrom (see chapter 9, p 134). Gainsborough is on the River Trent, south of the River Humber, indicating that the ore went by sea from that town and possibly by boat from Derby. In March 1782, the mine paid Robt. & Wm. Tonge of Stockwith (invoice dated 27 February1782), for a pair of ropes weighing nearly 5 cwt, the sum of £11.2s.5d. Stockwith is slightly to the north of Gainsborough and the northern port on the Chesterfield Canal. Hence these two ropes must have come down the canal with road shipment from Chesterfield; the inference being that they had come from further afield by sea.

The vessel used to transport the copper metal from Gainsborough to London would appear to be *The Ecton* and her master in July, 1784 was John Sims. (22) Who owned the vessel is not known. She is likely to have been a billyboy of about fifty tons.

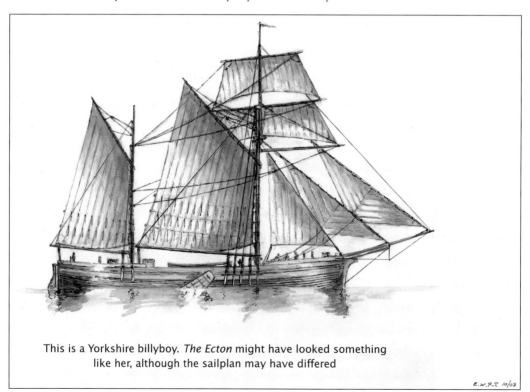

This is a Yorkshire billyboy. *The Ecton* might have looked something like her, although the sailplan may have differed

E.W.P.T. 10/03

One of the problems of canal transport surfaced in the Reckoning of February 1786. George Cresswell of Ashford had to fulfil an order for gunpowder and sent a consignment of 17 dozen (not clear what weight this represented). The invoice of 12th January 1786 (Nos 1 & 3 in the R. February 1786) was endorsed 'On Tuesday next your whole order shall be forwarded. The Canal was not opened (sic) on Tuesday or we shod then have fetched the powder'. Clearly bad weather had frozen the canal. Bad weather forced the mine to put men on snow clearing duties a little later (see under Chapter 13).

The Chesterfield canal opened on 4th June, 1777. Pilkington stated in 1789 that the business done on the canal was only sufficient to pay the interest on the loan of monies used to help pay for its construction. (23).

Ambergate to Brightgate

The following route from Ambergate Forge to Brightgate is suggested: it climbed up through Shining Cliff Woods towards Alderwasley. It then possibly then took the path to Lane End, crossing the Mere Brook. It then crosses over the B5035 to Intake Lane and descends to Cromford. The route then lay up Chapel Lane, Scarthin and on the old road to Ball Eye (which is marked on the 1840 O.S map) and then on to Townend, Bonsall, reaching Brightgate via Bonsall Cross.

Pen Farm Today

A visit to Pen Farm (August 2002) reveals nothing of the daily loading and unloading of coal and ore which formally took place here. Indeed there is not even an obvious levelled off area for the stocking of coal and ore. It certainly begs the question of whether materials were stockpiled. Perhaps not, with panniers being transferred from one animal to another. Too little is known about operations here. For instance, were coal deliveries brought by cart and transferred to packhorses for the onward delivery to Ecton via Wetton Mill or initially were pack mules used exclusively for ore and coal?

The original house survives, albeit extended at either end. In fact the 'original' portion of the building may well consist of two periods of development, according to the owner, Mr Spooner. The field between the house and the road to Butterton has yielded many horseshoes

Pen Farm

when ploughed (per Mr Spooner). These were shoes for horses rather than ponies which indicates the use of carts, but this may relate to a later phase of use after Pothooks Lane was built by the Duke. It also seems to imply a level of service industry with a blacksmith on hand.

The output of ore was delivered to the Pen by pack mule for many years after 1770. The annual raised ore tonnage needs multiplying by ten to assess the number of horse deliveries per annum from Ecton. With the coal deliveries in addition, there was considerable activity here. The coal and ore interacted as a back carriage and too many of the Reckonings give a combined tonnage making it impossible to accurately assess the volume of the deliveries, whether by pack mule or may be carts. The house at the 'Highmoor Pen', as it was known, was not built until 1784. The tile lathes came from Mr Beech's Shawe estate at Cheadle and the house was glazed by the man (James Keates) who was glazing at Whiston works (R. 2 November 1784).

References

1 Phillips, A.D.M., & Turton, B.J., Staffordshire Historical Collections, 4th series, Vol XIII, p 78. This paper gives the correct titles for each Act which are needed if seeking copies from the House of Lords Record Office

2 op. cit., p 79

3 pers. comm., Brian Rich, from Senior's Plan, 1617

4 Porter, L., & Robey, J., *The Copper and Lead Mines Around the Manifold Valley, Staffordshire, 2000,* p 64

5 Derby Mercury, 25th May, 1781

6 Alstonfield Constable's Accounts. Alstonefield Parish Chest

7 op.cit.,

8 Dev.Coll., plan press

9 Thanks to Brian Rich who suggested this route

10 Gerhold, D., Packhorses and wheeled vehicles in England, 1550-1800. *The Journal of Transport History,* pp 1-26

11 Farey, J., *General View of the Agriculture of Derbyshire,* 1811, Vol 1, p 380

12 Gerhold, J., op.cit., p17

13 Roberts, J., *The History of Wetton, Thors Cave & Ecton Mines,* 1900 p 177

14 Glover, S., *The Directory of the County of Derby,* 1829

15 Dodd., A.R, & E.M., *Peakland Roads & Trackways,* 2000, 3rd Edition, p 78

16 Thanks to Neil MacPherson who spotted the link between Duke's Lane and the now horizontal guide post with Windyway Cross

17 Farey, J., op. cit., p 380

18 Gerhold, op.cit., p 8

19 Pilkington, J., *1789, View of the Present State of Derbyshire,* p 312

20 Dodd & Dodd, op.cit.p.80

21 Thanks to Brian Rich, Neil MacPherson and Brian Foden who helped to discover this route

22 Derby Mercury, 15th July 1784, p 4, col 3

23 Pilkington, J., op. cit., p 281

Although taken at Frog Lane Colliery near Bristol, this view shows well what conditions must have been like at Hazles Cross and Foxt Wood Collieries.

The demand for coal for ore and metal smelting at both Ecton and Whiston was substantial, with tonnages running well above 10,000 tons per annum. Most of the deliveries were by cart to Whiston from the Cheadle Coalfield. Deliveries from there to the mine were by pack mule, as back carriage; ore being taken to Whiston (? along with roasted copper) on the outward journey.

The quality of Cheadle coal was considered by Robert Shore to be inferior to North Derbyshire coal. Additional coal – for the Ecton Smithy was supplied from the Axe Edge Coalfield, south-west of Buxton, but this seems to have stopped in the mid-1780s for a short time, perhaps because of an excess of coal being drawn from Hazles Cross or Kingsley Colliery. It is also suggested below that the mine's smithy may have received coal from the Derbyshire Coalfield, but it cannot be stated with any certainty.

Initial deliveries of coal to Whiston from 1770 were made by 'Mr Mitten', (see below) but no details of tonnage are available. Presumably the purchases were from Hazles Cross Colliery.

Coal deliveries at the end of 1779 and well into 1780 came principally from Ross Pit and John Beech's Shaw Colliery. These were both south-west of Whiston, across the Churnet Valley.

A substantial tonnage was delivered from these two pits, by two – and three – horse carts rather than packhorse or mule. The Ross Pit coal cost 5s. 6d per ton delivered, the colliery being close to the smelter, whilst the Shaw coal cost 4s.5¹/₃d (sic) per ton plus 4s.0d carriage. Following the appointment of Mr Flint, are preserved more substantial records which reveal that the Duke's own pit, Hazles Cross Colliery, was sending regular shipments of varying quantity to Whiston. From September 1780, the quantity of coal from Hazles Cross supplied to Whiston increased dramatically. In the Reckoning for August 1780, the quantity was 120 tons, a little above the regular deliveries, but the September 1780 Reckoning was 535 tons and deliveries of this magnitude continued thereafter (see p 197) reflecting the demand of the enlarged works.

(See Chapter 14 for detail on the capital acquisitions by the Duke generally)

The expansion of this colliery clearly followed. It had four shafts and a drainage level to the River Churnet – The Duke's Level – which must be approximately 1¹/₄ miles in length. It drains to the Churnet Valley, the outflow being at GR009479

Extension of the level would appear to have commenced in 1781, when 2,400 arch bricks were purchased 'for level'. It still drains a considerable area judging by the outflow.

The increase in the quantity of coal deliveries from Hazles Cross coincides with the purchase of 'Kingsley Colliery' from a Mr Mytton for £21,500 in 1780. (1) Thomas Mytton of Cleobury, N Shropshire took a lease from Messrs Dodshon & Paxton of Bristol, of the area around Crowtrees, Whiston and Oakamoor (c.1767). Mytton also leased land for coal mining north of Crowtrees in an area called Jack Elms, later Jack Stones, and now disappeared in the British Industrial Sand Quarry. Mytton's interest in the Kingsley Colliery dated back to at least 1766, but the mine may not have been working by 1773. (2)

Prior to March 1770, Thomas Mytton had driven a sough, which later was to become known as the Duke's level later, through his own land and land of William Dodshon (a Bristol woollen draper), his wife Francis and her son Michael by the late William Paxton of Durham. The sough commenced on common land above the River Churnet. Mytton leased the Dodshon/Paxton land for the purposes of getting coal, for 100 years at a ¹/₈th royalty from 10th March 1770. The sough had already been driven some way by the time of the lease. It was this freehold land plus an assignment of the above lease which the Duke purchased in 1780. By separate agreements, the Duke also worked coals under lands of adjacent owners (Dev.Coll., L/23/7). This document also has a crude plan which indicates where the various interests were situated. It consists of a case stated for counsel's opinion on the interpretation of initial covenants regarding the use of the sough, but dates from after the failure of Ecton in 1790.

Dodshon and Paxton both had land in the vicinity of Hazles Cross Colliery and Mr Dodshon (in the late 1780s there are payments to Mrs Dodshon) received royalties for coal extracted from beneath his land by the Colliery.

Hazles Cross also sent deliveries direct to the High Moor Pen for Ecton when demand exceeded the quantities of coal delivered to Whiston to provide back carriage for the pack mules arriving with ore from the Pen. Other deliveries went direct from the mine itself. The latter could have been by cart with back carriage of coal to the mine from Cheadle Coalfield. Some of the direct tonnages from the mine to Whiston reached 73 tons in a Reckoning (November 1780) reflecting perhaps 10 tons or more per week sent as back carriage.

Deliveries of coal from Shaw Colliery seem to have ended in August 1780 with the increased output from Hazles Cross. Output from Foxt Wood Colliery near Froghall also appear in the accounts from September 1780. The quantity was much less, however, generally being in the range of 130-180 tons per reckoning. Cross-checking with the records for shipments of coal to the Pen and Ecton, shows that at the Reckoning on February 1781, 182 tons 17 cwt 7 stone of coal was delivered from Foxt Wood to Whiston (per the Foxt Wood mine account) and the expenses account for Whiston shows a movement from Foxt to the Pen of 160 tons 18 cwt and to Ecton of 22 tons 2 cwt. This must mean that at least some of the coal from this colliery was going to Ecton or the Pen having first been dropped off at Whiston, or at least notionally booked in and out of the smelter. It points to coal deliveries going up the ore route via Winkhill Cross.

The Foxt Wood-Ecton deliveries were charged at 10s.0d per ton, which also indicates that the deliveries perhaps were booked in and out, i.e., there was only one charge, not two. Deliveries from 'Kingsley Bank' to Whiston at 3s.6d per ton and to the Pen at 9s.0d per ton reflect a similar level of charges (the Ecton to Whiston carriage cost being 6s.8d). The Kingsley Bank references appear in August 1779, but the exact pit is not known. It would not be Hazles Cross as the carriage costs from there were higher (to Whiston 8s.5d and to the Pen between 10s.8d and 12s.5d).

Some small quantities of between 2 and 3 tons of coal were also delivered in 1779/80 from 'Dillon' at 14s.6d per ton. This must relate to Dilhorne Colliery and was for initial purchases of 'smithy coal'.

The Basset family continued supplying 'smithy coal' to Ecton at 15s.0d per ton long after there were regular supplies coming north from the Cheadle Coalfield. Unfortunately, where this coal was purchased is not given, but the inference is that it was from elsewhere. If (and it seems likely) that a high quality coal was needed in the smithy, it probably came from the Derbyshire Coalfield. It is noted (see page 134) that Denby coal was of a quality superior to the Cheadle coalfield. The delightful packhorse bridge near Raper Lodge in Lathkilldale on the old road from Haddon to Youlgreave is known as Coalpit Bridge and this could have carried pack horses bound for Ecton laden with coal. The 'smithy coal' bound for Ecton, whether it crossed this bridge or not, was not of a great quantity.

However the tonnages of ore and coal crossing Wetton Mill Bridge were regularly between 500-600 tons per 6 or 7 week period in the 1780s. In round terms this equates to approximately 15 tons per day (Sundays excepted) week in, week out. Assuming that each pack mule carried 2 cwt or 10 deliveries per ton, this means an average of nearly 150 loaded animals crossed the bridge six days a week. There would be more if any did not carry back carriage and excluding all other ancillary crossings carrying other materials or passenger traffic between the mine and the Pen or Whiston, or from elsewhere, let alone traffic to Wetton Mill itself (it was a Corn Mill). The demand for coal must have risen with the completion of the new smelters at the mine in 1782 and 1784 and the opening of a brick kiln at Newhaven, some five miles to the east, via Beresford Ford and Biggin, by mid-1786.

In 1782 comes the first specific reference to the fetching of coal from Goldsitch, part of the small coalfield north of the Roaches, west of Ecton. It seems reasonable to assume that the smithy coal was being fetched from there at that period. As indicated above, it is not clear where the smithy coal came from previously. The volume remained largely the same at around 3 tons per reckoning, being delivered at about 15s.0d per ton. Goldsitch Colliery was being worked under a 21-year lease, granted in 1765 at £10.15s.0d per annum from Sir Henry Harpur and covering Goldsitch and Knotbury. (3) The lessees were George Goodrum and John Wheeldon of Derbyshire and James Slack. The lease included a forge recently started by Slack.

Unusually, one of the carriers in the early 1780s was a woman, Hannah Cluwlow, although she signed herself Hannah Beard from the September 1782 Reckoning. She carried coal to Whiston and Ecton and copper ore as back carriage.

The Hartington Enclosure Award of 1804 indicates that the road from Cisterns Clough, along Leap Edge, High Edge, Harley and via Earl Sterndale, High Needham, Vincent House and Madge Dale to Hartington was set out and known as the Coal Road, but the award makes it clear that this highway succeeded a much older road along which coal deliveries had been made prior to the award. (4) If coal was bought from Cisterns Clough Colliery and others nearby, this clearly could have been the route it took to reach Ecton – or at least Hartington.

Perhaps as a trial, in March 1786, 1 ton 4 cwt of smithy coal was delivered to Ecton from 'Dilorn' (Dilhorne), south-west of Cheadle, at 14s.6d per ton. There are a few earlier accounts of Dilhorne coal being delivered to Whiston but not to Ecton. The carrier was Samuel Steel.

Initial Profitability and Trading

The purchase of Kingsley Colliery cost £21,500. In the first six months, some 6,662 tons of coal was raised. This was valued by the mine at 5s.0d per ton. Superfluous quantities of coal were sold 'to the country' at 5s.0d, which was a little cheaper that the 5s.6d paid for Ross Colliery coal. Figures for the latter part of 1781 are missing, but most of those for 1782 exist. For six of the eight Reckonings of 1782, the figures show that 5,321 tons were raised and it is suggested that the figure for the year was some 7,000 tons.

The costs for the first six months were £1,060 (3s.2d per ton), while for the six Reckonings of 1782 the cost had been reduced to £645 (2s 5d per ton). It is suggested that the cost for the whole year is about £850, which also conveniently converts to a cost per ton of 2s.5d.

Adjusting for the missing figures covering the last seven months of 1781, it is suggested that income from August 1780 to December 1782 was about £4,400 (based on 5s.0d per ton). For this same period, it is suggested that the production cost was about £2,400. These figures are based on using 1782 figures for the seven months of 1781. If the figures for the first six months of production are used instead, the income hardly changes, while the costs rise.

However, using the 1782 figures, in the August 1780-December 1782 accounts shows:

Income	c. £4,400
Costs	c. £2,400
Profit	£2,000
Interest on £21,500, 2¼ yrs. 5%	£2,419
loss	£419
If interest was 4½%, the loss is	£177

However, Ross Coal was purchased at 5s.6d per ton. Recasting the figures at this level shows:

Total tonnage:	1st 6 months	6,662
	May - Dec 1781 say	4,100
	1782	7,000

17,762 tons @ 5s.6d	£4,885
less costs as before	£2,406
	£2,479
less Interest @ 5% as before	£2,419
Profit	£ 60

Clearly at this rate the pit was breaking even after allowing interest on the purchase price. However, this was not really good enough. It is shown in chapter 14 that Chatsworth capital investments, needed to yield an income well above 5% to cover interest costs, so this purchase was under-performing. Moreover, Ross Colliery was providing coal at 5s.6d per ton delivered. It has been shown above that the 1782 production cost at Hazles Cross (Kingsley) colliery was (2s.5d) per ton. Adding carriage cost of 3s.4d per ton, the total cost was 5s.9d before the finance charge (interest on the purchase cost). Ross coal was therefore cheaper. By comparison, Shaw Colliery coal had been costing 8s.5⅓d per ton delivered. However if John Heaton saw the investment just as a hedge against price rises, then he would, no doubt, be happy with the mine's results.

Foxt Wood Colliery yielded much lower tonnages (see below). For 1782, its costs were around 2s.6d per ton. However, carriage costs to Whiston were only 2s.0d per ton. Its coal was 1s.3d less than Hazles Cross, its bigger neighbour. Despite significantly lower output, this must have been the reason why it was retained. This assumes that coal quality was the same, but on the whole, it is believed that Foxt Wood did in fact produce a lot of poorer coal.

Agricultural Improvements

Documents in the Devonshire Collection reveal that the 5th Duke of Devonshire was working the Thatch Marsh and Goit (sic) Pits in 1790. The northern part of this area consisted of the Goits Moss Colliery, Moss House and adjacent land, which had been purchased in 1778 from Messrs Dickinson and others for £2,350. (5)

This inventory for the purchase of lands excludes Thatch Marsh Colliery, which must be on land held by the Duke in 1773 (because its purchase is not listed in the inventory of post-1773 purchases). In 1780, Thatch Moss and Goit Collieries were let to Robert Longdon of Countess Cliff Farm, Richard Wheeldon of Cronkston Grange and Isaac & Edmund Wheeldon of Buxton. The method of payment was to have a significant effect on the value of the Duke's land. The lessees were to burn and spread lime on land belonging to the Duke in an area stretching from Hind Low to Cronkston Grange (so indirectly the first two named may have had an extra benefit if they held land involved). (6)

Farey (7) recounts that in 1783, the Duke improved a large area of heathland, to be improved under the direction of his Agents, Mr Robert Longsdon (sic) and Mr George Brassington, by spreading lime. 'The effect though slow, was striking; the heath being exterminated by the lime, a sweet and good herbage has succeeded'. The result caused the Duke to have all of his heath land and other poorer soils limed to improve it for hay, rootcrops and cereal production. The Apes Tor limekiln, situated at Apes Tor Shaft, where stone was removed from the mine, commenced burning stone in 1785, yielding up to four kilns full of lime per mine reckoning. In August 1786, i.e. after the hay had been carried, coal deliveries commence to Wetton Hill together with a small amount of gun powder in. This indicates that lime production had started for the Wetton estate, the gun powder being to free limestone at what is now Townhead Quarry. The coal for the Ecton and Wetton kilns came from Foxt Wood Colliery, which produced poorer, slack coal than Hazles Cross Colliery. Thatch Marsh coal was not used at Ecton although its coal was of poorish quality, like Foxt Wood, being leased as indicated above.

It is interesting to see that the experiment south of Buxton, starting perhaps in 1781 – despite what Farey says – was quickly taken up to improve yields elsewhere on Devonshire lands and can be seen in the Ecton accounts. The resulting extra yields must have improved the value of the land let alone the produce, ultimately adding greater yields in the form of higher rents, to the Duke. Yet the strange thing is that the benefit of liming the land was nothing new. Clearly no one had focussed upon the benefits of liming the limestone heathland. (Chatsworth expenditure records show that land there was being limed in 1761, for instance at Cow Close field, and even earlier).

Hazles Cross Colliery

Output

The Kingsley Colliery was supplying coal to Whiston in 1779. How it came to the Duke is unclear. Whether it was offered to the Duke; why it was felt that this mine was a good prospect etc are not known. In 1780, approximately 2,200 tons were sent to Whiston, with a sudden increase in the volume from the September reckoning. (This amount is calculated making an assumption for the tonnage in March and December Reckonings). The only figures for 1781 are in the first three Reckonings and amounted to 1,414 tons. Coal production in 1782 rose, with some of this going direct to Ecton and the Pen.

Thus, in February 1782, 939 tons went to Whiston, Pen & Ecton. In March 800 tons went to Whiston and Pen and in June (May figures have not survived) 809 tons went to Whiston. The output may well have been approaching 6,000 tons for this year. In 1783, the missing accounts predominate, but with only three figures to go on, it is noticeable that they are in four figures for the first time: the mine's output could conceivably have passed 10,000 tons pa. The

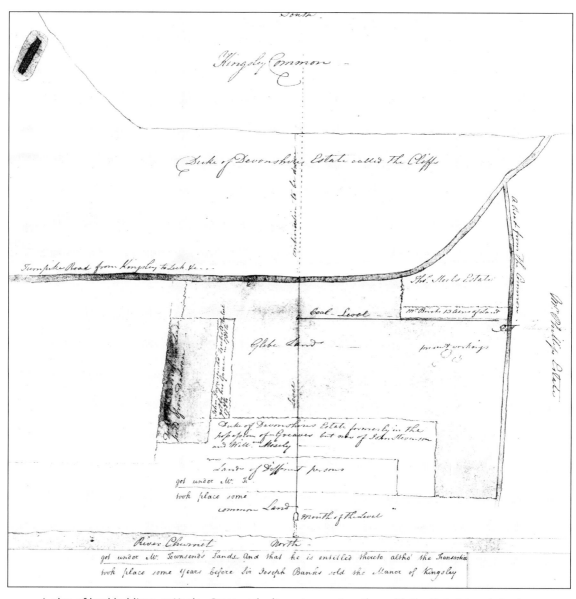

A plan of land holdings at Hazles Cross and adjacent areas together with the Duke's Level. It shows the holdings as at the late – 1770s.

The slight depression in the bottom left hand side of this photograph probably marks the site of the infilled New Pit

intriguing and unanswered question is why, given a surplus sold on (i.e. not sent to Whiston), was coal still purchased from Ross Colliery.

Most of the figures are missing for 1784, but output for 1785 was 10,571 tons although a large amount, probably in excess of 20%, was sold 'to the country'and not used within the business. Significantly, coal output in 1786, the year of maximum ore output, showed a slight decline in total output and about 1,000 tons was sold elsewhere. See p 197 for a summary of output and expenditure.

There was no attempt to run the colliery on the same basis as Ecton. Measurements, terminology, wage structure etc all followed Cheadle coalfield practice. Consequently some of the terms used are unknown so far as Ecton is concerned; e.g. the following are items supplied by Ralph Beadmore, a local blacksmith in 1781/82 (R.Voucher Box 1783): a pare of pinsons; Reathes; fettling an axe (? sharpening it, but he charged 6d, which was half a day's wage); shoes (? horse shoes, at 4d each).

Additional to the land owned by the Duke, there were workings under land owned by Mr Dodson, who was paid 7^{1}/$_{2}$d per ton for his coal under Glebe land, with payments to Mr Sewood at 5d per ton (there are various spellings of his surname); and other land belonging to a John Townsend, who was also paid 7^{1}/$_{2}$d per ton. Underground there was a shallow level and a deep level, which was part or became part, of the 1^{1}/$_{4}$ mile long drainage level known as Duke's Level.

A surviving plan of the surface of the colliery, showing the position of the shafts was reproduced by Herbert Chester. (8) Four shafts are shown. Originally there were the Gin Pit and Smithy Pit. A new shaft was being sunk in February, 1781 and there are references in November, 1783 to dialing for a new shaft and the colliers' bill for a new shaft and some deadwork (i.e. not coal production). The main four shafts would appear to have been the Gin Pit, Meadow Pit, Daniel Carr's Pit and New Pit.

In addition to these four shafts, a further shaft commenced in Glebe land in June 1782. There are references in the surviving accounts to the purchase of a second-hand horse gin being brought to the 'Cros Works' for £10 at that time, together with a payment 'To the men for Ernest and Clod Ale taking Pit to Sink 2s 0d'. This relates to a small advance on wages and ale on taking the bargain to commence sinking. The shaft was not very deep, for in the August 1782 expenses the shaft was being put in order 'for getting coale by Bargen'. A further shaft on the Duke's land is mentioned in the August 1782 expenses too and in September: 'To the men for 11 yards being the remainder of New Shaft in Duck's (sic) land'. A reference at the same time

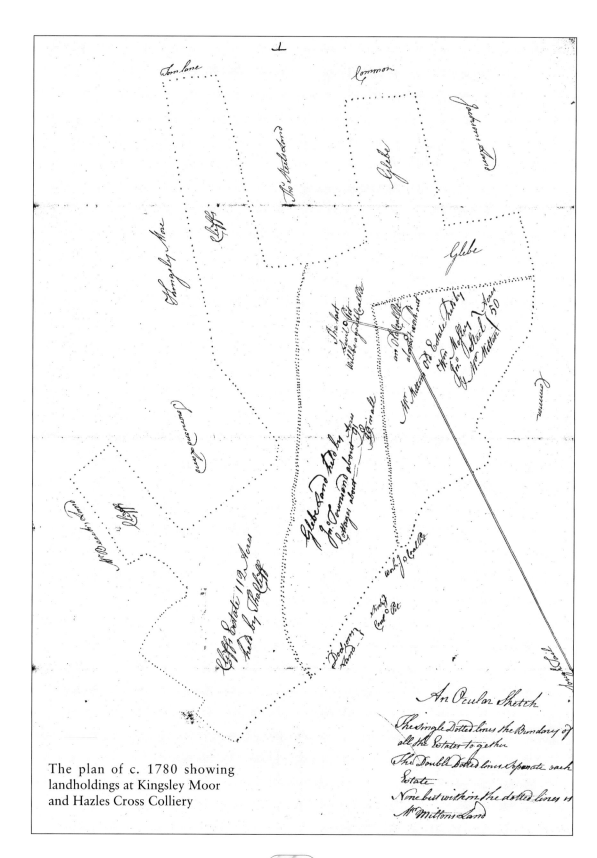

The plan of c. 1780 showing landholdings at Kingsley Moor and Hazles Cross Colliery

to 19 tons being raised the 'New Shaft' indicates some success, but not from which of the two new shafts it was raised from.

Output

For the years 1783-87 inclusive, over 10,000 tons of coal were moved annually to Whiston or directly to The Pen. Most of it went to Whiston, but in any event over 30 journeys a day (except Sundays) were made with a one ton cart, including coal sold 'to the country' i.e., to third parties. The tonnage bound for Whiston or Ecton amounted to 64,445 tons from autumn 1780 to 1788.

The Chatsworth Plan

A crude drawing (see p 192) of Hazles Cross survives at Chatsworth, (AS/3102), which contradicts the Chester plan referred to above. It clearly shows the four shafts. The most easterly, i.e., the one nearest Kingsley, is marked 'sinking'; the nearest one to it is marked as 'working'. The two westerly shafts are marked 'will be a good Coal Pit' (the southerly of the two), whilst the northerly one is marked 'an Old Coal Pit almost work'd out'. The handwriting on the map is that of Cornelius Flint, which would date the map to 1779-early 1780 (after his appointment and prior to the Duke's purchase, as the various ownerships are given). The Glebe land is shown but the most interesting bit is the orientation of the Duke's Level, shown as the 'sough'. This is different from Chester's plan, based upon a now lost original. Was this an earlier drainage level? Probably not, it would seem that the Deep Sough (Duke's Level) had reached Hazles Cross Colliery by 1780. From this, it is possible to make a reasoned attempt at identifying the names of the various shafts. 'The Old Coal pit' is probably Gin Pit; the 'last levil Pit' – the Smithy Pit or the Meadow Pit; the 'working pit' – is probably Daniel Carr's Pit and the 'sinking pit' is New Pit.

It is tempting to try and align some of the field boundaries with Flint's plan, but the shafts would seem to be in the wrong place. Their position is taken from the Chester plan. However the western extension of the Glebe land looks like field 164 and the area marked 'Cliffs' and bounded by 'Kingsley More' and 'Tom Lane' looks like field 166 and maybe 154.

Detail from the Accounts

The expense accounts give away only a little detail to help us to an appreciation of what was going on and there is even less at Foxt Wood. Sales of surplus coal seem to have started in March 1781, when there were 225 tons stockpiled at the colliery. Payments were made for corn for the Duke's Engine horses and at that time there were four lots of contractors. William Barnes supplied 2,400 bricks a few weeks later and there is a further payment (R. May 1781) to William Stoneyer for making bricks. It is not clear if these were for a building or shaft lining. An unusual item was a payment in March 1782 to Mr Gould for '3 yards flannil for 2 wascoats for sum wet work, 3s.6d'. Purchases of flannel would appear to become an annual purchase for waistcoats to help keep the men dry.

In 1781, the Gin Pit horse gin was repaired and 2 wheels were made to go 'over the pit', presumably replacements. These were made by John Milner who also provided 6 yards of pump trees at 2s.6d per yard. Two lengths of pump trees, (wooden pumping pipes), one containing a non-return clack valve, may be seen erected in the Mining Museum at Matlock Bath, Derbyshire. They were recovered from Royledge Copper Mines by Len Kirkham, Peter Thompson and the author and must have been similar to those made by John Milner.

The initial expenditure records indicate that 22 people were paid wages, including four 'lads' and Mary Carr, the gin driver paid 3d a day for 11 days. The daily rate of pay was 14d but some were at a rate of 14s.0d and 15s.0d which may be for a contract. Daniel Carr was paid for 'the get of' 757 tons of coal at 1s.6d per ton which will account for other miners, although we do not know how many. Initial work included driving 18 yards (the fathoms measurement was not used) in the Deep level, but the location in the level is not clear. An analysis of the first six month's activity shows that 6,662 tons of coal were raised, valued at 5s.0d per ton – £1,665, and the costs were £1,060 (£3.18s.0d per ton). Costs in the year 1782 were brought down to under £2.10s.0d per ton.

The manager was John Heath who disbursed wages and paid invoices and produced a statement of expenses and coal sales for each Ecton reckoning. Heath was paid £20 for supervising Kingsley (Hazle Cross) Colliery and £10 for Foxt Wood.

Illumination was by candles and small quantities of gun powder for blasting was purchased from Charles Young at 14d and 18d per lb, in August 1781 and July 1782. Candles and gunpowder were dangerous commodities in most coal mines unless they were well ventilated to remove inflammable gas. A William Hill is reported by Chester (9) to have been killed on January 11th. 1783 'in one of the Coal Pitts at the Hazles Cross Mine' and, was buried by Coroners Warrant (quoting Kingsley Parish Register). The cause of death is not given, either in the Parish Register or in the mine accounts. In fact there is no William Hill mentioned in the accounts (there is a William Hall) and if is not Hall, it must have been a collier working on a bargain with other men and not on a wage (i.e. being paid per ton raised). These men were not named.

The September 1782 accounts also carry two unusual payments. The spare land was mowed and four people gathered in the hay. John Heath claimed for 'caring the hay I charge nothing but I paid for drink to Mowers 3s 8d'. With ale at about 2d per pint, there was clearly a lot of hay being cut. The following year there was a payment for meat and drink for the mowers and hay makers. The second payment of September 1782 was 'To John Tatler for taking care of the Coale when the men did't work on the 16th, 9s 4d'. There were no royal or political events on the 16th September that were of national importance. Was this for a local event? John Tatler is mentioned in August 1785 with an even more unusual entry: Paid for '20 days for care of the Coale when they did not work for twelve months at 7d per day 11s 8d'.

This must relate to Sundays and other days over 12 months and the need to keep an eye on pilfering of the coal stocks.

It is not possible to determine the number of employees for only the labourers were listed. The colliers were paid at a rate per ton of coal produced (1s.9d). There were usually 4-6 men labouring at each of the main shafts. Sinking and Heading (called driving at Ecton) was paid usually as a price per yard. Other men (and a few lads) were involved in other work including drawing stone to the pit bank etc. The amount of work was usually only a few days per Reckoning.

In May 1783, work was progressing at Daniel Carr's pit, the New pit (to be called the New Gin pit); and the Gin pit (later the Old Gin pit). There was also a Meadow pit a little later, so a reference in December 1783 to the New Pit in the Meadow is confusing. The New Pit must have been brick lined, for in February 1784, 17,000 bricks were purchased off Mr Mytton (for £8.10.0d). Six months later there is a reference to 'makeing 21,000 bricks at 6s 6d per thousand', but this would seem to predate the construction of a brick kiln at the mine.

The mine clearly employed children underground, although Salathen (he was known as Sal) Hall's lad was working with his father drawing spoil at 4d per day and may have been on the surface. This was in February 1784. An unnamed boy was hurt underground at about this time, and Dr Jeffery's invoice for treating 'the boys Arme' came to 15s.0d (May 1784). The only other reference to calling out the Doctor was to one of the labourers early in 1787, when William Wetwood badly hurt his leg 'in the works 5s 0d'. He usually worked underground, so that may be assumed. Curiously these labourers hardly ever were paid for a full Reckoning of 6 to 7 weeks. As we do not have details of the coal-getters, perhaps they supplemented that activity with labouring, for which they received a daily wage. Towards the end of the year, the New Gin Shaft saw activity cutting a water course down the shaft side. Some men were paid for 16 day's work at 1s.3d a day for this, but young Thomas Hill did just one day at 3d and John Stevenson worked for 2 days at 5d a day, indicating that he was older. The only reference to

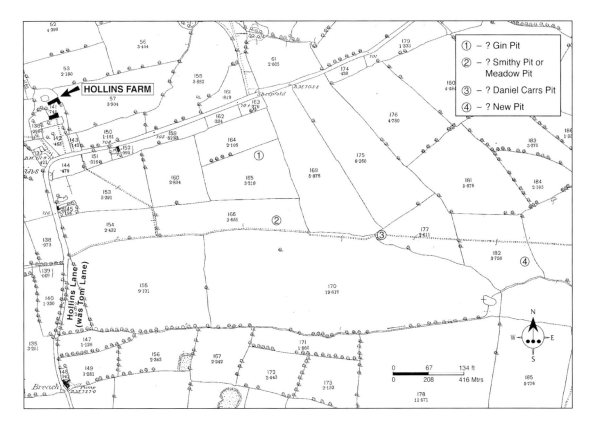

① – ? Gin Pit

② – ? Smithy Pit or Meadow Pit

③ – ? Daniel Carrs Pit

④ – ? New Pit

female employees is the early reference to Mary Carr, the gin driver.

Throughout the 1780s, there are references to filling in shafts and removing the brick lining, but it is not clear if these were shafts from the surface or underground. The management of water was clearly important, despite drainage down to the deep level. References to the purchase of flannel was for jackets or waistcoats to help keep the water out. One wet job must have been tackled in December 1785 when men were 'Paid for Drink Putting up a rowler in the wet shaft.' A rowler seems to have been some means of raising water or perhaps in this case a means of catching it and bringing it to one side of the shaft. (10) The flannel came from Mr Chawner, a mercer of Cheadle. His son was to lease the mine in 1819 from the Duke following its closure in 1818. (11)

Getting water out of Daniel Carr's Pit seems to have become important in mid-1786 when a gutter was laid 'throw the works'. Sometimes a gutter was laid for ventilation, but this would be in areas where the air was poor, such as on headings, coal faces etc. At this time is a payment to Joseph Cornell, 2 days at 2d per day. He must have been a small child for this is the only occasion that 2d a day has been found (R. August 1786). Gutter laying was then done in the other three pits, so the idea had clearly proved successful.

The use of lads underground was generally to pull the coal out of the faces towards the shaft so that it could be drawn up to the surface. The section on Geology below indicates that the seams were under 3 ft high. The coal must have been drawn out on corves, which were like a barrow but with no legs or wheel. It was pulled by a chain attached to a leather girdle known as a 'byatt'. A new byatt chain cost 9d in September 1786. In such low seams, the puller would be crawling on all fours until the main passageway for haulage and air was reached.

By the end of the decade, there were more shafts and a shallow level. There are references to the New Pit in the Duke's land (as distinct from Glebe land), the Coak Pit in the Duke's land and the Old Pit at the Duke's Barn, which may be the Old Gin Pit. The problem with water may have been resolved by January 1789 when there is a reference to Turning the water down the old works. Early in that year there are many references to putting up stone which had been brought from the Cagebrook. Whether this was to give permanence to the waterway or just an indication of poor ground is not clear.

There are no references to horses underground, but there was at least one horse, the gin horse, but he/she worked on the surface and also went off in the mine cart for postwood (pit props). There are references to the purchase of oats by the strike to supplement the grass mown in the fields around the shafts which was cut and carried annually. In one poor year (March 1787), a haystack was purchased for £6 from John Heath. As with hay, more was paid for old oats than for new ones. The difference was 1s.0d per strike, a labourer's daily wage at Ecton.

A new cart 'and Gearing to it' was purchased at the end of 1786 for £7.17s.6d. Among its first uses was to bring stone 'to the roads and Manure to the Land' for which a horse was hired for 14 days. The mine had a stone pit and road maintenance was an ongoing problem for which the Kingsley Parish was notionally responsible. In 1811, Mr Heaton, the Duke's auditor, charged for his expenses 'to Conferences on getting the roads in and near your Grace's works at Kingsley properly repaired by the respective townships.' (12)

A house was built in 1787, 'at Kingsley' and may well be Hollins Farm or the cottage around the corner of the road. It was glazed in June of that year just as work would have been starting on the construction of a brickworks at the mine. It cost 19s.0d for the brick oven. The brick maker was Robert Gelley who wasted no time and had made at least 53,500 bricks by the November Reckoning. Although the accounts record the delivery of 9 loads of sand in November 1787, there is no note of clay deliveries. What were the bricks for? A new shaft was being sunk and 'bricking the pit side' in November 1787 reveals part of the answer. However the Deep level was also being extended and references to arching it provides the rest.

The 1880 OS map shows a 'largish pool' immediately to the south of the area in the middle of the two eastern shafts. One wonders if this was the site of the clay pit for the making of the bricks. The site is now lost as it was subsequently developed by Berry Hill Brickworks Ltd of Stoke-on-Trent as their Kingsley brickworks. Their marl pit, to the west of the buildings, may still be seen from the footpath immediately to the north.

Of the three shafts close to this path, the one in field 166 (See p 195) is still visible from slight settlement of the in-fill. This would appear to be true for the shaft in field 182 (the path now runs a little further to the south and close to the depression). The shaft in field 177 would appear to be somewhere close to the position indicated, but no clear sign of it can now be seen. The shaft in field 165 was not visited. No sign of the brick oven or the coke oven could be seen, but the former is certainly lost below the later brickworks (which closed in c. 1960s) and maybe the coke works was adjacent to it. There are no spoil heaps remaining. (Inspected 18 October 2003)

As new reserves of coal were required and exploited, the insatiable need for postwood (pit props) occupied much activity. The £40 purchase of timber from the Hurts on their Casterne estate south of Wetton was shared by Ecton and Hazles Cross (with tons of charcoal from the branches (cordwood) going to Whiston.

However more was needed and sourced from many wooded areas. What is striking is the record of the movement of this timber viz:

June 1787	'635 Horses at two toul gates when went for wood £2.12.11d'
June 1788	'Paid at Blakely Lane Toolgate for 76 horses 6s 4d'
September 1788	'Paid at the Sheephouse Toul Gate for 212 Horses carrying Postwood to the works 17s 8d'
	'Paid at Blakely Lane Toul Gate for 155 Do. Carrying Do. 12s 11d'

Blakely Lane Gate was at GR 978470 and Sheephouse Gate was at Leekbrook (GR 987540). The latter gate would be on the route to Barleyford Wood at Swythamley on the River Dane. Another gate would have to be passed at Pack Saddle Hollow at GR 918695. (13) If these were the two toul gates mentioned in June 1787 one needs to examine the September 1788

Coal Production						
	Hazles Cross Colliery					
	Total Output	to Whiston/ Ecton	Resting	Expenses £	Sales *	Profit/Loss
1780	3695	2340	1355	451	339	-112
1781	**7967**	5042	2925	2358	731	-1627
1782	**7154**	5860	1294	856	323	-533
1783	**10147**	8977	1170	1183	292	-891
1784	11630	10187	1443	1383	361	-1022
1785	10571	7824	2747	1301	687	-614
1786	10129	8869	1260	1507	315	-1192
1787	10753	8309	1889	1566	472	-1094
1788	**8736**	6789	1947	1338	487	-851
1789	**8460**	6970	1490	1300	372	
Total	89242	71167	17520	13243	4379	-7936
1790	6661	4219	2442	905	610	-295

* Col4 x 5s 0d

	Tonnage	Value *	less annual cost	Net Profit		
1780	3695	924	-112	812		
1781	**7967**	1992	-1627	365		
1782	**7154**	1788	-533	1255		
1783	**10147**	2537	-891	1646		
1784	11630	2907	-1022	1885		
1785	10571	2643	-614	2029		
1786	10129	2532	-1192	1340		
1787	10476	2619	-1078	1541		
1788	**8736**	2184	-851	1333		
1789	**8460**	2115	-928	1187		
Total	88965	22241	-8848	13393		
1790	6661	1665	-295	1370		

* Tonnage x 5s 0d
Bold includes estimates

	Foxt Wood Colliery					
	Total Output	Value	Expenses	Profit/Loss		
1780	359	72	40	32		
1781	1267	253	195	58		
1782	1365	273	172	101		
1783	**1320**	264	219	45		
1784	866	173	180	-7		
1785	827	203	286	-83		
1786	**918**	184	375	-191		
1787	648	279	380	-101		
1788	**1178**	247	317	-70		
1789	Not known					
Total	8748	1948	2164	-216		
1790	Not known					

reference, when 212 horses went through Sheephouse Gate but only 155 horses went through Blakely Lane. This means that the two incidents are unrelated and confirm the use of another route to and from Hazles Cross to avoid Blakely Lane Gate. This route would be the road shown on the lst Edition of the OS map of 1840 from Greendale to Consall and on to what is now Felthouse Lane and paying at the gate there.

However if Sheephouse was the first at which a toll fell due (the second being Pack Saddle gate, then a route bypassing the gate at Felthouse Lane was used and this is indicated again on the OS map of 1840 – From GR 971495 north west of Consall, a road went to the bottom of Basford Bridge Lane and then to Cheddleton Bridge.

An important development is first mentioned in August 1788 and it is the production of coke at the mine. The first reference is 'Delivered to the works [Whiston] 905 9c [905 tons 9 cwt] and coaked' Thereafter coke was sent to Whiston and Ecton.

Thus at the end of the 1780s the Colliery would seem to consist of 4 shafts, two deep enough to merit a horse gin for winding, pens for the stocking of coal; a stable; woodyard for stacking pit props, a brick oven and clay store; and a coking oven.

It will be noticed that the reduction in smelter demand started in 1788, with nearly 1,700 tons less being despatched in 1788 compared to 1787. Similarly there was a reduction in output from 10,500 tons to just over 8,700 tons. There was no indication of increased marketing to maintain demand at its maximum. Although production in 1789 was about the same as the previous year, in 1790 the volume reduced substantially to 6,661 tons in total. Similarly the tonnage dispatched to Whiston in both 1788 and 1789 was about the same at a little under 8,000 tons, but in 1790 it dropped to 4,219 tons.

In the Reckoning of February 1788 is a bill from Sparrow & Co. for 10 tons of coal, endorsed 'Cockhead Frog.' (Cockhead is a local seam of coal) presumably delivered to Froghall, at 5s.3d per ton plus 1s.6d freight – so it had not come far. The question it poses is why was it purchased. Was the curtailing of output at Hazles Cross due to reduced demand coming from Whiston or was the mine failing? The smelter may have been trying another colliery's coal to see how they handled it, if it became necessary.

In 1785 work at the beginning of the year was concentrated at three shafts - New and Old Gin and New Pit, plus Meadow Pit by March. Later in the year, two pits were abandoned and back filled after removing the brick lining. As coal production advanced, pit props – post wood, as it was called – was being brought from many places – Castern; Swythamley (on the River Dane); Ipstones Park; Broad Oaks; Lady Park; Bradnop (? Ashenhurst Hall Estate); Consall Wood (adjacent to Lady Park Wood); Woodhead; Hazles Green; Tomfield Sprink and other places. The location of these are marked on the map on p 120.

An indication of the use of boys to pull wagons of coal to the shafts, often in seams insufficient to enable the drawers to stand, was a reference to Thomas Hill 'a draw boy' who was paid for 23 days work at 7d a day (roughly half the adult male rate) in March 1785.

The Deep Level

References to this are assumed to refer to the Duke's Level, the $1\frac{1}{4}$ mile long drainage level. Herbert Chester (13) states that it was started in 1784, but he is wrong, it predates 1770. In 1785, there are references to 'sloughing the deep level'. Sloughing possibly means clearing the level of rubbish, but one cannot be sure. Payment was made for driving the deep level in June 1786, plus another payment for 'three person going down the deep levil, 10s 6d' – a significant payment. A year's 'sough rent' was paid to Sir Joseph Banks (presumably as a wayleave for crossing his land) £6 p.a.

With production in 1785-86 running at c.10,000 tons p.a. (it is likely that production in 1783-84 was similar but records are missing) the need to keep the pit dry was important and a lot of water must have been removed by this level, which also seems to have been extended to drain pits south of Hazles Cross Colliery. There is no note of the use of boats on this level as occurred at the Duke's colliery at Thatch Marsh, south west of Buxton, where the drainage level was also used for removing coal by boat (it was also called Duke's Level).

The estate of Sir Joseph Banks was sold in 1790 to James Beech. The Sough rents would have continued as before but in 1811 Beech was trying to increase the rental. There followed discussions with Mr Heaton, the Duke's accountant. However Heaton reported that Beech's application was 'doubtful in consequence of the coal for which it [the Dukes Level] had been originally reserved having become exhausted.' (14)

Geology

The Geological map for Ashbourne and Cheadle shows the surface area of Hazles Cross Colliery as being Westphalian A : the top series of the Carboniferous sequence. This included at least 20 seams of coal but a plan in the Geological Memoir (15) indicates that the area of the colliery was above the Woodhead coal where the main seams consisted of the two Dilhorne Seams, plus the Parkhall Sweet Coal, Alecs, Cobble and Rider Coals. Just how many of these occurred at the colliery is not recorded.

The local ironstone was 585ft or so below the Woodhead coal so it would not have been found by the Duke's miners. The nearest section of formations to Hazles Cross Colliery is at Hazlewall Colliery (16) which consisted of the Mans seam (2ft); the Cobble Coal (3ft); the Rider Coal (1ft 6in) and the Woodhead Coal (3ft), at a depth of some 787ft below the surface. Hazlewall is south of Hazles Cross. It would appear that the Duke's Level was at a horizon above the Froghall Ironstone band too. Given the value of the copper ore to the Duke, it's ironic that the coal mine was draining water directly above another ore which was to prove so valuable some 70 or so years later and after the Duke had relinquished his interests in the area.

Hollins Farm

Hollins Farm deserves a mention, especially as the hedgerows nearby contain a high percentage of holly. Prior to the improvements in agriculture of the mid- to late 18th century, fodder yields were often insufficient to sustain stock throughout the winter. It was therefore common to grow holly, the higher and less thorny growth being cut and fed to animals. The areas of holly growth were often on the perimeter of a parish. (17)

Another reason has been advanced for the explanation for Hollin place names on the perimeter of a parish (as is the case at Hazles Cross). This is that the name was associated with places where a stock man could find secure grazing for his animals and a place to sleep, or if a cattle drover, somewhere to find conviviality before retiring to sleep with his animals. (18)

Such places would be a farmstead usually standing on its own with a group of little paddocks and enclosed lane leading to the farm. Hollins Farm meets this criteria, if the lane to the farm is from Tomsprink on the nearby A52.

It has been suggested above that Hollins Farm may have been built by the Duke, but the nearby cottage may have been the mine house if, as may be the case, Hollins Farm has a much older history.

Shaw Colliery

Herbert Chester in his history of the Cheadle Coalfield clearly did not know about the activities of John Beech. His son purchased the Shaw(e) estate from the disposal sale of Sir Joseph Banks in 1790. It included the manorial rights at Kingsley and fetched £3,300, against the expectations of the Banks agents. In fact James Beech appears to have experienced some difficulties in settling the purchase price. John Beech died on 20th October 1787 and the Kingsley Register describes him as being 'of the Shaw, Sqier'.

Chester (19) states that 'Beech must have started mining operations before 1800' and clearly means James, but the Ecton accounts show that coal was being supplied in 1779 (the detailed invoices prior to this are not available). Coal was sold at 4s.5$^1/_3$d (sic) per ton plus 4s.0d carriage to Whiston. Despite some substantial tonnages per reckoning, supplies seem to have ended once the Duke purchased the Kingsley colliery. From the December 1779– August 1780 period, the Reckonings indicate that 1,844 tons were carted to Whiston.

The current Shaw Hall is of 19th century date, with a drive off Shawe Park Road, the road to Cheadle from Kingsley Holt. Although coal deliveries ended, the Ecton mine continued to purchase timber from 'Mr Beech of the Shaw' especially ash and beech trees. The loss of the coal contract must have been a substantial loss, especially as the nearby Ross Colliery continued its supplies to Whiston.

Ross Colliery

This mine was certainly being described in the Ecton Accounts as belonging the Messrs Gilbert by May 1783.

It supplied Whiston by November 1779 (when detailed records of coal deliveries to Whiston begin in the Devonshire Collection). Even after this time, the records are frustratingly incomplete. However, it is likely that some 2,800 tons of coal were delivered to Whiston in 1782 and the deliveries for 1780-81 may have been similar. The coal cost 5s.6d delivered to Whiston. Delivery figures for 1783 are largely missing, but may have been substantially less.

The Gilberts had large interests in mining and quarrying in the area and needed slack for their Froghall and Cauldon limekilns, although those at Froghall were not built until 1786 (at a cost of £312.12s.4d). (20) Farey (21) refers to Rossbank Colliery, being $^1/_4$ mile south of Lees in Kingsley, Staffordshire, in his list of Collieries, but is not clear as to its proprietors or even if it was still working.

Lead (22) may be referring to Ross Colliery when he refers to the Gilbert's interests in a coalmine on the 'south west side of the Churnet Valley'. This was leased from a Mr Whitehall (for 31 years at a $^1/_8$th duty from 18th May 1759) working the Woodhead seam. (23) The Gilberts had been behind an amalgamation of mines in the area, formed in 1762, to which they leased their colliery. However in 1777, the Gilberts objected to a payment of £150 between two of the other partners. In 1780 there was a further disagreement and as a result the partnership collapsed despite the 1777 dispute deciding against the Gilberts on a referral for Counsel's opinion. Chester gives details of the disagreement (24) but indicates that the Gilberts withdrew from coal mining in the Cheadle Coalfield in favour of their interests at Worsley. This clearly is not the case. They must have continued under their lease, selling a lot of coal to Whiston despite the Duke having two collieries in the area.

Their connections with the Duke may have acted in their favour, for with the purchase of Kingsley Colliery (Hazles Cross) in 1780, purchases of coal from Mr Beech at Shaw Colliery terminated. Perhaps more importantly, despite being much cheaper per ton, Shaw coal cost 4s.0d per ton carriage, making it 8s.5$^1/_3$ per ton delivered against 5s.6d per ton delivered from Ross Pit.

Foxt Wood

Geology

The Geological Memoir (25) shows a section through a shaft 'Near Foxt'. It is marked on the associated plan as being nearer Foxt Wood than Foxt village. The shaft section shows the main coal seam as being the Ribbon coal with two thin seams above it. The Ribbon coal on the section indicates a width of 2ft 3in. These seams were beneath the Woodhead Coal. A working at Grid Ref., 02674815 yielded 'Coal 11$^1/_2$ in on dirt 2in on Coal 11in' (26). At a depth of approximately 100ft was a seam of 16in of Froghall Ironstone – the calcareous ironstone which caused the 'iron rush' in the 1850s. There are no references in the accounts to indicate that the Duke's miners mined this stone or even recognised its significance. Yet if it was not found, the miners could have only been a few feet above it. Given that the coal was not of the best quality, judging by the few records which survive, it is ironic that the ground contained this valuable seam. The mine accounts mention problems with faults and this may account for the difference in the two sections. No plan of the workings at Foxt Wood in the Duke's era survive.

Activity at the Mine

On the 19 June 1780, at the George Inn, Leek, Staffs (now demolished for road widening, but on the corner of Church Street and St Edward Street) a local auctioneer had for sale the Fox Wood (sic) Colliery and a moiety of another colliery at Jack Elm (sic), in Kingsley parish. (27) It is tempting to think that the purchaser was Mr Mytton, the vendor of Hazles Cross Colliery to the Duke. In the same year Mytton is known to have had an interest in a mine at Jack Elms. He may have sold on the Foxt Wood land to the Duke a short time afterwards. The Duke did take out a lease of land at Foxt Wood, although the details are not known, and it may have been either for a lease of the Colliery or a lease of more, contiguous land.

Foxt Wood Colliery was much smaller than Hazles Cross Colliery. The workings were shallower and in the accounts there are several references to sinking [a new shaft] and the in-filling and removal of bricks from an 'old shaft'. This makes location of the workings at any particular time difficult to determine. Today, the area still retains several spoil heaps (pit lows) (See p 204) Some are covered with scrub and at least one hawthorn of significant size indicating great age of the spoil heap. In the late 1780s, much slack coal was extracted from 'Foxt Lane' and taken to the limekiln on Wetton Hill, but it is not possible to determine precisely which pit this was; there are several pit heaps near to the lane.

Adjacent to the area of Foxt Wood Colliery is Whieldon's Wood. John and Joseph Whieldon received a royalty from activities at the mine, based upon £55 per acre worked. Timber from the wood was used in the mine by John Whieldon, who was a carpenter. The former and adjacent pub to the mine still proudly displays its name: The Woodcutters. From time to time royalties were also paid to a John Brown.

The mine was worked on a similar basis as Hazles Cross, with day rates for labourers and the colliers being paid for each ton of coal obtained (in 1780 for instance, it was 1s.11d per ton). Consequently, as at Hazles Cross, the number of people involved is not known. Only towards the end of the decade, in January 1789 was some work set by 'bargain'. Whether this was different from the price per ton though, is not known. What is known is that Foxt Wood employed a woman underground. A couple of records survive indicating that Ann Brindley was working the same days as the men in the Reckoning for March 1787. However, whilst the men received 1s.2d per day, she received 6½d per day. She would not have been employed drawing up the shafts or similar work, because the number of days involved would have been fewer. She must have been drawing corves from the working faces to the main haulage way and perhaps moving coal from there to the shaft bottom.

Corves (like wheelbarrows with no legs or wheels) would have been dragged on all-fours out of the confined seam. The seam thickness was only 2ft 3ins (0.69m) as mentioned above. In December 1785, there is a reference to 'Paid Aron [Beardmore] for assisting Macking Real Road underground for a wagon.' This reference to railing a haulage level is the only one found for Hazles Cross or Foxt Wood, so it is unclear whether the use of wagons on rails was used in all of the two collieries' haulage levels as at Ecton. It is convenient to assume so, but so much of the methodology of working and the terminology was completely different from the copper mine. There is no reference to underground horses, so the waggons would be manually pushed or pulled to the shaft bottom, including the slack pit (? Stocking Pit) where Ann Brindley worked. The method of pulling corves or tubs is given under Hazles Cross.

A feature of the wage structure which differed from Hazles Cross was the distribution of burn coals – free coal for workers. It has not proved possible to determine the basis upon which it was provided and it usually involved only a handful of people. It was charged to the mine account at the rate of 4d per person per week. The mine was under the charge of John Heath, as at Hazles Cross.

Children as well as Ann Brindley were employed underground. There are many references to dray boys. (Draying basically meant carrying or moving material, e.g. spoil. In June 1783 there is a mention of 'draying a wind rope from Cross'.) Children – they were all boys – were paid 6d-7d per day. Boys on a lower rate of 3d-4d a day probably worked on the surface or were younger.

Work During the Decade

Shortly after commencing work, a new shaft was sunk. The February 1781 Reckoning refers to the purchase of 2,400 bricks and at the same time mentions that this shaft was already producing coal (90 tons against 183 tons from the 'old shaft' still in production). As new shafts were sunk, or perhaps a level driven (the level pit in February 1783), a cabin and fleaks were built for use of the workers/colliers there. They were probably cheap and cheerful: there is a reference in February 1783 to straw for cabin and 3 fleaks – perhaps for the cabin roof and for in-filling intertwined branches used for weather protection around the cabin or perhaps a shaft top.

In Derbyshire, near Wensley, there was a Straw Fleak Grove in 1702. (28) The cabin was over the shaft top. In October 1785, John Whieldon was paid for 'Powls [poles] for Cabin ove Foxtt Wod pit.'

During 1783, there was work on the new level, including arching it at the end of the year and 'sinking a shaft for the level' early in 1784 together with carrying wood to it. Driving the new level continued throughout 1784 and into 1785. There were clearly problems with ventilation and over 100 yards of 'air guttering' was laid to alleviate the problem. Whether someone was operating a pair of bellows or this was natural ventilation is not clear. The situation of this level is not known either.

It is highly probable that underground plans of both here and Hazles Cross Collieries were not made at the time. Certainly none survive at Chatsworth except p 192. Amongst other purchases at this time was 'pitch used for blasting' and flannel to make jackets for use in wet conditions in the new level. In February 1786 the mine bought a pair of byatts for 3s.6d; a thong (3d); and 2 pairs of Girdles (5s.6d) – all connected with the removal of the coal from the headings, or coal faces, and nothing to do with the purchase of underwear! They were parts of the leather gear which enabled the puller to pull a corve or wagon laden with coal.

A list of purchases of slack from Foxt Wood exists with the February 1786 accounts. It is interesting to see who was purchasing it. The quantities are 'loads':

'John Smith for Caldon Lo Coy	1541	£23.	2.	0
James Duon for Hemingslo	850	12.	15.	0
James ? of Hilsdale	610	9.	3.	0
J Simson of Grindon	435	6.	10.	0
John Mellor of Cordon	252	3.	15.	6
Georg Chadak	88	1.	6.	6
Samul Bostack not paid	200	3.	0.	0'

Clearly the majority of it was going to two quarries which are working today – Cauldon Lowe and Hemingslow, to burn the limestone in their lime kilns. The quantities are unclear. A little later, slack was being sold by the load, which is known to have been 1 cwt, at 5s.0d per load. Consequently, Samuel Bostock was not purchasing 2 cwt, but more like 12 cwt and the relationship between that and 200 is not obvious. Much of the slack output was sent to Wetton Hill (or Hills as it was then called) shortly afterwards.

In June 1786 there is the first reference to a deep level, i.e., there were then two levels. Alder wood was being purchased at that time for pump trees, and a continuing supply of postwood (or pit props) was being fetched from wherever it was available. A 'boatman' was paid for bringing a boat load to Froghall a little earlier in 1786. Supplies were also coming from Cloughhead Wood, north of the Colliery.

In addition, as at Hazles Cross, was the purchase of 'rails and stoops'. Rails could be wooden rails for a wagon way and stoops could be the sleepers, but caution is suggested. They were often purchased with 'slobs', which were wooden packing pieces behind wall and roof supports, so they are probably part of the wall and roof support system.

A little help is found in the accounts for another query. At the beginning of 1787, stone and clods (presumably for the roof?) were brought for a smithy. At the same time a load of bricks was fetched from Kingsley. The Duke's brickworks had not started production at that date, so this confirms the existence of a brickworks prior to that. Whether the Duke purchased this earlier one is not known, but no record of such a payment exists and the records of capital expenses by the Duke at this time are fairly comprehensive. Where the other works was therefore needs to be determined.

Today, the working of this small pit seems difficult to fully appreciate. Some of its pit heaps survive in a kind of silent testimony of a long disappeared way of life, or at least the difficulties of winning coal from a seam 2ft 3in thick. A photograph of working a small seam (albeit at Bristol) will give some idea of how the coal was won and how awkward was the job of removing it on all-fours (See p 185). So much of what was then commonplace has now been forgotten. An example was the work in January 1787 of Thomas Davenport who made ten journeys from Joseph Walton's wood (described in the summary account as Whieldon Wood, nearby). Getting the wood out of the steep valley side required the expert use of seven horses pulling the timber clear. The invoice makes it clear the timber was carried, not dragged, and all the horses used each time.

In June 1787, Smith and Knifton of Oakamoor supplied 15 rolled iron plates 'for...the men to work under', indicating the need for more substantial support for the roof in poor ground. It was not all soft going so far as the rock conditions were concerned, for regular but small quantities of gunpowder were being purchased from Loton Tipper, the area's equivalent of Robert Low at Warslow. The extraction of slack, which was sold at 6s.0d per ton indicates that it was either of better quality to that produced previously, or the valuation of coal in the Colliery accounts at 4s.0d per ton was too low.

The absence of plans of these workings means that the shafts suggested as representing the Duke's workings are not supported by documentary evidence. However this is the area known as Foxt Wood to this day and some of the workings are close to Foxt Lane where it is known that slack was being extracted. Chester (29) indicates that he believed the mines to be further north nearer to Whieldon Farm, but gives no reason for suggesting this. Certainly the pit heaps at Foxt Wood indicate shallow workings, characterised by the Duke's mine. It closed in 1812. (30)

1780s Production at Foxt Wood

Foxt Wood was very much a small enterprise compared to Hazles Cross and, one suspects, other pits in the area. Its output and profit was small, but it clearly served its purpose of delivering a poorer quality coal to the lime kilns at Ecton and Wetton and the brickyards at Whiston and Newhaven. The production figures indicate a small loss for several years, but this is unlikely to be as bad as shown. Several Reckonings include tonnages for coal and slack together. The slack was being sold at 6s.0d per ton, higher than the price paid for Hazles Cross coal (5s.0d) and 50% up on the coal price at Foxt Wood. As little coal was sold from

This page: mine tips at Foxt Wood with a shaft (left) situated on the left of the middle photograph. Opposite: OS Map of 1900 showing Foxt Wood

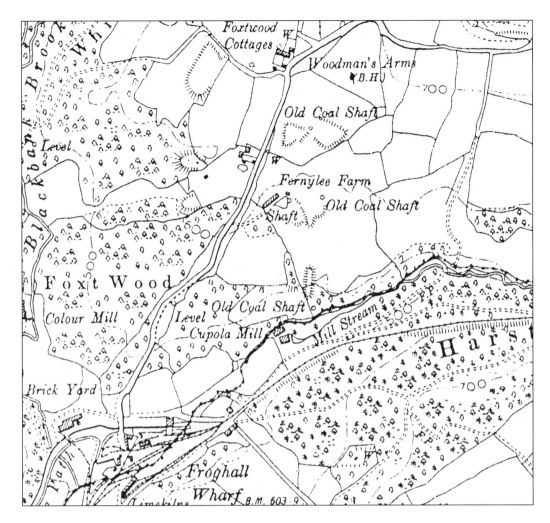

here, the internal price of 4s.0d per ton used shows only marginal profitability, but there is no way of knowing if this was a reasonable price for the concern to have applied to it.

Coal was sold by the ton and slack by the load (1 cwt). Fortunately, just one Reckoning account gives enough detail to be able to work out that a load equates with 1 cwt! It was mentioned above that the colliers switched to working by 'bargain' from January 1789 instead of being paid by the ton raised. Thereafter the Reckonings give no details of the tonnage raised.

From 1781, the output of the Colliery ranged in the 1,270-1,370 tons region for three years and then fell to 866 tons in 1784. Slightly lower the following year, it rose 100 tons in 1786 and then went above 1,000 tons in 1787-88 as The Stockings Pit started to produce the more valuable slack, used in lime production. However the exact quantity of slack produced is not clear as some months show a combined total for 'coal and slack'. These figures have been shown as valued at 4s.0d per ton and therefore the losses in 1787-88 are likely to be less. Indeed, the pit may have been close to breaking even and in some Reckonings in 1788 made a profit. As indicated above, figures for 1789-90 are not available. Today we equate slack with poor quality coal, whilst at Foxt Wood it was more valuable than the coal. Total output from mid-1780-1788 was a little over 9,000 tons with the mine more or less breaking even over that period.

Chapter 10, on Roads and Transportation, examines the route the packhorses would have taken to reach the Duke's Lane. To the west of Windyway Cross the route is clearly marked by guide stones still in position.

1   Dev. Coll., Notebook of Expenses of the 5th Duke, 1774 – 1812

2   see Chester, H., *The History of the Cheadle Coalfield, Staffs*, 2002, p 46, when a miner from there was seeking parish relief

3   VCH Staffordshire, vol. 7., Leek and the Moorlands, 1996, p 52

4   DRO Q/RIc32 referred to in Roberts A.F., & Leach J.R., *The Coal Mines of Buxton*, 1985, pp 18-19

5   Dev. Coll., Notebook of the 5th Duke's purchases, 1773-1810

6   Dev. Coll., L/76/20

7   Farey, J., *General View of the Agriculture and Minerals of Derbyshire*, Vol. II, 1815, pp 436-437

8   Chester, H., op. cit., p 52. The source of the plan is not given

9   Chester, H., op.cit., p 53

10 Rieuwerts, J.H., *Glossary of Derbyshire Mining Terms*, 1998, p 130

11 Chester, H., op. cit., p 76

12 Dev. Coll., AS/901,

13 Victoria County History: Staffordshire, Vol 7, the Staffordshire Moorlands, pp 99 & 217

14 Dev. Coll. AS/901

15 Chisholm J.I., et al., *Geology of the Country Around Ashbourne and Cheadle*, 1988, p 57

16 op.cit., p 58

17 Spray, M., Agricultural History Review, 1981, Vol XXIX Holly as a Fodder in England, pp 97-110

18 Atkin, M.A., Nomina, 1988-89, Vol XII, Hollin Names in North East England', pp 77-88

19 Chester, H., op.cit., p 62

20 see Lead, P., *Agents of Revolu*tion, pr.pt. c.1989, p 170

21 Farey, J., *General View of the Agriculture and Minerals of Derbyshire*, vol 1, 1811, p 208

22 Lead, P., op.cit., pp 118-19

23 Chester H., op. cit., pp 36-37

24 op.cit., *p 41*

25 Chisholm J.I., et al., op.cit., p 57

26 op.cit., p 63

27 *Derby Mercury* 26th May 1780. Coincidentally, this paper also carries an advert for the sale of assets of Robert Shore

28 Rieuwerts, J.H., *Glossary of Derbyshire Lead Mining Terms*, 1998, p 74

29 Chester, H., op. cit., p 54-55

30 Chester, H., op. cit., p 55

SALES & PROFIT

Once coarse metal production started at Ecton, output and sales were low, chiefly, one suspects, because it was all for the benefit of the Executors of the 4th Duke (later called the Trustees of the late Duke's younger sons) rather than for the 5th Duke who had management of the mine. The fact that the smelted ore was of poorer quality may also be relevant. Only some 31 tons of coarse metal was produced and most of it was sold to Roe & Co (25 tons). Cooper & Rotten purchased no metal at all.

During the period 1761-1768, all the ore was sold to Patten (2,197 tons–£30,287); Cooper & Rotton (1,860 tons–£26,976) and Roe (1,790 tons–£27,235). The total sales were 5,847 tons and a value of £84,498, the values including the small tonnage of metal (see p 4). These figures differ from those shown in the audited accounts, but are based on each Company's own figures sent to the mine during the Shore fraud enquiries. The difference perhaps relates to the audited figures not being based on a calendar year. If one adds the audited figures for 1769, the difference is reduced to 63 tons of ore more in the audited figures.

Nonetheless, the breakdown of sales gives a good idea of where ore was being sold.

Ore and Metal Sales

| Year | Ore | | | | Metal | | | Value | | | (£) |
	Roe	Cooper	Patten	Total	Roe	Patten	Total	Roe	Cooper	Patten	Total
1761	-	113	162	275	-	-			1,416	2,244	
1762	231	269	190	690	-	-	-	3,095	3,661	1,798	
1763	166	251	343	760	-	-	-	2,728	3,567	4,724	
1764	264	333	211	808	-	-	-	2,006	4,501	2,879	
1765	381	217	107	705	7	2	9	6,606	3,311	1,457	
1766	283	212	367	862	7	2	9	4,974	3,724	5,826	
1767	240	465	236	941	5	1	6	3,925	6,796	3,758	
1768	225	-	581	806	6	1	7	3,901	-	7,601	
Total	1,790	1,860	2,197	5,847	25	6	31	27,235	26,976	30,287	
											84,498

[Figures from details submitted by each Company, except for 1768 when the mine figures show a larger amount.]

Ore was sold by the system of ticketing. In 1771 both Roe & Co. and Patten (calling themselves 'The Warrington Copper & Brass Company at the time) spelt it 'Tickett'. Samples of ore were assayed by the smelters, who then bid for the ore at so much per ton, in writing. Only a few Ticketts survive, all from 1771. Payments due by the mine were generally paid at the mine, the amount being receipted by the supplier. Whether the cash due to the mine was sent to Ecton is not clear, but it would appear to be the case and would avoid the necessity of bringing huge sums of money regularly to the mine from Chesterfield for the Reckonings.

In May 1761, the accounts record 'bill for meat and drink for ye Gentlemen at sales £1.19.3'. In the following August is 'Mr Davenport for one Galland of wine £0.8.0d', which is rather expensive by today's prices. Although there are specific additional references: May & June

1762. 'Elizth. Chadwick Bill for Meat and Drink at Weighs' and Nov 1764 'Thos. Talor bill for Tabaccow at Weighdays £0.2.10d', there are no more in the surviving accounts, but it is difficult to believe that refreshments were not provided. The occasional bill for rum and hops/ malt gives credence to this.

Ore Sales

In the previous account of Ecton's 18th century history (1) the 'output' for 1781 is stated by John Robey to be 4,000 tons and indeed it is. However this is confusing as it consists of approximately 3,500 tons of ore raised and 500 tons of dressed ore. For the purpose of this book, raised ore consists of both ore as indicated in the accounts as 'raised ore' – believed to be principally, if not excusively, 'Botham' ores – plus 'Hillock ore', being ores extracted from 'coarse ores', which would have contained a higher percentage of gangue minerals, e.g. fluorspar or calcite and even rock, depending upon the vein width. 'Botham' ores consisted of ore from large deposits and the only inferior, or coarse, ores from that source would be from the edge of the deposit.

'Dressed' ores consisted of beaten down 'Botham' ores – reduced to the size of a nutmeg according to Efford in 1769 – and 'Slimes' the fine particles of copper ore retrieved by separation in water. In terms of raised ore values, to add dressed ores would appear to be a duplication and the figures used in this book treat the two entirely separately. If your author is incorrect, the two need adding together, but before the latter is addressed, one needs to enquire where the extraction costs for this additional amount are to be located in the mine's expense account; they do not exist.

In 1786, some ore raised is termed 'Grove ore', believed to refer to ore raised from veins rather than the pipe deposit, or from other mines on the hill in the Duke's possession. 'Botham' is the old way of spelling 'Bottom' and should be pronounced as such. The ore raised figures do not always differentiate between lead and copper and it is important to bear this in mind.

1780s Ore and Metal Production

Sales figures for copper metal after 1781 have not been located, so 'output' has to be judged against the production of copper metal. The consistent parameter which has been used is the cake copper dressing (literally) figures from the invoices submitted by John Orme. His tonnage equates to the figures of tonnage carried by the two regular carriers of copper cakes from Whiston to Ashbourne.

Using these and adding notional figures (with care) where the invoice is missing, it has been possible to assess the annual production. The initial astonishment is that production fell in 1782. For the last half of the year production was running below 40 tons per 6–7 week reckoning and this rate ran into 1783. After production running at around 600 tons in 1780-81 and at that rate (broadly) in the first half of 1782, the rate dropped to produce a figure for 1782 of about 450 tons.

Ore production may have been slightly lower in 1782, but the overall picture does not indicate a reining back of ore output. Coal consumption was not less, rising significantly in fact. Output from Ross Colliery fell significantly, however what was the reason for the reduced metal production? Ore production in the period 1780-1783 remained fairly static despite metal output of 600 tons per annum in 1780/81, as mentioned above. The mine could have afforded to maintain production higher than sales, yet the 1782 metal production was 75% of the previous year.

Even with a large quantity of ore 'on the bank' at Ecton, it was mainly of poorer ores. The mine could stretch its metal output by concentrating on using only the richest ores except for the minimum of poorer ores needed as a flux. With ore output running at 2,200 tons or so, ore at a richness of 20% (and it was unlikely to be higher than this) would yield 440 tons of metal.

With metal output actually at 600 tons, an additional 800 tons of ore at 20% yield would be needed. It is doubtful if they would have that quantity in reserve for very long. Maybe the mine had more in stock than had been thought.

Perhaps the lower metal production of 1782-83 reflects the difficulty of finding a market, maybe in the face of aggressive marketing from Thomas Williams of Anglesey. Caution needs to be drawn over the output shown for 1783, as no figures are available for the four mid-year Reckonings. If the deduced figures are too low, an increase does bring the total for the year to a level more in keeping with the figures for 1782 and 1784-85. Such a move reinforces the uniformity of production at around 450 tons per annum.

Coal consumption during this period varied between 8,500-9,500 tons per annum, the actual figures depending on missing totals as with ore and metal output. Despite coal being required for the Ecton lime kiln and the Newhaven brick kiln, the quantities used here would not have been great enough to materially affect the total volume required. It would seem that, as a ball-park figure, ore smelting required something like 3.5 tons of coal to a ton of ore during 1781-85.

Ore output, having apparently fallen a little in 1782 recovered and continued to rise annually, with a figure of 3,100 tons in 1785, the first time the volume was over 3,000 tons. Output may have reached 3,500 tons in 1786, possibly the year of peak production, but the figure of 4,000 tons (Porter & Robey, op.cit., p 106) cannot be substantiated. The total ore output for 1780-89 was about 26,000 tons.

The metal output for 1781 was confirmed by Farey: '12 tons of refined copper were produced weekly from the mine.' (2) What is clear is that the following quote from Bromfield (3) re the period 1781-85 cannot be substantiated: it is wrong – 'Records of production and sales at Ecton would seem to indicate a slowing down in output at the mine, although it might remain uncertain that this was connected with the national crisis in the copper trade'. There was no slowing down at the mine; just the opposite in fact.

Profit & Loss

Perhaps the title of this section could have been better worded, for the Duke's activities yielded few losses for decades. Moreover, profit and loss implies revenue accounting whereas the mine made no distinction between day to day activities and capital expenditure. Thus, the erection costs of Whiston smelter and its subsequent expansion were all absorbed in the revenue accounts. Insufficient detail survives to take them out, but clearly as time went on, the profit became understated by an ever increasing total of capital expenditure. Moreover, the huge number of bricks and tiles purchased by the mine seems to indicate that the Wetton estate costs were to some extent, being absorbed by the mine. (e.g. what were the 36,000 tiles (or thereabouts) purchased by the mine – as distinct from the 4,000 purchased at the same time by Whiston – really acquired for? It seems inconceivable that they were used at Ecton)

Work under the Duke started on 10th October 1760. By the end of 1769, sales of ore and coarse metal (of which the latter was an insignificant part) amounted to £96,872. Expenditure during this period was £44,375, yielding a profit of £52,497. These figures are from the surviving audited accounts. The latter are available until 1774 and the above figures indicate a profit of 54% of turnover.

In the period 1770-79, the profit was 35.5%, having dropped because of development costs at Whiston, the Collieries and at Ecton. Expenditure in the 1760s had averaged £4,930 p.a. until Whiston smelter opened in 1770, with revenue at an average of £10,760 and profit averaging £5,830. Thereafter, the figures are £7,785 and £12,064 and a profit of £4,279 p.a.

The 1770s suffered from a collapse of the metal price in 1775 from £92 p. ton to £77-£82 p. ton, with some evidence of a discount for volume. This came as ore sales were abandoned in 1774. It is indicated below that in 1780 there was £20,000 worth of ore in stock. Twenty tons of ore was sold in 1782 at £15 p. ton. At this figure, over 1,300 tons remained to be smelted. Notwithstanding the price drop, the tonnage smelted rose significantly. Care needs to be exercised in making comparisons between the figures for 1770-74 and those for the next five years. The initial figures are from the audited accounts, which ran on a year ending 31st March, while the figures for the last five years are for calendar years. Moreover the figures for 1775 are from July only.

After the extension of the smelter in 1780, business levels began to alter dramatically. Expenditure rose in 1780, but this reflects the capital outlay. It reached £15,800 with revenue at £24,878. In 1781, expenditure rose to £17,000 or thereabouts. Figures are available for the first half of the year and for 1782 and an estimate has had to be used for the last half of 1781 drawn from levels either side. The revenue in 1781 rose dramatically however to £44,577, a huge leap to give £27,500 (61.9%) profit. This reflects not only increased production, but increased demand for the metal. See further analysis below.

A letter dated 8th July 1780 survives. It includes a note of a previously unknown visit to Ecton on 4th July 1780. It states that:

'upwards of 300 men, women and children are employed and at Whiston... about 200 more. This is I believe the best Copper Mine in the Kingdom and besides the payment of wages and every other Incidentiall Expence clears upwards of £15,000 per Annum and had they more Smelting Furnaces there can be no doubt of its clearing considerably more. Near 20,000 Pounds worth of Copper Ore lie on the Banks ready for working up'. (4)

No doubt the writer had been advised of these figures whilst at the mine. It is likely that the number of employees at Whiston includes the colliers of Foxt Wood and Hazles Cross. If the employee figures appear plausible, one is inclined to take the profit and value of ore on the bank at face value too. Tonnages of ore raised rose from around 1778 and this must have reflected in improved sales and profitability. Given the lack of full information and the rise in profit, once Whiston was extended, to £27,500, it is suggested that for 1778-79 the profit was probably about £15,000 p.a. However the figures on p 4 show a lower and more cautious assessment, based upon the only actual records available.

Clearly the mine became a substantial creditor to the purchasers of ore and then metal. In 1772, an incomplete account of the year shows Roe & Co., owing £1,280; Cooper & Rotton £7,979 and Patten £8,931, amounting to £18,190 – a huge amount of money. In later years the Duke advanced money to the debtors to enable them to ease their cash flow (at 5% interest), presumably at times of volatility in the market.

The level of profitability in the 1770s was influenced by the inability to sell tonnages above 100 tons prior to 1777. Levels were generally in the 80s and there was a dependence upon ore sales, which stopped in 1774. This followed the agreement with Dawes, which opened up the London market. It was the East India Company contract that improved sales in 1776, although the sales figures appear under 1777. Despite much improved sales in 1777-79, the revenue from copper for 1770-79 was only £120,644, against £96,872 for 1760-69. The profit for the same period was £42,794, (1760-69 £52,497). Thus, the rise in turnover saw profit down by £10,000 or so. This reduced profit includes capital expenditure at Ecton and Whiston which really needs adding back.

Sales figures do not survive for the 1780s, only for 1780-81. The only guidance comes from the amount of ore dressed at Whiston, as mentioned above, and these figures have been used for 1782 onwards. Some figures are missing for specific Reckonings and careful estimates used to complete annual totals. From the 1775-80 ore sales book, it is known that costs of sales were about 4%. The price on the London market in 1781-91 was £102.6s.8d per ton (5) and less 4% gives a figure of £98 p. ton in round terms. However in 1781, Ecton was selling copper metal at £76-£87 p. ton (which reflected a welcome rise in price). Either these represent sales negotiated ahead of the price rise, or Ecton ore was being discounted yet further than the 4%. A single note of 1788 indicates the sale of under 2 tons of copper metal to Lilley & Roberts at £72 p. ton. In 1780, they bought a ton or so at £70 p. ton when the East India Company was paying £78 p. ton on a significant quantity, so the 1788 price has been ignored. The price used is £77 p. ton on the Table on p 4, which is much less than the London standard price. This is an average price but the comfort is that the profit for the period is known from John Heaton's own hand. (Dev. Coll., L/60/20)

The profit (Michaelmas to Michaelmas) for the period 1760-1775 was £78,234. Thereafter until 1780, the profit was £31,225, whilst the sales were being undertaken by Mr Dawes. In an endeavour to increase profitability, Mr Heaton undertook the management of the sales thereafter. The purchase of Kingsley Colliery (Hazles Cross) was, according to Heaton, a move to eliminate the risk of exposure to price rises. The profit from 1780 to the end of 1791 was £184,480. The total from 1760-1791 was £293,938. From 1729-1791, the Duke's profit was £302,218. It was apportioned as under:

4th Duke	£8,277
4th Duke's Executors	£11,200
5th Duke	£282,741
	£302,218

The ore tonnage raised between 1760-1789 was 41,829 tons and ore sales were 9,056 tons.

A Year in Focus

A complete set of account summaries for the eight Reckonings of 1786 enables a closer look to be taken of the expenditure in one of the busiest years. Total expenditure was £20,800. Of this, clearly the mine was the main cost centre accounting for a little over 72%. Of that sum, 77% consisted of wages (chiefly ore extraction costs), 8% for carriage costs and other purchases 15%. Some of the latter items would also include hidden carriage costs to the mine and some of the timber costs include sawing up the trees etc.

Whiston expenses amounted to nearly 21.5% and the Collieries, after allowing for coal sales, amounted to 6.3% of the general Whiston expenses. Quite a lot consisted of coal delivery payments and if these are put with the Ecton carriage costs – some of which also included coal deliveries paid at Ecton – the total carriage costs were some £4,000 or 19.4% of total expenditure. (Regrettably, although all the summary sheets for 1786 survive, the individual expenditure sheets for May and June are missing. Estimates have been used for these, both for costs and the tonnages carried). Total coal and copper movements amounted to approximately 11,150 tons at a cost of about £2,800.

Ecton	Wages	£11,578	
	Carriage	£1,208	
	Overheads etc	£2,262	
Total		£15,048	72.3%
Whiston	Total Costs	£4,445	21.4%
Collieries	Total Costs	£1,323	6.3%
Total		£20,816	

Carriage Costs	
Ecton	£1,208
Whiston	£2,821
	£4,029

The Cost of Raising Ore, 1760s & 1770s

Regrettably it is not helpful to try and make a comparison of this over several decades. The decision to smelt ore at Whiston increased costs significantly and a comparison with the pre-1770 figures is therefore not comparable. It is useful to compare 1770-79 costs against those after this period when the smelter was producing a higher output. However the work is not helped by a lack of some of the Reckoning costs.

The analysis is given as it will act as a source of comparison for other mining historians. It also shows, for instance, that the cost of ore raised per ton, set against total costs, doubled after the Whiston smelter opened. This must indicate more 'coarse' ore (Hillock or Grove ore) being mined with higher levels of extraction and dressing costs.

From 1762, when ore raised reached a general level of production, maintained over several years, the cost per ton, was generally under £5. This is set against total expenditure and included some capital expense, e.g. building furnaces at Ecton. From 1767 costs p. ton rose as production was reined back ahead of the final decision to build a smelter at Whiston.

Throughout the 1770s, not all ore was smelted at Whiston, some continuing to be sold (see chapter 9). However, total costs approximately doubled from 1770 onwards. Figures for 1775-76 and 1779-80 are not available, but 1777 seems to be broadly in line. Ore output increased in 1778-79 and costs dropped in 1778, but estimated figures for 1779 may be tainted by capital expenditure at Whiston.

Profit per Ton Raised, 1760s & 1770s

The average profit for 1761-1764 was £4.57 p. ton, rising to an average of £9.6s.6d p. ton for the period 1765-69. Again figures are tainted by the reduced ore production of 1767-69. The figure for 1770 should be ignored as it includes most of the capital cost of enlarging the smelter. The average profit for 1771-74 was £8.6s.7d p. ton. Production was not increased after the smelter was built. The miners must have known of the greatest of the deposits in the pipe working during this period, but the figures to the end of 1774 indicate that production was not stepped up to exploit it. Although the figures for 1775-76 show a loss, the 1777 figures show only a marginal increase in output above 1774. This may be partly explained by a desire to reduce the volume of poor ores, which were in stock and had reached 3,500 tons by 1772.

Output jumped in 1778 to over 1,000 tons and the profit per ton probably reached over £14 in this year (the profit of £15,000 for the year is an unconfirmed assessment based on data available (the notes taken by a visitor, see above)). The profit figures for the 1780s reached £10 per ton in 1785, but generally were similar to the 1770s.

It is considered that an analysis of the cost per ton of ore raised against total cost is not particularly helpful, although it may be noted that the expanded output saw the cost per ton drop to nearly a half (1773 – £11.16s.4d, 1786 – £5.19s.1d). Following the expansion of the smelter in 1780, total costs of production tripled (1776 – estimated at £7,000, 1786 £20,900).

In the 1780s, the costs for 1780-1782 were of the order of £16-17,000 per annum, but as ore and metal output rose, the total production cost (and this includes the Collieries) rose above £20,000 to £22,270 in 1783. It stayed above £20,000 until the end of the decade except for 1785, when total costs fell back to £16,426.

The Overall Picture

Phillips (6) gives figures for ore production, sales and profit for the period 1776-1817. Assuming these to be correct, by adding the figures from 1760-75, it is possible to gain a picture of the mine's performance from 1760-1817. The figures are:

1760-1817	Ore Tons raised	Sales £	Profit £
1760-75	12,064	165,239	78,234
1776-1817	53,857	677,112	244,734
	65,921	842,351	322,968

For the sales to be as high as they are, they must include Clayton Mine, otherwise Phillips got his figure wrong. The figures from 1760–1790 which account for the bulk of sales from the Ecton Mine, are given on p 4.

The First Twenty Five Years

Carefully adding projected figures where the actual ores are missing, it is possible to arrive at totals for the ore raised and the profit on the trading activity of the combined mine smelter, collieries etc. The actual profit would have been higher, for the accounts do not exclude capital expenditure. It is emphasised that the totals should be regarded as being in general terms although it is unlikely that most are wide of the mark.

Ore tonnages for the period are mostly factual with a few best guesses where Reckoning summaries, which list raised ore tonnages, are not available. The similar situation exists for expenses. Profitability can be judged reasonably well and is expressed purely as revenue less given expenditure. It is impossible to draw up a balance sheet or assess the amount of capital employed. Revenue figures for 1782 are missing and are included at a total of £167,200.

The headline figures are:

Raised copper ore:	29,780 tons
Raised lead ore:	c 1,004 tons (this is likely to be substantially understated)
Operating costs	c £230,000
Profit	c £221,484

The Profitability of Ecton Compared to Parys Mountain

There remains an interesting comparison of profitability of the Duke's activities relative to those of Williams who actually manufactured copper metal into sheets, bars etc, even tokens for use as an alternative coinage. Williams himself had a part interest only, so the profitability of his concerns (the Parys and Mona Mines organisations) is of more interest. Harris in *The Copper King* attempts to give some indication of output and profit, but was severely hampered by a lack of documentary evidence. He states that Anglesey output was 3,000 tons of metal in the mid-1780s; in 1798 it was about 1,700 tons and in 1799, 1,000 tons. The Mona Mine contribution was over 1,000 tons in 1792; in 1798 – 716 tons and in 1799 – 484 tons. Harris includes a guess of Ecton metal output in 1799 as being 200 tons, which is way out. The figure was much nearer 50 tons.

With Ecton metal output in the 1780s running at below 500 tons p.a., clearly the impact in a national market running at about 7,000 tons p.a., was low (7), but what of the profit?

Harris reveals that the Mona Mine made a profit of £19,260 in the period 1785-88, compared to an estimate for Ecton of £95,762, (see p 4), with the Mona Mine organisation as a whole (i.e. the metal manufacturing side included) making a profit of £87,128, i.e., £29,000 p.a. (8) However huge amounts of capital had been borrowed by the Parys & Mona concerns. Their capital was in excess of £½ million. (9) Consequently in the period 1785-88, Ecton was more profitable than the Mona Mine, (even including the manufacturing side) if not the two Anglesey Mines combined in terms of profit, which does seem possible. Care has to be taken however, for the actual profit is not known, on an annual basis. However, the average price per ton adopted on p 4 does give a figure which matches the total profit for the period 1775-

1791, which is known. (see under 'Profit and Loss' above). It is not likely to be materially different. Moreover, the comparison of Ecton with Parys Mountain as a whole excludes the combined Ecton/Clayton Mine or in other words the Ecton Hill revenue.

This is of interest because Williams wrote in 1788 to the Earl of Uxbridge about his Mona Mine income (Uxbridge had major and pressing debts): 'Whatever you may think of your profits they far exceed those of any six or eight Cornish Mine owners with the Duke of Devonshire put together ...' (10). He did not realise how wrong he was. The only capital expenditure not made out of revenue at Ecton was the £21,500 Hazles Cross Colliery purchase. All other capital really needs adding back to the profit of the enterprise but no attempt to do this has been made. Nevertheless, it would not have been a lot of money compared to the capital employed by the Parys/Mona concerns as a whole.

It is also clear that traditional stories in the Staffordshire Moorlands about Ecton being the richest mine in the country at one point cannot be wholly substantiated because the Parys Mountain figures are not available for comparison. However, there is a strong case for suggesting that the story may be true.

In the 1780s Ecton had another claim to fame: it was the deepest mine in the country, being 202 fathoms (at least) in 1788. In fact it was likely to have been deeper than this. The measurement relates to the depth of the main haulage shaft (the Balance Shaft) only. It had passed 500 feet from the surface prior to 1759 and probably was the first mine to reach 1,000 feet deep. See 'Depths of Workings', chapter 6.

Lead Ore & Metal Sales

A bi-product of the mine was the lead ore – galena or lead sulphide. It was sometimes found in association with copper ore – increasing the dressing costs as a result, or alone. Chadwick Mine seems to have been principally a lead deposit and it is known that work resumed there under the Duke in 1761. The quantities recorded as being raised were never great, the total for 1761-69 being 42 tons, but 1769 sales are recorded in the figures for 1770. Of the 42 tons, nearly 28 loads (about 7 tons) were sold to C Roe & Co in 1767 at £1.10s.0d per load. It may be that there was more impetus in searching for copper ore than lead ore, as the former was more valuable. Prior to the sales of the lead ore in 1767 to C Roe & Co it had been sold to J Barker & Co. The value of ore sold between 1761-67 was £207. (11)

The figure of 42 tons of raised lead ore compares with the sales recorded in the audited accounts where the total sales are shown as 142 loads 3¼ dishes (approximately 35½ tons) sold for £207.0s.9d. The price obtained was 30s. per ton in 1761 and 1767. It dropped to 27s.0d in 1763 before recovering. There were no lead sales recorded in the audited accounts for 1768-1769.

Unfortunately the income figures from lead metal sales have not survived. However some of the tonnage figures have and it is possible to derive some figures. The tonnage sold in 1783 was 365 tons from four Reckonings. The other four are missing, but the output for the May-Sept Reckonings could be expected to be at least 150 tons (the average for the last three Reckonings of that year was over 105 tons per reckoning, so hopefully exaggeration is unlikely).

Willies (12) gives an annual figure for lead sold in the Hull market. He recommends a reduction of 15% for the 'middleman' who shipped it from Derby to Hull in the case of Ecton. He gives a price of £17.75 per fother or less 15%, £15.09 for 1783. 415 tons (i.e. 365 + 150) calculated above, is virtually 400 fothers (of 2340 lbs each). Applied to £15.09, gives approximately £6,000 sales revenue for the year. It is interesting to note that the tonnage of lead sold in 1783 was as high as that produced in Derbyshire, all of which was absorbed in the immediate area. (13) So whether the Ecton lead found a market in the Derby area or went down river to Hull via Gainsborough is not clear.

The figures of lead sales revenue in the 1780s on p 4 are based on prices per ton given by Willies.

Prices

	Botham Ore		Slime Ore		Coarse Copper Metal		
1761	£9.00	£14.17.0	nil				
1762	£12.12.6	£16.11.6	nil				
1763	£13.0.6	£17.6.3	£9.12.9	£)			
1764	£13.6.0	£14.5.9	£8.10	£)			
1765	£13.10.0	£17.7.3	£8.1.3	£)	£88	£96	
1766	£13.14.0	£17.7.6	£10.15.6	£)	£95	£100	
1767	£14.6.0	£16.10.0	£8.5.0	£)	£100	£101	
1768	£13.12.6	£15.18.9	£9.3.6	£)	£99	£101	
1769	£16.5.0	£20.2.6	£9.5.6	£)	£96	£	
1770	£16.1.6	£17.10.2	Nil		£100	£	
1771	£15.10.9	£16.10.6	nil		£100	£	waste ores sold
1772	£15.7.6	£16.7.6	nil		£92	£100	waste ores sold at £6+/-
1773	£13.3.0	£13.18.6	nil		£92	£	waste ores sold at £6+/-
1774	£10.15.6	£14.0.0	nil		£92		waste ores sold at £6+/-
1775					£77	£82	? disc for volume
1776					£77	£80	
1777	£13				£77	£78	E.I. Co @ £77
1778			Thoyts 78 & 70		£77	£82	E.I. Co @ £82
1779			Thoyts 70		£72		Cazalet 66-68 (81 ton)
			(end of 1778 lot)				E..I. Co. at 73
1780			Thoyts 70		£71	£80	150 tons sold at £73
			(end of 1778 lot)				E..I. Co. at 78
1781		£15	nil		£76	£87	sheets at £101
1782					£??		
1783					£??		

Prices thereafter not available

References

1 Porter, L., & Robey, J., *Copper & Lead Mines Around the Manifold Valley, Staffordshire*, 2000

2 Farey J., *General view of the agriculture & minerals of Derbyshire*, 1811. Vol 1, p 354

3 Bromfield P., *Industrial workers in a Peasant Community: Manifold Valley parishes in the 18th century, with special reference to workers at Ecton Copper Mine c. 1760-1820*, Ch 3, p 13, unpub. thesis, Keele University.

4 Dev. Coll., Voucher Box, 1780

5 Grenfell, J., 1814, *Observations on the expediency and facility of a copper coinage of uniform weight and a standard value according with the mint prices of gold and silver bullion.* Copy in the Goldsmiths Library, Senate House, University of London

6 Porter, L., & Robey, J., op.cit., p 107

7 Harris, J.R., *The Copper King*, 2003, p 98. Republished by Landmark Publishing

8 op. cit., p 159

9 op. cit., p 142

10 op. cit., p 143

11 Dev. Coll., Voucher box 1760-74, Doc 2/26

12 Willies, L., 'A Note on the Price of Lead' *Bull. PDMHS Trans.*, 1969, Vol 4, Pt 2, pp 179-191

13 Farey, op. cit., p 379. This is a quote from the VCH for Derbyshire but it is wrong!

One gets the impression that the life in the Moorlands was not a particularly comfortable one, with income from agriculture not producing a comfortable living.

Bray (1) in 1777, states that 'Whetton is a very mean village, the inhabitants employed in mining. It is a poor vicarage of £20 a year, the church served about once a fortnight.... The land lets for 10 to 40 shillings an acre. The carting at Ecton Mine is of much service to the farmers here, who earn a good deal of money at it.' In fact those lucky enough to work at the mine saw a steady wage, paid on every reckoning day (every 6 or 7 weeks) and in legal money – not the private coinage of the huge Parys Mountain Copper Mine on Anglesey which forced the workers to shop and spend their hard earned money only at or around the mine.

However Bray was not entirely correct in describing the villagers as being employed in mining. It gives the impression of land lying idle while the people worked the minerals under it. This was not the case. The corn mill at Wetton Mill presumably ground locally grown corn and oats while turnips were grown as a cash crop in Wetton (2) in the 1780s. This evidence of the growth of turnips would seem to refute Pilkington's comment in 1789 that the turnip-rooted cabbage was not known in Derbyshire 'but is very acceptable food for horses as well as cows and sheep.' His specific reference to the adjacent county may be ignored in this context. (3)

Document AS/1471 in the Devonshire Collection also refers to the purchase of 'turnip sead (seed) in Bakewell in March 1788, and payment for its collection. Elsewhere is a reference to the purchase of a 'bead' (bed). Pronounced 'sade' & 'bade', we have an insight into a little of the local 18th century dialect. For the previous year, 1787, the same set of documents refer to the purchase of hay seed, clover seed, seed oates (sic) and turnip seed. In that year are receipts for the sale of turnips (£10) and 'Oats on the Inclosure in Wetton Pasture £135. 1. 0d.' There are also expenses for 'Limeing, Draining and Inclosing other improvements in Wetton Pasture and erecting a Habitation for Lawrence Fallows.' This was clearly a period of change in the village; not only had the pattern of work changed since the contraction of the mine, but several other properties had been erected additional to the house above and the provision of a shop in 1796 (see this chapter). In 1794 a new house had been built for George Gosling plus 'three different other Habitations, for miners in the Fields near the Town of Wetton.' The latter had had to have a heavier slate placed upon the roofs. Wetton Mill house was also extended in this year and a new roof placed over the original part. (4)

There is a reference to a shop at the mine in the papers relating to the assets of Robert Shore (see Chapter 4). The Devonshire Estate converted an old building into a shop at Wetton for James Newbold at Wetton in the year ending Lady Day 1796 (5) Whether this was connected with the poverty in the village in 1795 when the Duke had to send in cart loads of oatmeal and coal (see Chapter 6, 'The Mine Fails'), is not known but the Duke would not have wished to see his tenants in this position again.

A few details of village personalities at about this time survive. In 1785, Thomas Carr was the village Constable and Mr Fallows the Overseer of the Poor. There were two Thomas Fallows in the village in 1791, one described as 'Gent' and the other a carrier. Thomas Carr was also the Estate Bailiff and was paid annually for 'calling out the tenants', presumably on Rent Days (there were two in each year). (6) One wonders how much crime existed for the

Constable to concern himself with. Reference is made elsewhere herein to coal being taken from The Pen, which may be the reason why a house was built there and seemingly occupied by Thomas Rudyard (who was Wetton Churchwarden in 1791).

One incident has survived from 1766 through an advert (7) 'That all Persons who have any TOOLS, or other Things in their Custody, belonging to the Mines in Sir Roger Burgoyne's Manor of Ecton, are required to deliver them forthwith to Mr William Dean, at Ecton, or they will be prosecuted as the Law directs.' It would be nice to know what was behind that.

The Estate accounts also record the payment in July 1796 of 16 year's subscription (£168) to the 'General Infirmary of the County of Stafford', due 1 January 1796. Whether any of the miners availed themselves of this is not recorded. The same account refers to the construction of a second limekiln in 1796 at Wetton for Wm Richardson at a cost of £10.15s.0d. (8)

Although not conclusive evidence of the use of the hill for the growth of cereals, the 1739 lease of the Ecton Mine from the Duke contained a covenant requiring compensation to be paid for damage to corn and grass from mine tips etc. Wetton Mill ground oats to produce oatmeal. (9)

In 1785, the Mill Close at Wetton Mill must have been under the plough, for a payment was made for removing small stones for five days at 1s.0d per day. (10) Land was being fertilised too. In March 1785, John Taylor was paid 2s.6d per load for nine loads of 'dung laid upon the land in Mr Wild's possesion' plus 9d a load for delivery.

Hay was cut seasonally although there was little to spare for the demands of the mine, which was forced to find supplies from Winster. Efford, writing in 1769, (11) states that very fine wheat, barley and oats were produced in great plenty on Ecton Hill, presumably on the east side and on the fields around Broad Ecton Farm. This conflicts with the more general statement made by Pilkington in 1789 that ' In the neighbourhood of Ashbourn, the business of the dairy is principally attended to. Very little grain besides oats is grown here'. (12)

Whether nearby West Side Mill was working in the late years of the 18th century is not clear, for in the mid-1780s, Wm Mellor 'of the Mill' as he put on his invoices, was a carrier for the mine, fetching purchases from Bakewell (e.g. iron items), fluorspar and making regular journeys to Newhaven and back.

However one gets the impression that more land was under the plough than now. Equally, the landscape carried a view of more timber. There was clearly a much larger wood at Castern than now and much timber was sold from there to the mine by the Hurts. Even more timber went to the Duke's Colliery at Hazles Cross near to Kingsley. Similarly, there was a wood at Biggin Grange which sent timber to the mine and which has now disappeared. The Duke had purchased Biggin Grange in 1758. (13)

Many properties were still thatched, including buildings at the mine, although some buildings were tiled – one would expect the furnace buildings to be tiled. Tiles came from Froghall and Ipstones. Twenty three yards of tiles for 'Wetton Mills Kiln' were fetched from Chesterfield in 1785, but these may have been of a different type or quality. (14). Perhaps the dressing floor buildings were kept thatched for a different reason – the thatch was presumably warmer, retaining better heat from its occupants. Thatch was bought from Pikehall at 3. 6d per load.

Getting to Work

Unless there was access to a cart, getting to work or home meant a walk, often a long one. Other than the obvious need to get to work or home as soon as possible, bad weather made matters worse, often for days on end. A walk for a villager from Alstonfield, Wetton or Butterton in bad weather would be no joke. Arriving wet-through at work would presumably mean working in wet clothes for six hours or maybe ten hours before the trip back home. During the bad weather of spring 1786, James Chadwick and 17 others were paid a shilling each day for 'opening roads in the snow'.

Footpaths shortened the distance to Wetton and Alstonfield, but there was no quick route to Butterton unless there was an unofficial way past Swainsley to the Butterton road which came to the bridle road between Warslow and Grindon, high above the valley. Even then it would depend upon stepping stones across the river, as Stamps Bridge at Swainsley was not built until the 19th century.

Social Conditions at the Mine

Dressing the Ore

Although under the superintendence of a man, this was a job principally for women and children. The buckers or breakers of the ore sat at long benches beating with flat hammers. They were under cover and worked at least six hours per day, possibly ten. Working under cover was unusual in the Peak, but probably the sheer volume of work made it necessary. Children as young as six worked at the mine, according to Wm. Efford. (15) There are occasional records of a woman and a child working together for the price of an adult wage.

There does not appear to have been a canteen, at least there is no mention of one, although there is only one reference to the mine shop where candles, powder and riddles could be bought. There is no mention of perishable consumables for human consumption in the invoices, but some of the other items e.g. soap, could possibly have been made available. Coal would seem to have been a contender, but without revenue accounts one cannot tell. If there was no canteen, presumably the staff ate where they worked.

There is no mention of toilet facilities for the surface workers, but there were two rather small and separate buildings on the river side of the Clock House Smelter. These probably were the male and female earth closets. The mine was a regular purchaser of soft soap which may have been used by the workers upon reaching home. One can imagine the ladies on the dressing floor wanting clean hands before they left for home and also wanting to ensure that their children employed by the mine were equally clean.

Sanitary Matters

By the early 1780s in addition to the miners passing through on their way to work or home in the afternoon, there were some 100 smelters and labourers about the works and probably at least that number of dressers, knockers etc., treating the ore on the two dressing floors. On top of this, suppliers would call and of course the jagger men would be taking away ore and regulas and arriving with the coal. Prior to this date, the number of employees would have been smaller, but not appreciably so.

Above, it is suggested that there were probably two privies, attached to the Clock House Smelter. The daily accumulation of toilet waste must have been significant, although, perhaps understandably, no attempt has been made to assess the volume. The 1893-94 Inquiry into Slate Mining in North Wales identified that human waste production on the surface was not disposed of in any satisfactory manner. In fact it was very much the contrary. (16). It was the cause of much concern and no doubt, it was asserted, contributed to ill health in the area.

What then happened at Ecton? The dressing floor waste (ground rock) was dumped in the river, to be washed away by winter floods. This was inorganic waste; the disposal of toilet waste in this manner would have resulted in huge accumulations and sickness down river for those depending upon the river for drinking water.

Potter's plan of 1809 shows a footbridge across the river from the works for no apparent reason. Perhaps the waste was disposed of here in trenches. There is evidence of rent paid for a field, which was owned by the Harpur Estate in the Wetton accounts. Was this the field in question?

Historians of 18th century diet, may find this field an area of rich residual pickings, if that is the right expression!

In North Wales, the slate miners, while underground, went to the toilet where they could, often in unused parts of the workings which happened to be conveniently nearby. (17) One can assume that this was a regular practice elsewhere. On top of this would be horse manure, which probably lay where it fell except in the whim. One can imagine the horses being well looked after underground, the area of the whim where the horse walked being kept swept of manure.

The Mine School

Very little is known about the school built by the Duke at Ecton for the small children of his workers. It is unknown to what extent it was used just for teaching or whether it was also a convenient crèche. It closed when the National School opened in Warslow according to one 16-year-old ore dresser. (18)

However this would appear to be incorrect for Warslow had a school held in the west end of the church in 1784. A school building was erected by subscription in 1788 and enlarged in 1834 by Sir George Crewe. (19) Perhaps the lad had this in mind.

When did it open? A building was erected at the mine in 1781 which may be a candidate and crucially, this dates its opening prior to the school building in Warslow of 1788. In the Reckoning of June 1781, the mine purchased a 50 gallon 'mettle boiler' plus three doors, three grates and three door frames. Were these for the school? The doors and grates would indicate a building with three rooms – could this be one for the boys; girls and the teacher? The boiler could presumably be for the school too. Regrettably there does not appear to be a payment for a teacher! If the school existed then the reason for this cannot be accounted for. Regular payments to George Wild seemed to offer an explanation until it was found that he was an overseer of the collieries and later employed at Ecton.

Melville Attwood giving evidence for the Commission on the Employment in Mines in 1842 stated that there was no church school nearer than Wetton. (20)

The school is known to have existed however and miners' depositions for the defence of the New Dale Mining Co. Ltd (21) mention it. Some of the men recalled throwing stones at the Hayesbrook Mine's former Newcomen Engine boiler which lay by the tips to the Dale mine. They did this on their way to the Ecton school from their homes in Warslow. The date of this would be c.1820 or perhaps a little earlier.

Children Underground

The available records do not give any clue to the use of child labour underground. We have to be content with the use of terms such as '[name] a lad'. After the Royal Commission Inquiry into the use of Children in Mines, in the early 1840s, the age was raised slowly. The use of children underground continued nearby at Cowclose Mine, near Warslow Hall (22) but generally the practice at Ecton was not great. In other parts of the country, particularly in coal mines the use of small children was common and was practised in the Hazles Cross and Foxt Wood Mines. In 1842 the use of children as young as seven was common in the Ruabon district of N Wales, for instance.

Although the age limit was gradually lifted, a Henry Hall (an Inspector of Mines for Lancashire and N Wales) commented as late as 1900: 'I don't think they take much harm and they always seem very merry, though some of them are very little chaps. It may make a great difference to a workman's family where there are six or seven young children, when the eldest begins to earn even the rent of the cottage' He was referring to children aged 12 years (23) but his comments were just as relevant over 100 years previously and perhaps to children who were younger.

In August 1782, four 'lads' were allocated six candles each while driving underground and three 'lads' were allocated a candle each while 'Blowing Bellows at A[pes] Tor' (Candle and Powder Account) See chapter 5 for details of children employed on the dressing floor. Geisler

(24) refers to boys underground in a confusing comment, but one which it is felt referred to the pushing of waggons through Ecton Sough.

Gratuities

It is known that the 4th Duke, like his son, went to visit the mine and the event was recorded by John Harpur and William Efford (re the 4th Duke). Harpur stated that he descended the ladderway to the 4th chamber. The 3rd was at the 34 fathoms level so he must have descended some 250 feet or so.

It is recorded that he left the miners ten guineas to spend on drink and the accounts record on 1/10/1763 'to Wetton Tenants and these Minors (sic) at his Graces Order £12.12.0d.' So it would seem the tenants received two guineas to spend on drink and the miners (at 1/8d a gallon, the price pertaining in 1780) something like 126 gallons or 1,000 pints in round terms! In 1783, the expense accounts record '[to] C Flint added to the Money that His Grace the Duke of Devonshire left when he was at Ecton 12s 6d' (i.e., he added another 5%, which John Heaton chose to remburse). On this occasion, the Duke left the miners £16.5s.0d. He went also to Hartington where he left the [bell] ringers £1.1s.0d. (25)

The Revolution Feast

One could be forgiven for thinking that the payment of £21.11s.6d for 'Expenses of a Feast to the workmen in the Memorable 5th of November 1788' was a celebration of Guy Fawkes Night or the successful starting of the Boulton & Watt Engine (it was actually trialed three weeks later). The 5th November 1688 was the day that William of Orange stepped ashore at Brixham, Devon, an event partly orchestrated by the last Earl and first Duke of Devonshire.

Other Events etc.

In March 1770, Robert Shore claimed his expenses £2.19s.3d 'for sundries on his Grace's birthday' He was celebrating his 22nd birthday, having acceded when he was 16 years old (and apparently inherited an annual income of over £60,000). (26)

In August 1779 occur the first references to gratuities (effectively a pension). Both Richard Naylor and William Shore received 4s.0d per week, along with 'Widow Baker' (2s.0d) and 'Widow Sheldon' (1s.0d) per week. Presumably these payments to widows resulted from mine accidents, where there were dependent children. In February 1780, the 'Widdow Lovill' started to receive 2s.6d per week, all the other amounts remaining the same. By the end of 1784, the numbers had declined to two people – Mrs Baker and Mrs Sheldon on the same pension as before.

The Christmas Party, 1780 seems to have been a good example of Cavendish largesse. It was held at the mine as Sampson Stubb's invoice states that he delivered 20 gallons of ale from Warslow. In all, the party feasted on 136 gallons of ale at 1s.8d per gallon (2½d per pint); 261 lb of beef at 3d a lb; 264 pieces of bread (22 dozen) which may have been one per employee, giving an otherwise unrecorded number of employees at that time; 44lb of cheese at 2¾d per lb and a quantity (? 1 lb) of best tobacco pipes. The total cost was £16.7s.0d. A further party was held a year later and it is reasonable to assume it was an annual event, although in one year at least it appears that it was held in January.

The Reckoning for November 1782 included for two deliveries of 4 strikes of malt (on 26 August & 9 November) and 2 cwt of hops, which may indicate that the mine was making its own beer for consumption at the Christmas dinner! The malt cost 3s.0d per load (of 6 strikes) in August and then 4s.0d on the second delivery. Hops were 10d and then 12d (? per cwt). The same account (per C Flint) also includes six bottles of rum at 3s.6d per bottle for use on paydays. The December 1784 account shows that the making of their own beer was still in favour!

Amongst miscellaneous expenses at Whiston in early autumn, 1786, is the purchase of half a load of malt (18s.6d) and 2cwt of best hops (2s.0d), so maybe someone would soon have been preparing refreshments for the smelters' Christmas festivities too.

Health & Safety at Work

In 1769, Efford reported on the poor state of the ladderways which give access to the pipe workings. One can only think that this deterioration had occured after the Duke's visit, if it was above the fourth chamber or vault.

Towards the end of 1761, payments for a bed at £4.18s.4d and a 'Blanket & Cas (casement)' 9s.2d were probably for accident victims. Robert Shore had bedding at the mine (and later at Whiston) but it was his own (he resided at his home in Snitterton, but clearly stayed at Ecton in the manager's house, once built).

The blanket etc. came from John Bestall and he was paid on 2nd Janaury 1762 'for sundry's attendg Thos Swindale Kild in ye Mine 6s 6d'. Later that year, in May, Mr Doxey (presumably a local doctor) was paid 'for ye cure of Wm. Manifold Hurt in ye Mine £7.19.6d' and on 31st December 'for the cure of Josh. Mycock hurt in ye mine £4.6.6d', which if nothing else, shows that the high costs of private medicine and health care are nothing new.

There are some high costs of providing 'flanil etc.' and 'lining cloth etc' during the decade, which perhaps had more to do with the provision of accommodation and corporate hospitality than health care. It should be noted however, that flannel was purchased later by the Hazels Cross Colliery to make waistcoats for men employed in wet parts of the mine. However the doctor was needed again in March 1766 when Elizabeth Sleigh attended on 'John Tompson Hurt in ye mine' followed by Mr Doxey's bill for attending him, paid in February 1767 (£1.10s.0d). More intriguing was the payment of £8.13s.6d in November 1769 to Isaac Greenhough 'bill for Coventree Doctor'. The nature of the injuries demanding a specialist from Coventry are not known, but must have been serious. This was at a time when even a broken leg was life threatening and the treatment for infection was pretty basic, often lacking in effectiveness.

In August 1774 is the following reference: 'John Chadwick bill fetching the Crowner 10s.6d'. This was problematical until it was realised that it followed the death on 29 July 1774 of Solomon Barker at the mine, which is recorded in the Butterton Church Register. Grasping the spelling of Coroner was giving difficulties to the book keeper. Presumably he had to be fetched from Leek. Permanent Coroners' Courts are a feature of modern times. It was common for him to head for the stable and his horse in the event of fatal accidents, his hearing often being held at a local inn to which the body seems to have been taken. In the case of the mine, it no doubt would lie in the mine house, after its construction in 1780.

In 1779 Dr Eli Cope was charging 5s.0d a journey to visit injured miners and 2s.6d extra for a night visit. In August 1779, he went to Holmend [Hulme End] in the night to see Will Chadwick, administering 'applications to [his] head and side', treating him with 'apodeldoc' which cost 1s.0d extra. Opodeldoc is an external application, or soap liniment, which was 'extrememly useful in bruises and sprains etc. The part affected is to be frequently bathed with this liniment and as for as possibly (sic), kept constantly covered with it. Two ounces of opodeldoc and two drachms of laudanum form the anodyne liniment, which is still more efficacious in sprains and contusions; in rheumatic pains and similar local affections'. (27) Opodeldoc consists of soft soap (8%, camphor, oil of rosemary, water and alcohol). (28)

In June 1782, Martha Wheeldon was paid for 'ye cure of John Goodwin when he was Bruised and Burned by a shott in Ecton mine (10s 6d)', which had occurred in 1780. This was followed in 1781 by a more serious case when she attended on 'ye cure of John Hiberd Bruised and Burned Boath Hands, Armes, face and one legg by a shot in ye mine'. These occured when a fuse failed to ignite properly. The miners had a dilemma of hanging about not knowing whether it had gone out or was burning very slowly. In these two cases it seems likely that the men had approached the fuse as it had gone off.

In September 1785 there is a payment to William Salt who was sent to Leek for the doctor to attend Samuel Phillips. The reason is not recorded, but he was paid 1s.2d for 'horse and Toulbars'. Some accidents took time to heal and in 1786, Anthony Buxton received five weeks' wages at 8s.0d per week after 'he was disabled from working at the Mine by a Hurt in the same'.

Martha Wheeldon seems to have administered 'Salver' to Thomas Brindley, also in 1781, when 'Burned with coper'. This is the first record of an accident at Ecton smelter. There were two men by that name (father and son) working at Ecton, both at the top of the pay scales for labourers, at 9s 0d per week. In March 1781, the father was also paid for 'Attendance of Furnaces' and perhaps he was the one who had the accident.

Smelter accidents appear to have been rare, although there was a major one at Whiston in November 1780 when Dr H Moreton was treating 'Miles Finnecan at Oakamore' (paid in the June 1781 account). At least the patient recovered and the doctor charged £1.11s.6d for 'journeys to Oakamore and the dressings and curing of an exceedingly bad burnt leg'. He too was paid 9s.0d per week and was a smelter rather than a labourer. Miles Finnegan continued to receive his wages whilst he was off work. It is reasonable to assume that this was usual at the mine too. Unfortunately the accounts for the latter half of 1781 are missing and the details re John Hibbard cannot be checked.

A reference to George Mather being hurt comes from supplier Robert Low who sent oil and salts, along with material for making ore bags and a table cloth! (R. November 1786). A little earlier Anthony Buxton was paid his wages while 'disabled' for five weeks (at 8s 0d per week, R. Junes 1786). Dr Cope's bill for April 1786-April 1787 indicates that he attended to nine people including the wife of John Hall, dispensing stomach tincture and opening bills. Other treatment included viz: Wm Millward's son – applications to his leg; James Bott, G. Goodwin; Peter Hope – dressings for head. He also attended to George Mather (see above) with applications to his face and hand.

The reference to the accident at Whiston seems to have been mercifully rare. Copper melts at 1,083°C. The next apparent accident was in the summer of 1788, when Luke Orme, believed to be the son of the smelter refiner and manager, received several burns 'in consequence of some hot Copper flying upon him.' He was seen at home by Doctor Jefferys who made ten journeys to attend to him (at 2s.6d each time). This cost, the medicines and his wage (5s.0d per week) were all paid for by the Duke.

The accounts of the collieries are meagre in the information they give, but additional to the fatal accident recorded for Hazles Cross (see chapter on coal), Doctor H Moreton submitted his account (Reckoning March 1787) for treating William Wettwood 'for airing a bad wound on yr. leg 5s 0d.'

The local doctor for the mine, Dr Eli Cope, would be a regular caller. Here is his bill (R. February 1786) It covers the period July 1785-January 1786:

				£	s	d
July	25	A Visit	WM Birch		5	-
		Application for Head	WM Birch		2	6
		Spirituous Embrocation	WM Birch		3	-
	27	A Visit	WM Birch		5	-
Aug	12	A Vomit	Saml. Phillips			6
	13	A Visit	Saml. Phillips		5	-
		Febrifuge Decoction	Saml. Phillips		3	-
	16	A Visit	Saml. Phillips		5	-
Oct	2	A Visit	Fr Burton wife		5	-
		Digestive	Fr Burton wife			6
	4	A Visit	Jas. Kirkham		5	-
		Spirituous Fomentation	Jas. Kirkham		3	6
	5	Balsamic Electary	Jas. Kirkham		2	-
	7	A Visit	Jas. Kirkham		5	-
		Spirituous Embrocation	Jas. Kirkham		1	6
		Purging Salts	Jas. Kirkham			4
	12	The Electary	Jas. Kirkham		2	0
		The Embrocation	Jas. Kirkham		1	6
	19	Do	Jas. Kirkham		1	6
Nov	3	Strengthing Plaister	Jas. Kirkham		1	-
1786						
January		Application, Dressings etc	Anthony Buxton		10	6
	4	Pectoral Mixture	Thos. Marsden		1	6
	11	Do	Thos. Marsden		1	6
				3	11	4
		To Board & Lodgings of A Buxton		2	0	0
				5	11	4

Clearly James Kirkham and Anthony Buxton were seriously injured. Falls of rock probably accounted for more injuries than anything else. It would be interesting to know if Francis Burton's wife was ill or injured. Her 'Digestive' cost virtually a day's wage. Bromfield (29) refers to the fatigue suffered by women in the arduous task of bucking, or beating, the ore. She quotes an unpublished thesis by J G Rule, who was referring to the activity in Cornwall. 'Even apparently strong females exhibited symptoms of pain in the side and back, giddiness and faintness' (30). If this happened at Ecton, there is nothing to indicate that the doctor may have been called to attend the unfortunate lady.

Severe Poverty of Redundant Workers

In 1795 following the redundancies at the mine, the loss of the income previously enjoyed was producing a severe problem in Wetton. An account of 10th February 1795 indicates the extent of the poverty being experienced and perhaps the hunger too. Eighteen households involving 76 people received 456 lb of oatmeal per week from Wetton Mill. John Redfern, the miller, charged £13.6s.0d for 7 loads and 144 lb of meal. Additionally, 32 households received 1 cwt of coal a week. The document covers four weeks. A bill survives for the delivery of 10 tons 10 cwt of coal from Kingsley Colliery, charged at 4s.0d per ton for the benefit of the Colliery's accounts. (31)

From August 1779, accounts survive which detail the wage payments for labourers including those working in the mine smelter buildings. They enable additional information to be gleaned about activities at the mine.

The wage for general labourers underground was 1s.0d per day – 6s.0d per week. Three 'lads' are specifically mentioned in August 1779. There were 39 labourers who worked 49 days or 49 shifts out of a total possible of 7 weeks (i.e. 49 days). One man paid for 60 days and another for 50 days were probably picking up back pay from the previous reckoning or wage for part-time work by someone else.

There were 16 'Smilters', all on 1s.4d per day except for three earning 1s.6d per day. The latter – Joseph Smith, Thomas Brindley and Ralph Salt – were possibly the headmen at the three furnaces (calciner and the two smelters: the Clock House and South Smelters). The cost of smelting for the 7 weeks was £49.9s.2d for a total of 680 days. In addition there were eight men at the lead smelter, each earning 1s.0d per shift. This fell to four men in 1786 presumably as production fell.

A total of 37 water drawers kept the mine dry. All of them were paid 1s.0d per shift and virtually all worked 7 days a week. Working a 7-day week also were the three strikers at Apes Tor. There were another five Parters and Strikers who also worked in excess of a 6-day week, (between 42 and 49 days), all eight were paid 1s.0d per shift. A striker did not 'hit' anything; he was the man who landed the tubs. Three strikers at Apes Tor Shaft seems to indicate round-the-clock working, chiefly raising water in barrels, although these men landed and emptied the barrels, rather than operated the horse-driven whim which hauled and lowered barrels in the shaft. The 37 water drawers were to be replaced by the water engine in 1784, although some men were still needed to draw water up to the bottom of the engine's pump-rod.

There were 13 labourers and 'stone getters' on 1s.0d per shift and 46 'miners & Co filing gravele' at between 8d and 1s.0d per shift. The length of a shift is not known. It may be linked to a longer period of work – perhaps eight or ten hours rather than six. Many of these men were paid at the rate of both 8d and 1s.0d per shift, but the reason was not stated. The total number of labourers was 128, all male. Females working underground was not practised at Ecton, at least during the Duke's time.

After this particular reckoning the number of names falls, but it is clear that someone was signing for groups of men working on contract, the total wage bill (£193.11s.0d in August 1779) not varying too much over the next few years. In fact a year later (August 1780), more people seemed to have been taken on, but a lot were part-time.

By the mid-1780s, the numbers of workers had increased, but the exact numbers are unclear as several teams were employed with an unknown number of members. The general wage was 1s.0d per day. The work ranged from drawing stone and water; sludging water 'at the Head of the Boatgate' and 'the Water Sump Lodg', i.e. removing accumulations of silt from water; making three saw pits at Castern; 'Burning and prepar'g Sinders etc getting stone for one kiln full of Lime'. The different labouring jobs arising through different features of mine activity was clearly very varied. Additional to those drawing at Apes Tor, there were 14 drawing water at 7s.0d per week, which may indicate 7-day week working. There were 4 lead smelters, two on 1s.4d and two on 1s.2d per shift, all paid for 63 shifts. By contrast there were 24 copper smelters who were paid by the week [all bar one (who was on 8s.0d) on 9s.0d per week]. The head man, Thomas Brindley, was paid 12s.0d per week. Amongst other sundry workers were three men timbering in the mine (on 1s.0d per day) and Titterton & William Rudgyard who were paid for weighing coal at the Pen, Titterton at 9s.0d per week and William at 6s.0d per week.

The ore dressing account of this same date (August 1779) is discussed under chapter 5.

Pat Broomfield's thesis examines at length the detailed working practices of individuals and has found that not a few men had the day off when they were paid. She also makes the point, which will be clear to readers this far into this account of work at the mine, that the mine offered regular, daily work in a non-agricultural environment. The need to turn up daily and undertake regular hours of work, often repetitive work, would have been a new concept in the district. Even Sunday working was necessary for key employees such as the water drawers. However some of the workers still took time off (two days) to go to Chesterfield Fair. (32) This was possibly not unusual, for Chester records that creditors from the Oakamoor forge were actually paid at Leek Fair in 1594 & 1607. (33)

There were fairs nearer too, for each of the local villages had, and still has, its wakes week. In 1900, 'Bull, bear, and badger baiting, cock fighting.... are still talked of as having been among the old Wetton Wake amusements, held at the Windle Hollow Alehouse Bowling Green when 'old Seth of Ipstones' brought his bear and the cock-pit was placed near the same spot.' (34) Roberts also advised (35) that Shrovetide Football continued to be played at Wetton in 1900. Today, nearby Ashbourne is the only place in England where the custom of playing hug football survives. (36) No doubt some of these pursuits were followed by the miners, but little is known.

Cock Fighting

Cock fighting was a traditional pursuit in the Staffordshire Moorlands and there is a local story of cock fights being carried on at Back Ecton at The Pepper Inn (now the Manor House) after it had been banned. The *Derby Mercury* of 22 April 1757 advertised a Main of Cocks to be fought 'at Richard Sheldons at Wetton, between the Gentlemen of Derbyshire and Staffordshire, on Thursday and Friday, Whitsun Week, 2 and 3 June for £10 a Battle, £50 the Main.' No doubt the local men had a flutter on it too.

Incredibly a cockpit still survives in the Staffordshire Moorlands. It has become infilled over the last 20 years, but the outline of it is still clear. Opposite the Royal Cottage Inn on the Leek-Buxton road is a lane to Gib Tor. Down this lane, at the end of the second field on the left, a few feet in from the corner by the lane may be discerned the flat area it occupies. Thanks to Tom Buxton of Royledge Farm for this information.

Women Employed in Trade

The number of women who worked on their own behalf was not great, but there were a few:

Hannah Beard was a carrier of coal between Hazles Cross and Whiston, sometimes taking it on to The Pen. Frances Bassett ran the Hulme End Toll Bar for a few years from the time it was built. It was being run by Wm Poyser by May, 1786, however.

When George Critchlow died in 1780, the invoices were made out by his wife Elizabeth for a while but probably the Pethills Forge was being run by her son, George. When he died unexpectedly in 1782, she sold the works to Francis Gosling.

Elizabeth Brindley was paid for 3 days' work at 6d per day for mending copper bags. (R. September 1786, Labourers' account). This was clearly an occasional job.

On 15th December 1786, a consignment from Liverpool, of a rope for the mine, having reached Stoke-on-Trent was sent on to Froghall via Wm Kenwright & Co of Etruria. They went via a Gilbert & Co's boat and the master was Love Lomax. The rope was being despatched by Messrs Renshaw & Lawton 'Ropers' of Liverpool and weighed a little over 10 cwt.

The following year (R. December 1787) the Whiston Smelter bought various locks and knobs (? door knobs) from Mrs Cath Goodwin. The money was collected on her behalf by James Ashton, the work's mason, but where she lived and worked is not known.

In March 1788, Ann Newton of Ashbourne commenced selling candles to the mine. They were sent via J Kirkland, carriage paid at 7s.6d per dozen. Her deliveries were 20 dozen at a time. Her handwriting (an assumption is made here) was rather large. One wonders if it reflected her character.

Joseph Wardle was a regular supplier for years of furnace bottoms and sand to Whiston works. In June 1788, the usual receipt on invoices (in the writing of Cornelius Flint) viz: 'Recd 21st Aug 1788 of his Grace the Duke of Devonshire by the payment of Cornls Flint the contents for Jos. Wardle' is endorsed 'and me Ellen Wardle', signing with a X. Whether he was unable to collect the payment (from Whiston) or whether Ellen was helping in his business is not clear.

Achievements of a Miner's Family

William Hardy, for many years employee at Ecton and a resident of Wetton, wrote *The Miners Guide* in 1748. (37) An advert for the book (38) describes Hardy as being of Wetton and 'who has been a Practitioner in the Mines for Thirty Years.' He married Mary Allen of Hope Dale, near Wetton. They had three sons, John, born 24th Jan 1752 an engraver, who engraved a portrait of Edmund Burke and 'A Venus de Medici'; William, a marble mason at Matlock Bath who died in 1826; and Thomas, a portrait painter in London, who died 14th September 1804. The latter painted viz: Lady Georgiana Cavendish; the Duchess of Cumberland; Philip Gell; and Mrs Gell amongst others.

The painting of Lady Georgiana Cavendish survives in the Chatsworth Collection. It is currently on loan to the National Trust and hangs at Hardwick Hall. (39) Thomas (born 1757) exhibited 31 works at the Royal Academy between 1778 and 1798. In 1783 he gave his address as being 'At Chatsworth'. He was working there in 1784, repairing the wall paintings in the chapel. It is likely that the Duke paid for his scholarship to the Royal Academy in 1778. He was living at 4 Gt Marlborough Street, London, when he painted five-year old Lady Georgiana Cavendish.

His brother, William, followed him to the Royal Academy, exhibiting in 1785, 1801 and 1803. His address in 1785 was 14, Old Burlington Street, a house on the Devonshire Estate. The Duke's trusted auditor John Heaton, lived at No. 6. The painting exhibited in 1785 is entitled 'A boy playing at marbles.' It was painted in 1784, portraying a Chatsworth page boy, John Lewis March and was painted by the order of the Duchess. (40)

References

1. Bray,Wm., *Sketch of a Tour into Derbyshire etc.*, 1783, p 147 (2nd Edition). The first edition is dated 1777.

2. Dev. Coll. AS/1471 which refers to 1788

3. Pilkington, J., 1789, *View of the Present State of Derbyshire*, pp 310-11

4. Dev. Coll., AS 917

5. Dev. Coll. AS 917

6. Dev. Coll., AS 1471, Vouchers of Wetton Estate 1785-91

7. *Derby Mercury*, 5th September 1766 p 4, col 2

8. Dev. Coll., AS 917

9. Dev. Coll., AS/917

10. Dev.Coll., AS/1471. The same document reveals that a load of tiles was delivered to the Mill from the Pen and three loads of 'paver slags' from the mine. These improvements followed the tenancy of the mill by John Redfern in 1785.

11. Efford W., *Gentleman's Magazine*, p 59

12. Pilkington, J., 1789, op.cit., p 292

13. Dev. Coll., AS/1053, p 84

14. Dev.Coll., AS/1471

15. Eford, W., op.cit.,

16. Wynne Jones, I., The *Victorian Slate Industry in Wales*, 2003 pp 43,63

17. Wynne Jones, I., op.cit. p 42

18. Employment of Children in Mines, Report of 1842 quoted in Porter, L and Robey, J., *Copper and Lead Mines around the Manifold Valley*, 2000 p 227

19. VCH *Staffordshire* Vol 7, p 63

20. see Porter, L. & Robey, J., op.cit. p 228

21. v.R.Roscoe – see Porter & Robey, op.cit., pp 231-34

22. Porter & Robey, op.cit., p104

23. Williamson, S., *Gresford: The Anatomy of a Disaster*, 1999, pp 153-154

24. Althin, T., Eric Geisler & his Journey Abroad, 1772 - 1773, *Med Hammare och Fackla*, Vol XXVI

25. Dev.Coll., AS/1717

26. Foreman A., *Georgiana, Duchess of Devonshire* p 17

27. Tindal, J., *Companion to the Medicine chest*, 7th Edit., 1817

28. pers. comm. Arthur & Barbara Williams, both retired pharmacists who used to dispense opodeldoc early in their careers

29. Bromfield P., *Industrial workers in a Peasant Community: Manifold Valley parishes in the 18th century, with special reference to workers at Ecton Copper Mine c. 1760-1820*, Ch 2, p 5, unpub. thesis, Keele University.

30. Rule, J. G., '*The labouring miner in Cornwall, c1740 - 1870*' unpub. thesis Univ.of Warwick, 1971, p 29

31. This record survives outside the mine accounts in Dev. Coll., AS/917

32. Bromfield, P., op cit., Part 1, p13

33. Chester, H.A., *Churnet Valley Iron: The Mills and The Mines*, 2002, pp 38 & 40 viz 'Pd to Collyers at Leek Fair £20.' [in 1607]

34. Roberts, J., *History of Wetton etc.*, 1900, p.154, Windle Hollow is the area north of Hope Dale. James Roberts was the local schoolmaster

35. op.cit., p153

36. Porter, L., *Ashbourne and the Shrovetide Game*, 2002

37. There is a copy in Derby Local Studies Library, Accession No 1452. The information on Hardy and his family is taken from a note in this book, which is endorsed 'Willm Bateman' of Middleton-by-Youlgreave. Thanks to Roger Flindall for supplying this note

38. *Derby Mercury*, 8 April, 1748, p 4, col 3

39. Painting Ref: PA 268

40. Graves, A., The Royal Academy of Arts, *Dictionary of Contributors and their work, 1769-1904*, 1905, Vol III, pp 390-91; Stewart, B., and Cutten, M., *Dictionary of Portrait Painters in Britain*, 1997, p 232; Correspondence file re Wm Hardy. Dev. Coll., office

In the 18th century, prior to the discovery of a large deposit of copper in Anglesey, the main source of copper ore was Cornwall, with a few other notable deposits scattered across the country – e.g. Alderley Edge, Cumbria and to a lesser extent, Ecton. Ore was smelted chiefly in South Wales to fine metal (cake copper) in which form it was sold and transported to manufacturers of copper materials or brass manufacturers.

When the Duke took over the works in 1760, the Ecton ore was being sold to three separate concerns, two of whom (Messrs Patten & Co & Messrs Roe & Co) were well established in the copper and brass metal market.

Despite the national output of copper ore being centred on Cornwall, there was a virtual stranglehold on the smelting of the Cornish ore by the Swansea copper smelters, who acted as a cartel. Cornish mine owners attempted to break this monopoly by importing coal and setting up their own smelting works in 1754, initially at Entrol and later at Hayle (where the community still carries the name Copper Houses). Despite the best endeavours of the Swansea concerns, the Cornish business flourished and was still operating at the end of the century. Mines elsewhere such as Ecton provided a useful alternative source of supply to copper smelters and manufacturers.

Britain was the biggest producer of copper metal in the world at the time. The deposit on Anglesey was owned by two people and two companies developed the mining of it – Thomas Williams with the Parys Mine Co., and Lord Uxbridge with the Mona Mine leased to Charles Roe & Co of Macclesfield, Cheshire. The low grade ore was initially extracted by opencast methods. Williams smelted his own ore near St Helens and had a manufactury in North Wales at Holywell. He developed a stranglehold over the metal supply through low prices (or at least lower prices than anyone else) and aggressive marketing. Upon the expiry of the Roe lease in 1785, the Mona Mine was worked by the mineral owner, as at Ecton, but in this case, the mine and smelting interests were under the daily control of Thomas Williams who was a shareholder along with Lord Uxbridge and their banker, John Dawes.

While the Roe lease subsisted, the Mona Mine could produce, notionally at least, as cheaply as the Parys Mine and Roe & Co remained an important competitor. Another was Ecton.

Here the Duke was mining and smelting cheaply and had the financial strength to reign back metal sales if necessary. For an account of Williams' activities see Harris, (1) but it does not include an assessment of the impact of the Ecton Mine on Williams' activities and that is really beyond the scope of this book. However it is worth a cursory look. Ecton was rich because of low production costs, high yields and the short distance to coal. Its ore volumes were not particularly high before the exploitation of the huge 110 fathoms level deposit, although the ore figures for the Clayton deposit would need adding on and these do not exist. Nor is there even any hint of the main period of production (see Chapter 6).

However as Williams' influence grew at the end of the 1770s, the availability of Ecton ore/ metal provided a useful alternative source of supply for those able to get it. This was not always the case, for initially metal production at Whiston was hampered by an apparent inability to break into the market.

In 1772, metal samples were sent to John White & Co in Houndsditch, London. He offered to assist in the selling of it but warned that 'London was crowded with Large Quantity of copper at this time'. (2)

In 1770, the year smelting began at Whiston, the volume of poorer 'Coarse' ores on the bank at Ecton was 2,000 tons. In 1774, instead of getting less, it had risen to 3,500 tons, awaiting dressing and reduction in the Ecton calciner and smelter. Paradoxically, the rise of Williams' influence on the national market must have created a stronger demand for Ecton copper and is probably the reason for the increase in smelter capacity at Whiston in 1780.

The annual copper metal production remained small until the East India Contract was secured in 1776. This was not for the supply of all of that Company's needs, as their requirement was some 1,500 tons p.a. (3). The Ecton metal output prior to this had never been over 100 tons, yet the first contract was for 199 tons (the figures shown on p 4 for 1777 include 1776). The year when the exploitation of the huge 110 fathoms level deposit began in earnest would appear to have been in 1778 – but only marginally so, as output of ore only rose 250 tons or so in that year and by 400 tons in 1779. The large increases occurred after the smelter enlargement of 1780. The mine presumably had reserves of ore, but the small size of the smelter was clearly the obstacle to growth.

Having held production relatively steady throughout the 1770s, the sudden upturn in supply of Ecton metal at a time when Williams was forcing the price per ton of metal downwards, thereby reducing the Duke's profits per ton sold, needs consideration. It can be no coincidence that the years of peak production – 1784-86 were perhaps the years of most volatility in the market, with prospects of mine closures in Cornwall, Cornish miners' unrest etc. By early 1785, Harris (4) states that many Cornish mines had reached the point of closure through the deterioration of ore prices. The addition of the Mona Mine interests meant that from 1785, Williams was producing a third of the national output of metal – approximately 2,300 tons compared to 4,700 tons from Cornwall. (5) It is particularly frustrating that full details of Ecton metal production and sales are not available for this time. The Parys Mine Co was formed in 1778 but its impact was in the 1780s.

The increased tonnages of raised ore at Ecton continued into the 1780s: in 1780 the figure for seven Reckonings is 1,387 tons (say 1550 tons for the full year); 1781:1,205 tons for the first half year alone and 1782: 1,866 tons for seven Reckonings, say 2,000 to 2,050 tons for a full year. Allowing for the fires to be lit in the new furnaces in 1780, manufactured copper metal rose to about 526 tons in 1780; even higher in 1781 (600 tons) before steadying off at 450-480 tons p.a., (1783 was a little lower at 380 tons).

The sales figures for 1781 survive and indicate that ore sales had virtually dried up. 20 tons of ore went to the Gnoll Copper Co at £15 per ton and that was all. Metal sales rose by nearly 527 tons. This indicates that there was a substantial amount of metal held in stock for sale. The majority of it went to the East India Company and to Cazalet & Cooke (221 and 234 tons each respectively). The standard price to Cazalets was £87 per ton, although some (presumably inferior) metals went for as low as £74 and £76 per ton. The East India contract was at a minimum of £85 per ton for cake copper with copper sheets being sold at £101 per ton, although it only amounted to 30 tons of sheet copper in that year. However Harris (6) indicates that the 1780 price was £88, reducing to £79 per ton for ore from the Cornish companies. It is suggested that the 1781 sales from Ecton were under the 1780 contract (all deliveries were made by April 6th).

The price of £101 per ton presumably reflected the cost of rolling, so Ecton had secured its order (delivered from 9/10/1780 – 6/4/1781) at £85 per ton for cake copper, £3 less than that demanded by Cornwall for its *ore*. Cornish ore prices were calculated on the price of cake copper less the smelting costs. It was known as the 'standard', although variations from this occurred, according to yield etc. Williams stated that Parys Mine Company 'cannot be out of pocket unless fine copper should sell under £50 per ton, and I am informed the Cornish mines cannot be worked to any profit if the ore must be sold under the standard of £80 per ton'. (7)

Had the Duke of Devonshire a clue about the profitability of his Ecton Mine, he would have replied to Williams: 'me too'. In fact he cleared his costs at under £33 p.ton in 1781.

The Parys/Mona ores were smelted at nearby Amlwch on Anglesey and the furnaces 'were charged with twelve hundredweights of ore every five hours and this quantity yielded about half a hundred weight of rough copper containing 50% of pure metal. About ninety smelters and other workers were employed at the works and at the adjacent rolling mill'. (8) This indicates a yield of the ore of 2%. The Ecton ore, mixing higher yielding ore with poorer ones, still yielded 10% in comparison (see chapter 9 for more detail on ore yields).

Williams could make high quantities of metal at low prices because of the sheer volume of ore and low extraction costs from his open cast working. He was even producing copper from the mine water, by electrolysis, in huge vats. The scale of this particular operation may be judged by the fact that the scrap iron used in the process was being brought from as far away as London. (9) However the cost of delivered scrap iron was high. Below it is stated that the profitability was not as high as at Ecton. Initially, volume offset this, especially for about a decade after Williams had control of the Mona Mine in 1785, but nothing meaningful can be deduced from available documentation.

The construction of the 'New Shaft' (Water Engine Shaft) at Ecton virtually to the 110 fathoms level indicates that this huge deposit of ore was known about at the time of sinking i.e. well before the increased output of ore and metal in 1780-81. Had the sinking been done with the idea of greater levels of exploitation, one could have expected to see the smelter being extended to coincide with the shaft's completion in 1776. This did not happen. Although the shaft must have improved haulage and general communication with the mine bottom, increased production was not part of the overall result.

It would seem that major purchasers of metal turned away from the perceived volatility of the Anglesey/Cornish metal supply to the more stable supply from the Duke. No doubt they wished more metal was available and the Whiston extension must have been a response to that. The expenditure of £21,500 on the purchase of Kingsley Colliery must have been done in the knowledge of an expected regular and higher demand for copper metal. Heaton records that it was done to avoid being at the mercy of coal price rises.

What has been dismissed is whether the Duke's decision to expand capacity was influenced by some need to counter Williams' activities. The Duke did have the ear of those in Government who would have been concerned over this. It is felt that the decision was purely on commercial considerations.

What cannot be analysed is the gradual increase in ore raised in the 1780s. Clearly the metal output of Whiston as extended was just under 500 tons p.a., (incorporating smelter activity at Ecton). Were ore volumes developed because of falling yield, ease of extraction or because of prospects of re-opened ore sales?

Harris (10) states that the only competition offered to Williams came from Roe & Co and the Duke of Devonshire, without developing the issue further. It does seem that the Whiston smelter played a small part in a now long forgotten drama which held the Cornish Copper Mines to ransom, affected output from the Swansea Smelters (the world's chief area for copper metal production) and rang alarm bells in the Admiralty regarding the availability of copper sheeting for the warm-water fleets.

Capital Expenditure by the 5ᵗʰ Duke

Between 1773 (the date of the appointment of the Duke's new auditor, Mr Heaton) and 1810, £620,901 was spent on capital expenditure, chiefly the purchase of land and tithes, but also including considerable construction costs in Buxton (see below for further details) and elsewhere. This produced a high level of income above the borrowing cost, which was 5% in 1810, but lower at 4.6% in 1782. The main periods of expenditure occurred after 1790. Expenditure prior to the construction of Buxton Crescent in 1784 were minimal with the exception of the purchase of Lord Byron's estate in 1774 (£51,000) and the FitzWilliam estate at Staveley in 1779 (£35,345). The only other major expense was at the Ecton business. In 1780 the Kingsley Colliery at Hazles Cross was purchased for £21,500. The 1780 Whiston expansion costs are unknown, for some reckonings are missing, but it would not have exceeded £2,500 in all probability. Expansion at Ecton took several years – driving Apes Tor Adit Level; construction of the balance engine in 1784 etc. giving a total capital cost of £25-30,000 including the Colliery (perhaps £27,500 being more accurate). (11) This amount of capital expenditure cannot be attributable to Heaton's successful attempt to increase income through land purchases. It was solely on the grounds of expansion of the mine. The need for the former clearly came later after the mine failed in 1790, as the schedule of purchases and revenue shows. The reason for the Whiston expansion seems to have been influenced by external factors related to the economic pressures of the copper industry at that time, as indicated above.

Detail of Capital Expenditure 1773-1810 (16)

The loss of revenue from Ecton must have impinged upon the seriously deep pockets of the 5th Duke. It is clear that a programme of capital expenditure on land acquisitions was undertaken by the ever-resourceful John Heaton (although the 6th Duke did not appear to have got on with him as well as the 5th Duke). This section compares the investments made prior to 1790 with those made afterwards and shows how the income loss was made up. However it was achieved with borrowings on a massive scale which were then made considerably worse by the 6th Duke. How that was tackled forms part of a story covered by John Pearson. (12)

Cannadine (13) states that in 1790, the Duke had spent £170,000 on purchases of land since 1773 and £63,000 had gone on the construction of The Crescent at Buxton. In fact £220,582 had been spent in total, not £233,000.

The figure for building work at Buxton to 1790 was £63,212 and John Carr's commission and other charges relating to this work was an additional £3,858, amounting to £67,070 in all. However this was not just for The Crescent, as Cannadine suggests; it also includes The Stables, later the Devonshire Royal Hospital, a significant undertaking in itself. A further £59,887 was spent between 1791-1810 on 'new buildings and improvements' which possibly includes the new church built by Jeffrey Wyattville.

The total spent on capital purchases between 1773 and 1810 was £620,901. Encumbrances in 1782 stood at £246,677 and by 1810, this must had increased to £376,640. Net income in 1773 stood at £38,635 net (after taxes, repairs, 'usual outgoings' and £16,907 interest and rent charges; the gross being £61,713). By 1810, the gross income had risen to £122,528. After deductions, the net stood at £79.660. (14) Not only had the gross amount doubled, the net income had improved from 62.6% to 65% of the gross figure. Moreover, in 1773, interest and rent charges were 27.4% of the total income. Despite high levels of capital expenditure and an increase in the rate of interest, this had dropped to 21.8% in 1810. It therefore would appear that yields were higher than the interest and other charges. If these figures are accurate, the profligate expenditure by his successor would soon change matters, but that is beyond the scope of this book. What is of interest here is that the capital expenditure was seemingly proving to have been prudent by 1810. The work by Heaton to replace the Ecton revenues had clearly met with some measure of success.

5th Duke's Expenditure on land purchases 1773-1810

Collection	1773-75	1776	1777	1778	1779	1780	1781	1782	1783	1784	1785	1786	1787	1788	1789	1790	1773-90	1791-1810	Total
Buxton		660		2350			150	8040			500	600		13141		1706	67070	79639	173856
Edensor			50		30						650			66	1050	1071		5276	8143
Woodlands (N Peak)				222															272
Chesterfield	51000			5000														20000	76000
Dore	11																		11
Hardwick								650							130			5355	6135
Hartington													1100					26224	27324
Shottle												75						947	1022
Staveley					35345										100			7530	42975
Wetton																		510	510
Tideswell																		38017	38017
Huntingdon																		9596	9596
Marton																136			136
Cumberland																674		28209	28883
Yorks-West Riding																		30578	30578
Yorks-East Riding																		35224	35224
Chiswick																		17527	17527
Ireland				362					354	160	39	2020	887	1147	1526	1010		88432	95937
Kingsley Colliery						21500													21500
Total	51011	660	50	7934	35375	21500	150	8690	354	160	1189	2695	1987	14354	2806	4597	67070	393064	613646

1   Harris, J.R., *The Copper King*, 2nd edit., 2003, Landmark Publishing

2   Dev. Coll., 1772 Voucher box

3   Harris, op.cit., p 132

4   op.cit., p 55

5   op.cit., p 53

6   op.cit., p 43

7   op.cit., pp 42-43

8   Rowlands, J., *Copper Mountain* 1966, p38 quoting Aikin, A., *Journal*, pp137-140

9   Harris, op. cit., p 45

10 op cit., p 45

11 Dev. Coll., *Income of the Duke of Devonshire in the Years 1773-1810* p 39. The capital expended estimate is based upon a notional £1,000 p.a., for 20 years and the rest on equipment, smelters at Whiston & Ecton etc

12 Pearson, J., *Stags and Serpents*, 1983, covered in several chapters

13 Cannadine, D., *Aspects of Aristocracy*, 1994, p 168 He states that the net income for 1813-1815 was £70,000 p.a. Either there was a reduction in revenues or his sources differ from that used by this author. It does not alter the thrust of the argument, however.

14 Dev. Coll., *Income of the Duke of Devonshire in the Years 1773-1810*, compiled by John Heaton, the Duke's agent

Conversion Table

Bushel	=	8 gallons
Cart load	=	1 ton
Dales or Deals	=	120 = a hundred
Draught	=	40 barrels drawn up a shaft (120 barrels to a shift)
	=	90 barrels wheeled from A to B
Foxtwood Colliery load	=	1cwt
Packhorse load	=	2 cwts
Peck	=	2 gallons
Piece	=	16 pieces of lead pigs = 1 fother
		1 fother = approx $7^3/_4$ tons
Rood	=	$^1/_4$ acre
Stone	=	4 strikes, 14 lbs
Strike	=	$3 ^1/_2$ lbs
Thrave	=	24 sheaves of corn (or presumably oats etc)

16 ounces	=	1 pound (1 lb)
14 lbs	=	1 stone
28 lbs	=	1 quarter
4 qtrs	=	1 hundred weight (cwt)
20 cwt	=	1 ton
21 cwt	=	1 ton (for copper ore)
2,240 lbs	=	1 ton (20 cwt)

The remains of the lacing of Clayton Engine Shaft (see Lace, under terms). In the late 19th century, the Cornish term "cased and divided" was adopted instead. The narrow vertical compartment (on the left side) housed the steam – hauled ore – skip from the shaft bottom, 960 feet below

TERMS USED IN THE MINE

Many unusual words have been noted whilst perusing the accounts and other records, such as Watson's descriptions of saddles and their component parts (see Chapter 2). Clearly some terms are the same as those found in Derbyshire lead mines (see Rieuwerts J, *Glossary of Derbyshire Lead Mining Terms*, 1998, Peak District Mines Historical Society Ltd). Some words however, are different and some have defied indentification. Even different words were used in the two collieries! These are all given below, together, in most cases, with the earliest date found and a short description. It clearly denotes a language now lost and not just the mining words, for some were clearly in everyday use.

Colliery Terms

Braking Stone: 'Whieling Braking Stone from the New Shaft for Duck's land,' Aug 1782

Brouse: '2 load of Brouse and Carnage to gin ring,' Feb 1785. This relates to hawthorn or gorse being used to make a platted windbreak

Clod Ale: Ernest & Clod Ale 'taking Pit to sink 2s.0d,' June 1782

Fang: 'Meaking fang for weater,' Dec 1782

Heath Kids: 'for kiding one thousand heath kids,' Dec 1785

Pileings: '2 thrave of wheat pileings at 2s.0d per ton for beding. 4s.0d,' Aug 1785

Riding: through faults, Aug 1785

Rowler: 'puting up a rowler in the wet shaft,' Dec 1785

Sloughing: deep level, Aug 1785

Trous: 'Carrying bricks and Clods and trous to hedge gin 5s.0d,' Nov 1783. This was probably to make a windbreak

Ecton Mine Terms

Back Joint: 17/6/1786, 'Driving a crosscut in the West Side to a Back Joint'. Working off the main vein on a side vein

Back Turnfoot: 25/6/1768, 'drawing from ye Back Turnfoot'

Back Turns: 26/3/1768, 'Stempling ye Back Turns' (Ed Goodwin). Putting in wooden supports in a shaft in an old working

Bareing an old work: 26/9/1761, opening up an old working

Belland dresser: George Betty in 1783. Belland was very fine particles of ore, probably just lead ore

Body: 22/3/1783, 'Driving from the East Run over the Body of the vein'. The main mass of the vein

Boreing hamers: 31/12/1763, hammers used when hand boring holes in rock

Bote Gate: 20/3/1761, the Boat Level

Botham: 27/3/1762, bottom

Bottom Turn: 11/2/1769, the lowest shaft

Bunding: A platform in the shaft, 28/3/1761. Also a platform for stacking deads

Capstone rope: February 1785

Christ: May 1786, 'Laying on the Christ at Maddars and Twigg's Houses' 2 days at 4s.0d

Cleefing: May 1780, Cleefing ash (wood) at 1s.6d per foot. Cleaving or splitting

Copers: 2/1/1761, the men working a bargain to extract ore at a fixed price per ton

Corves: 27/3/1762, a basket or sledge used to get mineral out of the mine or to a shaft or wagonway, by dragging along the floor. May have had runners or wheels

Counts and sets to the shaft: Three people employed in this position at 7s.0d per week, 29/11/1760

Crossils: November 1787, 'blasting crossils in the side of ye hill'. Thought to refer to the huge lumps of calcreted gravel still to be seen in the 'Dukes Gravel Quarry' at Ecton

Dales: 27/3/1762, Lengths of timber

Dead Water: 23/6/1764, 'Moses Kid & Co drawing out dead water, 15s 0d'. Likely to be standing water or water below the water table

Deads: 4/11/1786, 'Removing the deads'. Mined rock which does not contain enough mineral to justify transport to the surface

Deep soles: 4/5/1765, Anty Bestall & Co were driving the Deep Soles. ? bottom of the mine

Double Turn: 6/5/1786, 'Cutting room for a Double Turn upon the East Side'. Either two shafts close together or a shaft of double width

Draught: A measure of stone removal – for wheeling there were 90 barrels to a Draught and for drawing there were 40 barrels to a Draught

Dublex Horses: 28/9/1765, Wm Hambleton was paid for these. Could it be two horses?

Earnest of bargains: 2/1/1762, an advance on making a bargain or contract. One shilling each in August 1786

Easing stone: March 1788, '27 yards of Easing Stone for ye use of the slag mill.' Probably from Wetton Mill

Edish: March 1789, 'for Edish of the Medows at the mine £1 6s 9d'. Possibly the grass left after hay making

Engen: 18/11/1769, Ed Greenhough was paid £6.3s.0d for making an engen, or gin

Engine race: 20/11/1762, the walkway for the horse(s) at a gin

Engine Shifts: filling barrels to an Engine Shift – 120 barrels to a shift @ 2s 4d per shift; December 1785

Fanging: 26/3/1763, in Barker's Gate, 200 yards at 9d per yard. Probably the same 'fang' as in Colliery Terms above

Feathers: 31/12/1762, part of the plug and feathers for splitting rock

Flow Stones: These, according to invoice 22, had been purchased since 1784. A total of 3 doz (at 2d each) and 29 Barers (at 4d each) had been purchased between 1784 and 1786. Reckoning Sept., 1786

Forefield Turn: 14/11/1761

Freys: 15/11/1766, 'Rich'd Clay bill for a pair of Freys'. What these were is unknown

Garland: 28/9/1765, a half round pipe around shaft to collect water running down the side of the shaft

Gaun: May 1779, a one gallon barrel

Grove timber: Timber used in the mine, 29/11/1760

Grove watch: The mine clock, 3/1/1761

Goulds Wood: helping to cover a Groove Hole (old shaft), December 1783

Handaways: 15/9/1774 'Coarse handaways undressed – 3,500 tons'

Harks: getting harks, November 1780, from the Labourers and Smelters' account and refers to the hearth or smelter stones which formed the actual hearth in which the ore was roasted or smelted to a liquid state

Harring: May 1786, 'Harring thc lime' £1 0s 6d

Hatch: 16/9/1786, 'Ore got in a Hatch – 2tons 14cwt'. ? an ore bin

Helves: May 1780, 3doz pick and helves included in the powder and candle account

Knocking Barrows: November 1783, per bargain at 6d per barrow

Knocking forms: in list of equipment, 1760. Either seating in the knocking house or the hand held knocking plates used for breaking down the ore

Knock/sagots: March, 1782

Knocking shade: walling a; November 1782. The room where the ore was reduced by beating it, or bucking it, with hammers

Lace: 7/2/1784, 'George Harvey & Co assisting to Lace the engine shaft – 118 shifts'. This relates to the dividing of the shaft

Ladder poles: 22/3/1777, sides of a ladder as in a modern pole ladder

Landergate: 24/3/1764, Cutting a lander gate (Thos. Marsden & Co); a level with launders

Landers: 26/9/1761, launders or water channel (78 fathoms purchased from Edward Green) [Carpenter] for £7.16s.0d

Lanthorns: 15/11/1766, lanterns

Leading: Loading, 29/11/1760

Little Hom: 2/1/1762, driving a level at Little Hom. The field south of the engine house is known as Th' Om

Mandrels: in list of equipment, 1760. Long boring bars used for driving ahead of a face. Vital when there may be water ahead

Older Pools: 18/11/1769, alder poles

Opens: East side of the open; making a landing in an old opens. June 1785

Pick helves: in list of equipment, 1760. Handles

Picking boards, Picking Hoppets: in list of equipment, 1760. Where the ore was spread out for hand picking. The hoppet probably being used for moving the ore to or from the board or table

Pickle Dust: February 1781, ?; sent from Ashbourne to Whiston

Pints: drilling tools, 'Sharpening 988 pints at 3d per score (twenty)'. Invoice of James Ashton, mason, 1785

Pitching: 21/6/1783, 'Walling and Pitching the old level'. Pitching was making a stone floor. Also, August 1785: 'John Wright and six others waggoning stone to the Engine Rase (sic) pitching'

Puddle Gutter: 8/11/1783, 'Sampson Stubbs cutting a Puddle Gutter'. A water channel or launder

Pumpshoe: 2/1/1762, the bottom of the pump

Punning: August 1785, Wm Rowland punning regulas

Rag Turn Head: 14/5/1768, (mending it by Ed Goodwin)

Ragg Chain: A 60ft length was purchased, 3/1/1761

Rither: 23/3/1782, 'Driving a gate through the Rither'. A mass of unmineralised rock in a vein. Even in the main ore deposits these were not unknown

Run: Ditto

Saggotts: March 1782, knocking saggotts (from Labourers and Smelters' account)

Shack: December 1787, 'shack out of the lodge' by the barrel. Thought to be small stones and rubbish. In this instance it is likely to relate to the stone which fell overboard on loading the boats

Shooting: 21/6/1783, 'Samuel Phillips Shoot'g a Sump Head in the North End'. Blasting with gun powder

Sinking gear: 10/5/1777

Skeps: 14/5/1774, supports placed under the barrel/kibble at the top of a shaft to hold it steady whilst it is unloaded/loaded

Slime Tails: 16/12/1786, payment for Slime Tails (£3 0s 0d per ton)

Slime: 27/9/1766, the tiny particles of ore. In the 19th century the term was used for fine grade rubbish, not ore

'Sludging A Torr dam': August 1785; one of many references and not the earliest. Removing sludge to prevent silting up

Sludge Tails: 16/12/1786, payment for Sludge Tails (£3 15s 0d per ton)

Sludging and Railing: This may relate to removing accumulated detritus and laying rails, 15/8/1761

Soles: 28/3/1761, the bottom of a working

Stick Ashes: 11/8/1770

Striking House: 5/5/1764, 'John Touson making a Striking House'. Inset in a shaft side for loading barrels. Striking was the landing of a barrel at the top of a shaft

Striking ye forefield pump; 15/8/1767. Starting the pump

Stroke: 'Cutting a gate at the shaft side to stroke the water at level of Apes Torr Shaft foot'; August 1785

Stubs: 23/3/1764, Ed Fallow bill for stubs

Sumphead: 24/6/1780, 'Cutting Room at the sump head'

Sump ropes: December 1784

Swiffels and tokens: November 1780, this is mentioned in the invoice for the purchase of the chains for lowering horses into the mine

Tenting: 28/3/1761. The engine man was often called the tenter

Toolgate: 22/3/1777, tollgate

Trundles: November 1780, three wheelbarrow trundles from Thos Bassett

Turn Drawers: 25/6/1763, shaft winders; John Wilson & Co were turn drawers at 5s.10d per week. A turn was an internal shaft

Turn head: 15/8/1761, the space adjacent to the top of a shaft used for winding

Twitch: 18/6/1785, 'John Hall driving in a Twitch in the East Joint'. Where the vein contracted

Wagon gate: 26/9/1761, a roadway (gate) along which wagons are moved, probably equipped with a rail track

Wagoning and wheeling: Wagoning referred to pushing wagons (usually spelt waggons); wheeling was pushing wheel barrows

Water Turn: 15/8/1761, lifting water in a shaft

Waterman's candles: 19/11/1768, candles for the hand pumpers

Weight days: 10/5/1766, probably the weigh days when ore was sold

Wheelbarrow Gate: 11/2/1769

Wind: 13/5/1769, ventilation

Windgate: 2/10/1762, a roadway (gate) used for ventilation purposes

Wood Kidds: 16/12/1786. Sold from Castern at 4s.6d per hundred

Thanks to Jim Rieuwerts for assistance with the compilation of this list.

INDEX